Navagraha Purana

Tales of the Nine Planets

Navagraha Purana

Tales of the Nine Planets

V.S. RAO

Edited by
Preetha Rajah Kannan

JAICO PUBLISHING HOUSE

Ahmedabad Bangalore Chennai
Delhi Hyderabad Kolkata Mumbai

Published by Jaico Publishing House
A-2 Jash Chambers, 7-A Sir Phirozshah Mehta Road
Fort, Mumbai - 400 001
jaicopub@jaicobooks.com
www.jaicobooks.com

To be sold only in India, Bangladesh, Bhutan,
Pakistan, Nepal, Sri Lanka and the Maldives.

NAVAGRAHA PURANA
ISBN 978-81-8495-931-4

First Jaico Impression: 2016
Tenth Jaico Impression: 2023

Page design and layout: R. Ajith Kumar, Delhi

Printed by
B.B. Press, Noida, U.P.

For my parents
Subbalakshmamma and Varadaiah
who were the cause of my existence and
my wife Swarna Kumari
who is the cause of my happiness

CONTENTS

PART 3: THE GLORY OF THE NAVAGRAHAS

PROLOGUE

The Ganges, most sacred of India's rivers, flowed sedately past the ghats of Varanasi, paying homage at the feet of Lord Shiva as Vishwanath. These were the waters which had witnessed the passage of Rama, Krishna, Buddha, and other epic heroes and immortals, on earth. What secrets and ancient memories must the mighty river guard in its depths!

The evening sun shone forth in all its glory and painted the wind-rippled water in myriad sparkling hues of copper and gold.

Sage Nirvikalpananda gathered his four young disciples and descended the steps of the ghat to take the ritual bath ordained after an eclipse. As he offered his prayers to the Sun, Nirvikalpananda's heart warmed to the beauty of the golden orb which sat like the auspicious *tilak* on the brow of the West. The sage intoned his *mantra* to the Sun, his voice throbbing with devout harmony:

"Japaakusuma samkaasam kaasyapeyam mahaadyutim
Tamorim sarva paapaghnam pranatosmi divaakaram."

I offer my salutations to Divaakara (Surya), who shines like the japa flower, who is the son of Kasyapa, who is resplendent, who is the enemy of darkness, and who is the destroyer of all sins.

Prayer completed, Nirvikalpananda exclaimed in delight, "The sun seems to have grown in splendor after the eclipse!"

Chidananda smiled and said, "Naturally, master. His relief at having escaped total oblivion is obviously shining through!"

This evoked merry laughter from his friends.

Then, Sadananda turned respectfully to their *guru*. "Master, the eclipse has kindled in me a desire to hear the story of the splendid sun."

His request was seconded by Shivananda, who added, "Why stop with only the king of the planets? Master, bless us with a discourse on the origins and history of all the nine planets."

Vimalananda quietly pleaded, "Master, we long to immerse ourselves in the bottomless ocean of your wisdom. Enlighten us."

Gazing at his disciples with thoughtful eyes, Nirvikalpananda said, "It is only right that you learn the history of the Nine Planets. And Shivananda has a point: the stories of the *Navagrahas* are so intimately woven together that they can only be appreciated as a unified whole."

<hr>

With a serene smile, Nirvikalpananda took his seat on the small earthen platform lovingly crafted by his disciples. The cool river breeze, fragrant with herbs, carried the melodious chirping of birds. The rays of the rising sun formed a nimbus of light around him. He was enveloped by a cloak of devotion and wisdom. Looking fondly at the four *sishyas* seated before him, the sage commenced his discourse.

"I rejoice in your interest in the *Navagrahas*, my sons. The very intention of gaining knowledge, by paying heed to the spoken word, is commendable. The virtue of devotion can be attained through nine paths. When a devotee listens to words about God, sings his glory, or meditates on his mystical attributes, God blesses him with the quality of piety. God also gifts devotion to those who prostrate themselves at his holy feet, worship his divinity and exalt his greatness. Again, those who render God service, celebrate his friendship or offer their souls to him are rewarded with a truly devout nature. Of these, listening to insights about God is considered to be the supreme path to devotion, as the word firmly directs the listener's mind towards the Divine."

Nirvikalpananda continued, "It is but right that the stories of the Nine Planets be universally revered and propagated. The enlightened assure us that hearing, or reading, these stories is tantamount to worshiping the *Navagrahas* themselves."

Vimalananda humbly asked, "*Guruji*, does this mean that we are breaking our journey until you complete your sermon?"

"Yes, my boy. Let us focus single-mindedly on this crucial narration."

Sadananda piped up, "Master, I have a doubt."

Vimalanda protested in mock horror: "Not again! It's a miracle that Sadananda's head remains whole on his shoulders – it is always filled to bursting with doubts!" The other pupils laughed in unison.

Nirvikalpananda smiled and gently rebuked them. "Doubt is but the intellectual striving for truth. It is the first step on the path to wisdom. *Prasnopashith*, the question-and-answer method of oral instruction, is the best means of seeking and imparting knowledge."

Turning to Sadananda, the sage gently asked, "What is your doubt, my boy?"

The disciple replied, "Master, why do people worship the *Navagrahas* with such awe?'

"Good question, Sadananda. The Nine Planets are so powerful that people's devotion to them is tempered liberally with fear! After all, the *grahas* rule all living beings from the moment they are conceived in their mother's womb to the instant they draw their last breath. It is the configuration of the planets at the moment of birth which dictates an individual's horoscope and ordains his future. The *Navagrahas* are the embodiment of the infinite cosmic energy which turns the wheel of life – the wheel of *karma* itself. These nine demigods, worshipped with hymns and prayers in countless temples, actually circumambulate the corona of the universe constantly, manipulating every life."

The *guru* turned his solemn gaze on the upturned faces of his enthralled disciples. "The *grahas* define the boundaries of each life. Food, health, progeny, wealth, education, knowledge, glory – every single attribute of man is based upon the planets' unshakeable influence. They are the ultimate arbiters of a man's thought, speech, and deed. Their power over man and his destiny is set in stone."

As the *guru* paused, Vimalananda interjected: "Master, in that case, if the planets do not favour ..."

Nirvikalpananda silenced him with a gentle gesture. "I am coming to your point, Vimalananda." The sage continued, "Yes. If the planets condescend to look favorably on a man, his life will be filled with joy and harmony. If not, he becomes a storm-tossed boat, buffeted by inexorable waves of sorrow."

The four disciples digested this in silence.

Then, Chidananda asked, "Master, it is only human beings who come under the influence of the Nine Planets, right?"

"Not only humans, Chidananda. Demons, deities – every living being in creation must bow to the fate ordained by the *Navagrahas*."

Shivananda asked, "Master, does this include the epic heroes of yore?"

"Yes, my son. No one is an exception to the dictates of the *Navagrahas*, including the demigods. Why, the *avatars* of the Supreme God himself are subject to their influence."

The disciples gasped in surprise: "What?!" "Master, how can this be?" "Unbelievable, Master!" "No!"

Nirvikalpananda smiled and continued calmly. "My boys, ponder on the misfortunes which befell the epic heroes you so revere. What made Rama, the incarnation of Lord Vishnu, endure fourteen years of hardship in the forest? Did not King Dharmaraja and his brothers suffer twelve years of *vanavasam* and live incognito like paupers for another year? How did it come about that King Harishchandra was forced to sell his beloved wife and son and labor as a wretched watchman in a cremation ground? Why was King Trishanku fated to remain suspended upside-down in limbo for all eternity?"

"Master, all said and done, the Pandavas and the kings were humans. But, Lord Sri Rama? It's incredible!"

"Is it?" smiled Nirvikalpananda. "Well, Shivananda, consider this: Sri Rama learnt the hymn, *Aditya Hrdaya,* from sage Agasthya and recited this invocation to lord Surya during his epic battle with Ravana. What does this imply? Sri Rama needed to propitiate the Sun god and ask him to look favorably upon his endeavor to defeat the king of Lanka."

The disciples slowly nodded in thoughtful agreement.

"Again, in the case of King Dharmaraja, it was Saturn's malign influence which resulted in his losing everything, including his kingdom, wealth, army, brothers and wife, in the notorious game of dice with Sakuni. It was only the intercession of the Sun god, who blessed him with the inexhaustible *akshaya-paatra,* which enabled the Pandavas to successfully endure their forest exile."

Nirvikalpananda considered his disciples. "Surely, you now understand that all living creatures, without exception, are under the control of the Nine Planets."

Vimalananda spoke humbly on behalf of his peers: "Master, your compelling argument has convinced us of the unparalleled power of the Nine Planets. We are no longer skeptics."

The master nodded in approval. His voice took on a solemn timbre: "Come, my children. Let me now tell you the glorious story of the *Navagrahas.* Let me lead you on a voyage of discovery which will bestow enlightenment, and the benediction of the Nine Planets, on you."

Closing his eyes and folding his arms in devout prayer, Nirvikalpananda intoned his salutation to the Nine Planets:

'Harih Om!
Adityaadi navagraha devataabhyo namah
Adityaaya cha Somaaya Mangalaaya Budhaaya cha
Guru Sukra Sanibhyascha Raahave Ketave namaha.'

Salutations to Aditya and the other Navagrahas. I offer my salutations to
Aditya, Soma, Mangala, Budha, Guru, Sukra, Sani, Rahu and Ketu.

After remaining in silent meditation for a minute, the sage opened his eyes and said, "My dear disciples, time flows in four great cycles called the *yugas*. The *Kruthayuga, Trethayuga and Dwaparayuga* have passed and this present age is the *Kaliyuga*, a part of the *Vaivasvata Manvanthara* period of universal time. This cycle applies to all the fourteen *lokas*, or planes of existence – *Satyaloka, Tapoloka, Janoloka, Maharloka, Suvarloka, Bhuvarloka, Bhuloka, Atalaloka, Vitalaloka, Sutalaloka, Talaatalaloka, Mahaatalaloka, Rasaatalaloka* and *Paataalaloka*. The nine *grahas* appeared at the beginning of *srishti*, or creation. *Srishti* occurred in the *Adi Kruthayuga*. *Srishti* cannot be understood independently of *Maha Pralaya*, or total annihilation, as the one is the converse of the other."

ANNIHILATION AND CREATION

Nirvikalpananda continued. "The cosmic phenomenon of *Maha Pralaya* raged unchecked for four hundred human years, laying waste to the fourteen *lokas*.

"In the first phase of annihilation, a fierce drought ravaged the universe for a hundred human years. The three worlds were clamped in famine's iron grip. Bereft of water, the vital element of life, organisms perished in their entirety and the cosmos was devoid of life. The bone-dry *lokas* became tinderboxes poised on the brink of explosion.

"Even as the universe continued to reel under the unrelenting rays of the sun, there came a fearsome inferno. Lord Shiva assumed the awesome form of *Maha Rudra*, and launched into his *Rudra Tandava* – the fiery Dance of Destruction. Colossal, insatiable tongues of flame leaped from his gaping Third Eye and devoured everything in their path. This inferno of dissolution lasted for a human century and reduced the *lokas* to piles of blackened ashes.

"Before the smoldering fires could die out, the third phase of the *pralaya* commenced. Ferocious gales tore through the cosmos and these tempestuous winds roared incessantly for another hundred human years. Tornadoes and cyclones, in a continuous whirl of destruction, laid waste to all matter.

"Still unappeased, the *pralaya* worked itself up to a climax of torrential rain, which lasted for another hundred human years. Sheets of rain, almost opaque in density, attacked a cosmos already in the throes of death. A diabolic group of seven storm clouds merged to form a colossal elephant's trunk and trumpeted the end of the universe. *Samvartaka's* force left a trail of destruction in its cataclysmic wake. *Bheemanaadam's* downpour roared like frenzied thunder, while *Dronam* crushed the *lokas* with its humongous weight. *Indram* lashed the universe with knife-edged drops of rain. *Balaahakam* was a moving mountain of water and *Vidyuthpatakam* ripped apart the desolate wasteland with blinding flashes of lightning. The swirling rain waters became an ocean of annihilation. The universe lay submerged beneath the heaving waves. Absolute darkness shrouded the entire cosmos. All that existed was a monstrous void.

"But wait – in that vast emptiness, like a beacon of hope in the dark night of despair, floated a single banyan leaf. It shimmered a glossy green against the dark waters. On its leathery surface lay an infant of incredible, luminous beauty. Dark curls fringed a face as delicate as a blue lotus. In a gesture of ineffable charm, the baby boy suckled his own toe, holding it up to lips as red as the *bimba* fruit. The infant's eyes were closed in tranquil repose and the leaf cradled its precious burden, rocking it tenderly even on the stormy waters of the deluge.

"This exquisite child was none other than Lord Mahavishnu. But, this was not the beautiful Keshava who floated on the Ocean of Milk, reclining gracefully on Adisesha's coils. This was Sunya, a lone waif, symbolic of the Absolute, devoid of attributes, the very essence of being. In the adorable infant's tiny stomach lay the entire cosmos which the Sustainer had swallowed for safekeeping. As the baby lay in repose, in the transcendental consciousness of *yoga nidra*, or yogic slumber, he embraced all the tired souls who had wrestled with the cycle of birth and death, experiencing pain, poverty, strife and sorrow. Gathering them into his compassionate being, the Lord wrapped them tenderly in the calm of a deep slumber, which was healing balm to their wounds."

Nirvikalpananda paused. Bowing his head in prayer, his voice brimming with devotion, he recited,

'Kara aravindena pada aravindam
Mukha aravindena vinivesayantam
Vatasya patrasya pute sayaanam
Baalam mukundam manasaa smaraami.'

I meditate on that Holy Child who sleeps on the banyan leaf with His lotus-like foot in His lotus- like hand, placed in His lotus-like mouth.

The words vibrated in the stillness of dawn and seemed to echo from the waters of the Ganges. The four disciples remained spell-bound by the magic of their master's voice.

⚬⚬⚬

Nirvikalpananda resumed his discourse.

"Mahavishnu awoke from his yogic slumber and prepared to recreate the universe. Now, in the place of the adorable, sleeping infant, stood the creator in his awesome *Viraat Roopa*. His infinite faces, arms and legs encompassed space as the universal consciousness. Mahavishnu looked upon the waters of the great *pralaya* and there emerged from that cosmic womb, Brahma, as his *maanasaputra*, or mind-born son.

Brahma opened his curious eyes and gazed in wonder at the majestic form towering over him. Sri Mahavishnu reassured him: *"Kumara!* I am Sri Mahavishnu, from whom everything originates. In my desire to witness the progression of creation, I have assumed the cosmic form of the *Viraat Purusha.* I am *Viswa karta* and *Viswa bharta* – the Creator and Lord of the universe. I, *Parabrahma*, the Supreme Lord, have given you form as Brahma, my son, the first being in all creation."

Brahma bowed in reverence and said, "Father, I am honored. Tell me your will."

"My son, you are the ordained Creator of all life. Hosts of beings await your touch to come into existence: the god-like *devas,* the demons, the *garudas* and the *gandharvas*. Give life to the horse-headed *kinnaras* and *kimpurushas*. Let the *khechara* take flight in the skies, the *bhoochara* walk the earth and the *jalacharas* swim the seas. Go forth and discharge your sacred duty of *srishti.*"

Brahma's brow furrowed in confusion. "Father, what is the meaning of *srishti?*"

Vishnu expounded on creation. "My son, *srishti* takes four forms:

Sankalpa srishti, Sandarsna srishti, Sparsa srishti, and *Samparka srishti.* I have chosen you to be the instrument of the first form of creation, which is based on will. The other three forms will be executed independently by various beings."

The *Viraat Purusha* continued: "The worlds, with the hills, forests, rivers, oceans and all other requirements for life, will be generated by the power of my will. On your part, I decree that you will into being *maanasaputras* and their wives. These mind-born sons will not be bound by any ties of consanguinity. With their wives, they will procreate and fill the worlds with their progeny."

Brahma bowed in agreement: "Yes, revered Father."

Vishnu gave his son further instructions: "Similarly, to populate *Bhuloka,* you are to create Manu and his wife, Manupatni, as the progenitors of the human race."

Brahma, although eager to please, hesitated and stood before his sire with downcast eyes. Vishnu gently inclined his head in interrogation.

"Father, forgive my inadequacy. I confess that I have no knowledge of the act of creation."

The *Viraat Purusha* smiled and assuaged his son's doubts. "*Kumara,* penance is the key to all enlightenment. It will throw light on your duties and responsibilities and show you the path to their execution. Go forth with confidence. You will have the right to decree the fate of all your creation. Let the sequence of creation bring good fortune to the human race. Also, let the gods of the nine planets, who are currently in their subtle forms in the upper plane of light, take birth with gross bodies and rule human life. The happiness of human beings will depend on their worship of these *Navagrahas.*"

Even as Brahma paid heed to Vishnu's instructions, his eyes widened in amazement – all round him unfolded a miraculous panorama of *lokas,* oceans, hills, forests and rivers! The *Viraat Purusha's* will had taken concrete form.

<hr />

Brahma now recollected his own ordained task: *Sankalpa srishti.*

He closed his eyes in resolve and willed creation. Four sons emerged from Brahma's volition and looked round in wonder.

Brahma said, "I am Brahma, the Creator. You are Sanaka, Sananda, Sanatsujatha and Sanatkumara – my *maanasaputras,* sons of my will."

The four sons stood with respectfully folded hands before their father.

Brahma continued, "Dear sons, I have created you in accordance with the dictates of my father, Sri Mahavishnu. I will now create women who will be your spouses and beget offspring through you."

The four young children shook their heads in instinctive negation and declared in one voice, "Father, we are *satwa roopas* – forms of pure goodness."

Sananda said, "Our sole purpose is to gain and disseminate knowledge."

Sanatkumara firmly stated, "We do not wish to procreate."

Sanatsujatha nodded in agreement, "Yes, our only objective is the search for the *jnana* of enlightenment."

Brahma heard their joint resolution in astonishment and said, "My sons, you are of tender age and do not need to be consumed by the thirst for knowledge yet. Follow my counsel: reach manhood and enter into conjugal life with women. Then ..."

Sanaka determinedly interrupted Brahma's words: "Father, we intend to remain children and undertake lifelong vows of celibacy as *balabrahmacharins*. We wish to roam the universe, spreading the knowledge of the *Vedas*."

They made their respectful obeisance to the dumbstruck Brahma and left on their travel.

⸿

Brahma, realizing that his first step in creation had taken an unexpected turn, contemplated his further course of action. Aware that it was the decree of the *Paramathma* which directed every development, Brahma surrendered to his will and tranquilly resumed his task. He closed his eyes in deep meditation, assumed a yogic posture, and let the *pranava mantra*, the primordial sound 'Om,' reverberate in his being. His consciousness took concrete shape as nine *maanasaputras*, aged twenty-five years, clothed in pristine white, designed to carry out his will to procreate. Brahma looked at his mind-born sons with satisfaction.

The young men gazed round them and cried out in bewilderment, "*Aarya*, who are you? And who are we?"

"I am Brahma, first-born of Sri Mahavishnu. He has made me both the Creator and the first creation of the universe. You are Athri, Mareechi, Bhrigu, Pulastya, Pulaha, Kratu, Kardama, Angiras, and Vasishta – my *maanasaputras*."

Brahma smiled at them reassuringly and continued, "My mind-born sons, I have commenced the cycle of *srishti*. It is my wish that you, as Brahma's *maanasaputras*, produce the various races of *devas*, *gandharvas*, *kinnaras*, *kimpurushas*, *garudas* and *rakshasas*. Comfortable living arrangements are in place for you and you will soon be granted wives."

The young men exclaimed in surprise at Brahma's words.

Mareechi asked, "What does 'wife' mean, Oh father?"

Brahma said, "My son, a wife is a man's female counterpart and companion."

Bhrigu wondered, "Is such a female necessary, father?"

Brahma patiently explained: "Yes, indeed. The act of procreation requires the male and the female to live in conjugation. This is the secret of creation. You will understand this natural process in the course of time."

Brahma paused and looked solemnly at his *maanasaputras*. "My sons, Sri Mahavishnu has ordained that you, through your children, will be instrumental in a far-reaching phenomenon – the birth of the Nine Planets."

The young men, conscious of the importance of Brahma's words, listened in rapt attention.

The Creator continued, "The Nine Planets, who currently reside in spirit form in the luminous *tejomandala* of *anthariksha*, will be born to your sons with gross physical bodies and glorious forms. These *Navagrahas* will bestow power and prestige on all living creatures, most particularly on the human race. They will influence both the subtle and gross contour of men's lives, effectively ruling all their thoughts and actions. The Nine Planets will be the dispensers of joy, sorrow, poverty, wealth and every other aspect of mortal life. The Supreme Lord, in his mercy, has provided man with a reliable path to better living – the worship of the *Navagrahas*."

The *maanasaputras*, as one, bowed their heads in reverence to Brahma.

Vasishta, speaking for them all, asked, "Father, what is your will?"

"My sons, go forth and make your homes where you wish in this beautiful cosmos. Dedicate your lives to meditation on the Supreme Soul who is the Creator and Father of the Universe. Meditation is the key to enlightenment. It will dispel all your doubts and guide you in the fulfillment of your future duties. As I continue with the cycle of *srishti*, you will be provided with wives who will be your partners for life. With them, begin your task of begetting children filled with devotion to Lord Vishnu."

The *maanasaputras* replied in unison, "Father, we bow to your wishes."

Brahma smiled in satisfaction at the nine young men, so eager to obey his command, and bid them a fond farewell. "My sons, may the Supreme God bless your endeavor."

⚬⚬⚬⚬

Brahma went back to the task ordained by Lord Vishnu. As he sank into deep meditation, his entire being again throbbed with the *pranava mantra*, 'Om.' There emerged from his right thumb a twenty-five year old male, clothed in flaming red. Simultaneously, a young damsel, draped in white, materialized from Brahma's left thumb.

Brahma gazed upon his new creation and addressed the man: "Son, you are Daksha *prajapati* – my *maanasaputra*."

Turning to the woman, he said, "You are Prasooti, created to be Daksha's wife."

As the couple bowed in reverence, Brahma continued, "Daksha, take Prasooti's hand in your own. With this, you are now husband and wife. Live together in harmony as the ideal couple and beget progeny. May Lord Vishnu make your union fruitful."

Daksha and Prasooti received Brahma's blessing with respect and set forth to carry out his command.

⚬⚬⚬⚬

Brahma again resumed his sacred mission of *srishti*, closing his eyes in meditation and reciting the *Omkar*. A movement on his lap made him open his eyes in surprise: a charming infant gurgled up at him.

Brahma's heart melted in affection as the little boy's ruby-red lips lisped, "Narayana!"

Brahma cradled the baby in his arms and smiled tenderly. "Child, you are Narada, my son."

To which the baby again chanted, "Narayana!"

Holding this precocious infant before him, Brahma peered intently into his cherubic face. Before his amazed eyes, the baby metamorphosed into a twenty-five year old individual.

Brahma collected himself and said, "Narada, dearest of all my *maansaputras*, take your choice of the beautiful damsels in my creation and make her your wife. It is my wish that you beget multitudinous progeny with her."

Narada made but one joyous reply: "Narayana, Narayana, Narayana!" He paused and smiled up at Brahma, saying: "Father, my desired life-long companion is the holy chant, 'Narayana!' The only progeny I need is the bliss that fills my soul when I recite the Lord's name."

The confounded Brahma exclaimed: "Narada!"

"Father, will you kindly explain the significance of the name you have given me?"

Brahma calmed himself and patiently replied, "My son, I have chosen a very meaningful name for you. Narada signifies 'The Dispenser of Knowledge of the Supreme Soul.'"

"Tell me, father, should I not live up to that blessed name? Is it not fitting that I disseminate knowledge to all the worlds – instead of progeny to a wife?"

Brahma reddened with rage. "Narada, this is willful disobedience. I warn you – your intransigence cries out for punishment."

Narada smiled beatifically and bowed his head. "A father's discipline is but a boon to a son! I accept your sentence, father."

Brahma's face was suffused by the indignant passion of *rajoguna*. He pronounced his curse in thunderous tones: "Narada! Your arrogance condemns you to wander the *lokas* as an eternal bachelor. You will never experience the repose of abiding in one place."

Narada remained blissfully unperturbed and declared, "I am indeed blessed. My permanent bachelorhood, and constant travel, will better equip me to inspire widespread devotion to Lord Sri Mahavishnu. Reciting the glorious chant, 'Narayana, Narayana,' will be my cherished mode of penitence."

Narada bowed in gratitude before Brahma and departed happily on his eternal pilgrimage.

As the chant, 'Narayana, Narayana,' faded into the distance, the bemused Creator thought, 'My dear son, Narada, has consecrated himself to the Lord. This is in accordance with Mahavishnu's divine will. So be it. I can but accede to the Supreme God.'

Brahma resumed the task of creation. There emerged from his will a man and a woman, both radiant in pristine white attire.

Brahma addressed the young male: "I am your father, Brahma, the son of Sri Mahavishnu. You are my *maanasaputra* – the child of my will."

The man respectfully greeted Brahma: "My *pranam* to you, father."

Brahma smiled and went on: "Listen carefully, my son. I am known as *Svayambhuva*, or the self-manifested. As you have inherited a part of my essence, I hereby name you *Svaayambhuva* – son of Brahma. I also confer on you the illustrious title of 'Manu.' As the primogenitor of the Manu-group of my *maanasaputras,* you will be known as *Aadi Manu.*"

Brahma then turned to woman standing beside Manu. "My dear child, you are Satarupa Devi. I also name you Yuva Devi, to connote your youth and extraordinary beauty."

"My grateful respects, father," replied the woman.

Brahma commanded his son: "Svaayambhuva, take Satarupa as your consort. Through your conjugal union, mankind will emerge and populate the earth in large numbers. As your descendants, this race of humans will be known as *Maanavas.*"

Manu bowed in acknowledgement.

Brahma continued, "The human race will experience four stages of life – childhood, adolescence, adulthood and old age and end with death. Go forth and fill *Bhuloka,* the earth, with your progeny."

Manu asked, "Father, where can I find this earth you speak of?"

The Creator explained, "My son, your first step towards accomplishing your task is the attainment of knowledge. This will enable you to define the laws by which your descendants should be governed in order to ensure peaceful and happy lives. Penance is the sole instrument by which you can gain insight into your prescribed tasks. Take Satarupa and commence your *tapas* anywhere you choose. In time, I will enlighten you and show you the earth."

Having blessed and sent the couple on their way, Brahma sighed in deep satisfaction. The seeds of creation had been sown and the foundation laid for the emergence of the *Navagrahas* in material form. Svaayambhuva Manu and his other *maanasaputras* and *prajapatis* were on course to perform their prescribed duties. He had fulfilled all the tasks assigned to him by his Father, Lord Vishnu. Brahma smiled and let himself sink into the repose of tranquil meditation.

∞∞∞

The wheel of time continued on its inexorable, eternal voyage.

Brahma's various *maanasaputras* united with the spouses created for them. Atri, Kardama, Bhrigu, Pulastya, Pulaha, Kratu, Angiras and Vasishta married Anasuya, Devahuti, Khyathi, Bhuthi, Sambhuti, Kshama, Sraddha and Urja respectively. In fecund effervescence, all the *lokas* teemed with progeny.

A daughter, Kala, was born to Kardama *prajapati* and Devahuti. As instructed by Brahma, through sage Narada, Kardama gave Kala in marriage to Mareechi, one of the *maanasaputras*. A son, Kasyapa, was the fruit of their union.

Meanwhile, Daksha *prajapati* fathered five thousand sons, called the *Haryaswaas*. This he did, not through connubial relationship with his wife, Prasooti Devi, but by exercising his will and emulating Vishnu and Brahma who had created *maanasaputras* and *prajapatis*.

Sage Narada, on hearing of Daksha's presumptuous misadventure, interceded. The sage met the five thousand *Haryaswaas* and won their hearts with his wise discourse. He exhorted them to strive after knowledge and seek to decipher the secrets of the cosmos. Spell bound by Narada's magnetism, the *Haryaswaas* set out in search of enlightenment and lost themselves in their eternal quest.

The grief-stricken Daksha now created another thousand *maanasaputras* – the *Sabalaawaas*. Again, the sagacious Narada employed his powers of persuasion to dispatch the *prajapati's* new progeny on a quest to uncover the great secret of the universe.

Daksha, coming to know of Narada's role in the disappearance of his six thousand *maanasaputras*, cursed the sage: "Narada, just as you sent my sons on eternal voyages, so may you be a perpetual wanderer."

Of course, this malediction was merely redundant to Narada, who already happily shouldered Brahma's curse.

The sorrowful Daksha approached Brahma and complained bitterly about the loss of his sons and Narada's perfidy.

Brahma placated him, saying, "Daksha, Narada was but an instrument of my will." Brahma went on to explain his stand: "*Sankalpa srishti* – creation by will, is the primary mode of creation. This greatest and noblest form of creation is the exclusive prerogative of the Supreme God, Mahavishnu, and myself, as his son. No other hands, including yours, can reap the benefit of *Sankalpa srishti*."

Daksha bowed his head in shame. "Father, I emulated you in my ignorance. Guide me in the task you have assigned to me."

Brahma said, "Son, listen carefully. There are three other methods of producing progeny: *Sandarsna srishti,* in which the mere look of the male can impregnate the female. This comes into play in the case of the peacock. In *Sparsa srishti,* which is observed in fishes, the female conceives at the mere touch of the male. In the fourth and last method of procreation, *Samparka srishti,* offspring are produced by the conjugal, genital union of male and female bodies. Just as the *havis,* the ritual offering, is placed in the pit of the sacrificial fire, the male inserts his seed into the female's womb, where it fertilizes her egg, develops and takes birth as his progeny."

Brahma paused and looked at Daksha: "It is this intimate method of creation which establishes blood relationships among beings, and engenders strong bonds of affection between parents and their offspring. Daksha, I expect you to adopt *Samparka srishti* to create progeny with your wife, Prasooti. Go and fulfill your obligation towards me who endowed you with life and form."

Daksha bowed in acceptance and saying, "Father, I am now enlightened as to the right path of creation. I will carry out your decree," he set out to do his duty.

In due course, Prasooti Devi gave birth to Sati, who became Lord Shiva's consort. Prasooti then bore Daksha thirteen daughters: Aditi, Diti, Danu, Vinata, Kadru, Simhika, Krodha, Krura, Kapila, Muni, Anaayu, Kaala and Praadha. Daksha *prajapati* gave them in marriage to Kasyapa, the son of Mareechi and Kala.

Kasyapa and his thirteen wives were blessed with numerous progeny.

Aditi bore Indra and other demigods, called the *devas* or *aadityaas* – sons of Aditi.

The *daityas,* or sons of Diti, were Hiranyaksha, Hiranyakasipu and Vajraka. With their negative, *taamasic* qualities, they became the forebears of the *rakshasas,* or demons. Danu gave birth to the *daanavas,* another demon clan, which included Mayaasura, Viprachithi, Sambara, Namuchi, Puloma, Asiloma, Virupaksha and others. The *rakshasa* clan was further increased by the sons of Anaayu – Vikshara, Bala, Veera and Vrtasura. Again, the demon *kaalakeyas,* Vinaasaka and Krodha, were born to Kaala, while Krodha, another wife, gave birth to *asuras* called *krodhavasas.*

Muni became the mother of Bhimasena, Ugrasena and others of the *gandharva* clan. Praadha also bore a number of *gandharvas.*

Krura bore Suchandra, Hantha and Chandra, while Kasyapa's other wives delivered birds and animals as their offspring.

As they grew into adulthood, the diametrically opposed innate qualities of Kasyapa's sons generated an intense rivalry among them. His progeny coalesced into antagonistic groups based on inherent temperament. Indra became the leader of the *devas* and *gandharvas*, while Hiranyakasipu and Vrtasura wrested control of the various *asura* factions.

The deeply perturbed Kasyapa tried to unite his sons in amicable brotherhood and dispensed knowledge and good counsel impartially to them all. But his efforts were in vain: increasingly virulent clashes erupted frequently between the hostile *deva* and *asura* factions. Soon, these two groups became sworn enemies and could no longer live together in comfortable proximity.

The *daityas* and other demons set out to establish an independent *rakshasa* kingdom in the dense forest. Following their lead, the *aadityaas* and their clan proceeded to found their own *deva* kingdom under Indra's sovereignty.

With heavy hearts, the helpless Kasyapa and his wives saw their warring progeny go forth into the world.

Desiring luxurious accommodation, the young *rakshasas*, Hiranyakasipu and Vrtasura, approached their brother, Maya, and said, "Brother, we require magnificent residences befitting our position as sovereigns. You are best suited to build us royal palaces and splendid cities."

Maya immediately undertook penance to propitiate Brahma.

When the Creator appeared before him, Maya said, "*Pithamaha*, grant me the knowledge and skill needed to make me the greatest architect of the cosmos for all eternity."

The curious Brahma asked, "Maya, why do you seek this particular skill?"

"Grandsire, my *daitya*, *daanava* and *kaalakeya* brothers intend to establish great demon empires. I have been chosen to build grand palaces, fit for them as sovereigns."

Brahma frowned thoughtfully and cautioned him: "Maya, I need not remind you that Indra and the other *devas* are also your siblings. They too plan to found their own divine empires. I will make you the greatest architect in the cosmos – on one condition. You must deploy your skill impartially on behalf of both your *rakshasa* and *deva* brethren."

Maya accepted this stipulation and Brahma granted him magical skills which made him the chief architect of the universe. Maya constructed cities and palaces, which were incredible marvels of engineering, for both *devas* and *asuras*. The *deva* and demon empires grew apace and flourished.

———∞∞∞———

The bellicose Hiranyaksha, eldest son of Diti, without the least provocation, declared war on the *deva, gandharva, kinnara* and *kimpurusha* clans. Armed with a formidable club, the *asura* went on the rampage and established his reign of terror over all the *lokas*. To extend his sovereignty over the oceans, Hiranyaksha entered the deep sea and violently threshed the waters with his club, creating tumultuous waves which submerged the earth.

At this juncture, Svaayambhuva Manu, accompanied by his wife, Satarupa, had comprehended his assigned task of creating human beings. However, to his confusion, he could not locate the earth in which he was ordained to begin his duties.

Manu approached Brahma: "Father, I am prepared to fulfill my ordained responsibilities. But the earth is nowhere to be found!"

Brahma said, "Manu, in ages past, I created the earth as an appropriate habitat for the human race. The misguided Hiranyaksha, son of Diti and Kashyapa, has embarked on a course of destruction and is holding the earth captive underfoot in the vast ocean. It is beyond my power to reclaim the earth from the *asura*. Lord Srihari is our only recourse in this predicament."

Brahma closed his eyes in fervent prayer. There emerged from his right nostril a tiny, white boar – this was none other than Sri Mahavishnu coming to the succor of his creation. In an instant, the miniscule creature metamorphosed into a colossal beast. Blazing like the sun, the animal dove into the waters with a thunderous roar, met Hiranyaksha in ferocious combat and gored him to death. The gigantic boar then rose triumphantly from the oceans, holding the earth tenderly between its pristine tusks, and replaced her in her designated place in the cosmos. With this, the *Swetha Varahakalpa* – the Age of the White Boar – commenced.

Svaayambhuva Manu and Satarupa began their connubial life together and, through them, the human race populated the earth.

PART 1

THE BIRTH OF THE NAVAGRAHAS

THE BIRTH OF SURYA

Lord Vishnu's destruction of Hiranyaksha incensed the *asuras*,
particularly his twin brother, Hiranyakasipu, who took a terrible
oath: "I swear to avenge my brother's death by slaying his killer.
Vishnu, beware!"

The *rakshasa*'s all-consuming hatred of Vishnu was shared by Diti,
their mother, who passionately berated Vishnu for his role in her son's
death.

Kasyapa consoled his grieving wife saying, "Diti, take heart. Anyone
who poses a threat to the existence of the three worlds must perish at
the hands of Sri Mahavishnu, the universal Father and Protector – this is
the immutable law of the cosmos. Hiranyaksha was indeed fortunate to
meet his death through the Supreme Lord. Believe me, my dear, our son
has been granted redemption from his sins."

Aditi, on her part, was filled with deep remorse at the estrangement of her sons and their cousins.

Vinata and Kadru tried to console her, while Diti declared: "Sister, just as fledglings fly away from the nest once they have sprouted their own wings, so do children depart from home. Look at me: my children have left me; my beloved son has been killed by Vishnu. Yet, I staunchly bear my pain and soldier on."

Danu added, "Sister Diti is right. The only path open to us all is to accept our situation stoically and cope with our grief."

However, Aditi would not be comforted. As she sat in pensive sorrow under a tree, Kasyapa came to sit beside her. He took her hand in his and said gently, "Aditi, my wife, it is time you stopped tormenting yourself with the pain of parting with your children. After all, union and separation is the unchanging law of nature. Our sons have departed to build their own lives. This is but fitting and must be accepted gracefully by us all."

Brushing away her tears, Aditi said, "Swami, it is not the physical separation from our boys which grieves me. My heart bleeds to see our sons – children of one father and one family – torn apart by envy and hatred, and filled with mutual hostility."

Kasyapa gave a helpless sigh and remained silent.

Suddenly, Aditi sat up: "Swami, will you grant me a wish?"

Kasyapa said fondly: "Of course, my dear. It is my bounden duty as your husband."

Aditi said, "Then, bless me with a child who is devoid of hatred, envy, partiality and unjust discrimination. Grant me a son who holds at heart the welfare of the entire universe."

Kasyapa calmly replied, "Aditi, I can but remain a father to the children who are the cause of your sorrow. Only Mahavishnu, the Father of the universe, can grant your wish."

Aditi exclaimed in wonder, "Mahavishnu, Swami?"

"Yes, dear. Only the Supreme Being has the power to bless you with a child of such sterling character."

Aditi frowned in doubt: "Swami, will the great Mahavishnu condescend to listen to my prayers?"

Kasyapa reassured her with a smile saying, "Aditi, you seek a boon for the benefit of all the three worlds. God always looks with favor on such altruism. Confidently begin your penance to Mahavishnu."

Aditi touched Kasyapa's feet in respect and asked his blessings on her endeavor.

"May Lord Vishnu grant your wish," said Kasyapa solemnly.

Aditi withdrew into the seclusion of a tranquil *ashram* and immersed herself in rigorous penance. The intensity of her *tapas* astounded even Kasyapa, himself a seasoned practitioner of austerities. Aditi merged with nature and her entire being pulsated with the holy name of Lord Vishnu. In an instant, Sri Mahavishnu stood before her.

Moved to tears by the Lord's apparition, Aditi cried, "My God, you have come!"

Vishnu smiled in benediction: "Aditi, the ardour of your penance has captured my heart. What do you want from me?"

Aditi, voice hoarse with emotion, said, "Lord, you are the *Paramathma*: surely you know my heart's desire?"

Vishnu's eyes twinkled in merriment. "My child, indeed I can read your mind like an open book. But the voice of my devotees is sweet music to my ears. Let me hear your wish."

"*Bhagavan,* this is my humble request: Bless me with a child whose heart is unsullied by hatred, jealousy and discrimination. Let him dedicate himself to the betterment of the entire universe."

Mahavishnu smiled and said, "Aditi, your wish is granted. Look up at the sky."

Aditi gazed skywards in puzzlement.

"Who do you see there, Aditi?"

"Surya *Bhagavan* is shining among the clouds, my Lord."

"Now look around you, Aditi. What do you see?"

"Lord, I see a thorn bush and a flowering plant."

"Aditi, do the golden sunbeams spread their warm light equally on both the coarse thorns and the captivating blossoms?"

Realization dawning slowly, Aditi whispered in awe: "Yes, my Lord."

"Surya's impartial gaze falls on all creation with the same benign magnanimity. Devoid of envy and hatred, he strives perpetually for the upliftment of the universe. He is the child you seek." Vishnu smiled at the enthralled Aditi and continued: "Surya is a colossal, luminous orb in the galaxy. He also resides in my right eye in his ethereal form. This glorious being will be born as your son."

Aditi exclaimed, "God, I am indeed fortunate!"

"Yes, Aditi. It is my wish that the *Navagrahas*, who are pure incandescence, be incarnated in physical form to be worshipped by the human race on earth. You are blessed to be the instrument of my will. Surya, who is a part of my essence, will soon be your son. Grant him the reverence which you accord me."

As Aditi closed her eyes and bowed low in immense gratitude, Mahavishnu vanished. Aditi ran to give the joyous tidings to her family.

Kasyapa embraced her and said, "Aditi, you are indeed abundantly blessed. Follow the Supreme Lord's instructions and commence your worship of Surya at the earliest."

Aditi's twelve sisters excitedly discussed the new developments.

Vinata said, "Surely, Sister Aditi is the luckiest of us all! Lord Vishnu himself has granted her an audience. And now, Surya is to be born as her son!"

As the admiring group clustered round Aditi, Diti sniggered aloud and said, "Hah! Has it perhaps slipped Aditi's mind that she has a god-like husband who can grant her progeny at will? Why would anyone choose to go through the tribulation of penance to propitiate another god? It appears that Aditi is a glutton for punishment!"

Danu, Simhika and Kaala laughed and clapped their hands in glee at Diti's mockery.

Kasyapa frowned darkly and angrily reproached his wife: "Diti, your taunt only demonstrates your own arrogance and your abject ignorance of Lord Sri Mahavishnu's greatness. He is the eternal Father of the cosmos: it is he who created Brahma, who in turn gave life to your father, Daksha *prajapati,* and my father, sage Mareechi. When the resplendent Surya is also none other than Vishnu himself, it is blasphemous to belittle the worship of Surya *Bhagavan!*"

Aditi quickly intervened, saying, "*Swami,* forgive Diti – it is only her innocence which makes her speak thus."

Diti spat out at her: "Sister Aditi, I do not need you to be my champion! I can take care of myself, thank you!" Diti continued in a voice dripping with sarcasm, "Oh yes! Vishnu is our forefather. Obviously, that is why he decided to assume the form of a wild pig and kill Hiranyaksha, his great granddaughter, Diti's, dearest son. What an affectionate grandfather he is!" Diti sniffed in disdain and stomped off, followed by her coterie of supporters. Vinata, Kadru and Muni remained protectively around Aditi.

Vinata clasped Aditi on her shoulder and said, "Sister, ignore Diti's outburst. A great miracle waits to be manifested through you. As our husband advises, start your obeisance to Surya."

At an auspicious time designated by Kasyapa, Aditi embarked on her worship. Oblivious to the pangs of hunger and thirst, and the passage of time, she immersed her entire being in single-minded meditation on the sun god. Her devotion elevated her to a spiritual plane in which time, space and causation ceased to be relevant. As she hovered in a transcendental state beyond darkness and light, a sweet voice penetrated her consciousness.

"Mother!"

Aditi stirred.

"Mother!"

Again, the mellifluous voice clamoured for attention. Aditi emerged from her trance and opened her eyes. There before her was a whirling, radiant orb of light. Aditi's entire being was swamped by a mystical tide of joy.

She whispered in tremulous tones, "Who – who are you?"

The same honeyed voice emanated from the luminescent disc: "Mother, it is me, Surya. You reached out to me through the silent yearning of your psyche and I have answered your call!"

Aditi exclaimed in delight: "Surya *Bhagavan!* You heard my prayers!"

"I share your longing for me to be your son. Mother, let me be cocooned in the snug warmth of your womb."

Aditi, moved to tears by the tenderness of these words, stood speechless, as the adorable voice again echoed from the brilliant sphere: "Cradle me gently in your lap, mother, and feed me the milk of sweet nourishment and divine bliss."

Voice choked with emotion, Aditi said, "O my divine son – dearest child of my heart! How fortunate I am!"

"I am equally fortunate, mother. Return to the *ashram* and await my arrival. I will not be long."

The radiant orb disappeared. Aditi looked round her in awe. It struck her that she had gazed at the blinding disc of light without once blinking her eyes. Nor had she paid obeisance to Surya *Bhagavan!* Her pang of remorse was quickly extinguished by a tender smile. She thought, 'Never mind – after all, I am his mother!'

Aditi hurried back to the *ashram*, where she soon showed signs of growing pregnancy. The presence of the god of light in her womb was reflected in the resplendent glow which cloaked her body. Her face blossomed like the luminescent full moon. She bore the weight of her pregnancy sedately and joyfully continued to perform her duties to Kasyapa.

Observing her moving heavily about her chores, Vinata said, "Sister Aditi, it is not right that you take so much upon yourself in your delicate state. Let us take care of our husband."

Kadru too spoke out in support of Vinata: "Yes, sister. Rest assured that we will attend to our lord's every need."

Kasyapa himself condoned their stand saying, "Yes, Aditi. When you carry Surya, the god of light, in your sacred womb, it is not appropriate that you continue to perform menial tasks like a servant. Let Vinata and Kadru relieve you."

Vinata and Kadru served Kasyapa with single-minded devotion. Late one night, Kasyapa awoke from a deep slumber to find the two women gently pressing his legs in the darkness.

He exclaimed in surprise, "Vinata and Kadru, are you not asleep yet?!"

His wives replied in unison: "*Swami*, serving you is our best repose."

Greatly moved by their selfless devotion, Kasyapa smiled affectionately at them and said, "Your dedication warms my heart. I wish to grant each of you a boon. Name your desire."

Elated at this unexpected bounty, the generous Vinata said, "Sister Kadru, make your wish first."

Kadru pondered for a moment. Then, "*Swami*, grant me a thousand sons, with long, gleaming, limbless torsos. Let them slither lissomely across the ground ..."

Kasyapa interrupted her: "Kadru, stop! Do you know what you are asking for?"

Kadru smiled in calm confidence. "Indeed, my lord, I am clear that I wish to bear *naga kumaras* as my sons."

Kasyapa remonstrated with her: "Kadru, I beg you to reconsider: your wish for serpent sons is bizarre, to say the least. Let me grant you another gift."

However, Kadru stood her ground and staunchly declared, "*Swami*, this is the only boon I ask of you."

Kasyapa sighed resignedly and said, "Well, my wife, if that is what you truly wish, so be it." He turned to Vinata. "And you, Vinata, what is the boon you desire from me?"

Vinata replied solemnly, "Lord, grant me two sons who will surpass Kadru's serpent progeny in valour and might."

Kasyapa inclined his head in blessing, "So be it, Vinata."

Deeply perturbed by the turn of events, Kasyapa hurried to *Satyaloka* and sought Brahma's counsel.

"Revered grandsire, what does Kadru's boon portend? I am filled with dread."

Brahma reassured him, saying, "Kasyapa, fear not. Remember that it is the supreme will of Sri Mahavishnu which presides over all the cosmos. The Lord has ordained that, in addition to the various *devas, gandharvas* and *asuras*, you and your wives will also beget miscellaneous other beings like birds, animals, cattle and reptiles."

"But, *Bhagavan* ..." Brahma interrupted the agitated Kasyapa with a soothing wave of his hand.

"I understand the reservation you have in producing serpent offspring whose venom will pose a fatal hazard to all other forms of life. But, calm yourself. I will duly teach you the means of saving the victims of snake bite. Go in peace and fulfill your wives' boons."

The relieved Kasyapa bowed before the Creator and returned to his *ashram*.

One auspicious day, in the predawn hour, Kasyapa stood knee-deep in the calm waters of the river, immersed in meditation. Facing the east, he performed his ritual morning ablution.

At the same time, Aditi's twelve sisters gathered to attend to her confinement. As the labour advanced, the mother's birth pangs were miraculously experienced, not as pain, but as pleasure!

The glow of dawn painted the sky in soft pastel shades of red and gold and the entire *ashram* was enveloped in radiant warmth. Just as the rays of the rising sun flared above the horizon, Surya, foremost of the *Navagrahas*, took physical form as the virtuous Aditi's infant son. Lord Vishnu's decree came to pass. This was truly a red letter day in the annals of the infinite cosmos.

Even as the three worlds celebrated the sun god's advent, in *Vaikuntha*

– the Abode of Bliss, the reclining Lord Vishnu sat up abruptly and gazed thoughtfully into the distance.

Sri Mahalakshmi, beauty incarnate, looked up questioningly at her consort. "*Swami*, your mind is far away."

Turning His serene face towards her, Lord Vishnu held out his hands: "Lakshmi, come here and tell me what you see in my right eye."

Lakshmi approached him and gazed into the profound depths of his right eye. Smiling playfully, she said, "The only thing I see is my own image reflected in the lotus petal of your vision, my Lord."

Lord Vishnu gently shook his head in disagreement, the gleam of gold from his crocodile-shaped *makara kundalas* rippling across his exquisite blue cheeks. He said, "No, my beloved, you know very well that your place is in my heart."

Lakshmi's voice trembled with emotion: "Yes, my Lord, I am *Vishnupriya*. I am ensconced in your heart for all time. I pervade every atom of your body. We are inextricably merged – You and I are but parts of one indivisible whole."

Lord Vishnu nodded in benign agreement. "Well said, dearest. Our sublime union transcends all reason and emotion: it is beyond interpretation."

Lakshmi smiled. "Well, my Lord, now that I accept that I am not in your right eye, tell me who is the fortunate one who resides there."

Lord Vishnu said, "Lakshmi, Surya abides in my right eye in his ethereal form."

Mahalakshmi exclaimed: "Of course, my Lord! I know that you guard the sun in your right eye and the moon in your left. However, I must admit that losing myself in ecstasy in the fathomless depths of your lotus-eye sometimes makes me forgetful!"

Mahavishnu chuckled and continued, "Lakshmi, I have glad tidings for you. Surya has taken birth in physical form."

Lakshmi smiled mischievously. "In that case, *Swami*, Surya is no longer in your eye. You were wrong earlier!"

"No, my queen. Surya will continue to reside in my eye for all eternity."

"Is that so? But, if Surya is born elsewhere, and also remains in your eye, his radiance will be diffused – he will lose much of his luster."

"My dear, let me demonstrate the fallacy of your argument. See the two lamps before us. Use one lamp to light the other."

Lakshmi laughed. "My Lord, both the lamps are already burning merrily!"

"Look again, dearest. One of them has deliberately snuffed out its own light – it looks like it yearns to be lit by your lovely hand!"

Lakshmi looked suspiciously, first at her consort's twinkling eyes, and then at the now unlit lamp. With infinite grace, she picked up the burning lamp and lit the others' wick. Lord Vishnu came to stand close behind her. Encircling her within his arms, he bent to rest his chin gently on her shoulder.

"Now, observe the lamps carefully, my love. You have used the flame of one to light the other. Has the first lamp diminished in radiance?"

"No, my Lord."

Sri Mahavishnu led her to *seshatalpa* – the serpent bed. Sitting beside her, he cupped her glowing face tenderly in his hands and said, "Although one lamp was lit with the flame of the other, both lamps burn with undimmed brilliance – like your sparkling eyes, my beloved!"

The Lord smiled and continued: "The light of the lamp is inexhaustible. Similarly, our original divine essence is infinite – it is a limitless *avyaya* form of the Godhead. When we choose to assume various *avatars*, the original *moolarupa* wholly retains its power and dimension."

Vishnu went on: "In the ages to come, you and I will take numerous *avatars*. Through all these incarnations, our original forms will remain unaltered, without losing an iota of sublimity."

Mahalakshmi wondered: "So, Surya, who is shining here ethereally in your right eye, is also shining undimmed somewhere else in a gross form!"

"That is the inexplicable truth of my creation, Lakshmi," said the Lord.

Lakshmi leaned forward in interest. "Tell me, *Swami*, where and to whom has Surya been born?"

"At the start of creation, I decreed that the *Navagrahas*, who reside in space as spiritual beings, should assume gross bodies so that the human race can gain merit through their worship. My will is now taking concrete shape with Surya's birth as the son of the virtuous Kasyapa and his consort, Aditi."

"Your will is supreme, my Lord. And when will the other eight *grahas* take their *avatars*?"

Vishnu's eyes sparkled as he teased, "There is a time and place for everything, my queen."

Lakshmi rose indignantly, but bit back her spirited resort as the familiar "Narayana! Narayana!" echoed through *Vaikuntha*.

As always, sage Narada followed hot on the heels of his fervent chant and bowed in deep reverence before the divine couple.

Smiling in benediction, Lord Vishnu asked, "So, Narada, how are you?"

"In the best of health and spirits, *Bhagavan* – thanks to you! What have I to fear when protected by the armor of your grace? After all, you shower your blessings unconditionally on your devotees, as *Nirhetuka Krpa.*"

Mahavishnu laughed appreciatively. "Narada, your words remain as sweet as your melodies."

"My Lord, you gifted me this *mahathi* as soon as I commenced my sacred *yagna* of singing the glory of your divine name. Words and music are fused in my being – as long as both my tongue and my lute are but instruments of the chant, 'Narayana!' no harm can come to me."

Mahalakshmi, familiar with the workings of the sage, smiled. "So, Narada, what brings you hurrying here?"

"Mother, I bear tidings of great import!"

Vishnu asked in amusement: "And you think this breaking news has not yet reached our ears?"

"Narayana! You are omniscient! But, surely, you will not deny Narada, your humble devotee, the pleasure of being your herald?"

Vishnu laughed and said, "Narada, it is always a pleasure to hear you! Go ahead and make your announcement."

Narada bowed in acknowledgement and said, "My Lord, the pious lady Aditi has given birth to a son. The father, Kasyapa, plans to hold the naming ceremony at his *ashram.*"

"That is indeed good to hear, Narada. Go and invite *chaturmukha* Brahma, Lord Shiva, Indra and others to join the celebration. Let the universe rejoice at the birth of Surya, the harbinger of happiness."

With a joyous, "Narayana!" Narada hurried to spread the good tidings.

Kasyapa's *ashram* wore a festive look, as a resplendent celestial host filled its humble precincts. Lord Vishnu, Lord Shiva and Brahma stood apart with Mahalakshmi, Satidevi and Saraswati. Sage Narada, accompanied by Indra, paid obeisance to the divine couples. An unceasing tide of *devas* and *maanasaputras*, together with their spouses, joined them in homage.

Kasyapa bowed before the Supreme God, saying, *"Bhagavan*, our son is the precious gift of your grace to Aditi and me. Bless him with a name of your choosing."

Lord Vishnu said, "Kasyapa, my gift belongs not only to you and your wife, but to all animate and inanimate creation. Your son is the incarnation of Surya, the foremost of the *Navagrahas*. He will rule the planets as he moves through the twelve signs of the zodiac."

Vishnu paused at the puzzled Kasyapa's interruption: "Lord, what are these twelve signs of the zodiac?"

Brahma explained, "Kasyapa, Sri Mahavishnu has willed that all the stars which shine in the heavenly firmament form constellations in the shape of *Mesham, Vrhsabham, Mithunam, Karkatakam, Simham, Kanya, Thula, Vrichikam, Dhanas, Makaram, Kumbham and Meenam* – corresponding to the ram, the bull, the twins, the crab, the lion, the virgin, the scales, the scorpion, the bow, the goat, the water pot and the fish."

Lord Vishnu continued, "Your son, Surya, will move through these dozen signs of the zodiac over a period of twelve months, or one human year. He will reside for one month in every sign, or *raasi*. In each *raasi*, he will be known by a different name – these twelve names will be collectively called the *Dwaadasa Aadityas*."

Vishnu turned to his fellow gods: "ParamaShiva, Brahma and I will now pronounce Surya's names."

Lord Shiva smiled and nodded in agreement: "Mahavishnu, we await your lead."

Aditi came forward and handed the infant to Vishnu with great reverence. The Lord smiled down at the gurgling baby. Mahalakshmi then cradled the child in her own arms, tenderly kissed his radiant forehead, and placed him gently on an elevated dais.

Vishnu closed his eyes and intoned *"Om!"*

Even as the sound of the primordial *mantra* lingered in the air, the Lord looked down at the child and pronounced the first name: "Dhaata!" The onlookers held their breaths in wonder as a second child, identical to the original baby, appeared on the dais. Before they could release their collective breath, Vishnu announced, "Aaryama!" A third baby lay before their amazed eyes! Vishnu continued – "Mithra!" "Sakra!" With each name, a new infant materialized on the dais.

Lord Vishnu then turned to Brahma and beckoned him forward.

The Creator intoned, "Varuna! Amsumanta! Bhaga! Vivasvan!"

Lord Shiva stepped forward in his turn and proclaimed, "Pusha! Savitru! Twashta! Vishnu!"

Each name pealed with bell-like clarity in the hushed atmosphere. The spell-bound assembly gazed in awe as a new child appeared on the platform with the pronouncement of each name. When Lord Shiva announced the final name, "Vishnu!" a dazzling array of twelve identical, beautiful infants lay side by side before them.

The onlookers' excited murmurs subsided when Narada strummed his lute. As the sage melodiously chanted Surya's twelve names: "Dhaata! Aaryama! Mithra! Sakra! Varuna! Amsumanta! Bhaga! Vivasvan! Pusha! Savitru! Twashta! Vishnu!" every one at the august gathering showered the infants with fragrant blossoms and yellow rice grains, as the ritual *akshata* for a long life.

Mareechi, Kasyapa's father, paid obeisance to Vishnu, Shiva and Brahma and said, "The Holy Trinity has blessed our Surya with auspicious names. I am indeed fortunate to be the grandfather of the god of light."

Lord Vishnu smiled at him. "Mareechi, your daughter-in-law, Aditi, performed her penance with the noble purpose of obtaining a child who would treat all creation with impartial munificence. As the result of her altruism, she is blessed to be the mother of the king of the *grahas*. Aditya, the son of Aditi, will be the shining sovereign of the *Navagrahas* and will be worshipped by all."

"So be it!" Shiva and Brahma intoned in unison.

Aditi gazed fondly on the twelve adorable infants, her heart overflowing with love. She longed to gather them all into her arms and let them suckle to their tiny stomachs' content. Even as she reached out to embrace them, her twelve babies merged into one! Aditi cradled her radiant son in her lap and lifted him tenderly to her breast, crooning a lullaby, a beatific smile lighting up her face.

<hr />

The charming infant filled Kasyapa's household with joy. Aditi and her sisters lavished all their care and affection on the growing child. In no time, Surya was leading them on merry chases, as he crawled energetically about the ashram. To their wonder, a nimbus of light constantly illuminated the ground beneath the child.

One day, as Aditi wove a garland of flowers for the morning worship, Simhika came running to her with Surya in her arms. Aditi looked up at the urgency in her voice.

"Sister Aditi, look – the child's body is burning! I am unable to bear the heat – take him."

Aditi took her son and said, "No, Simhika, I can find nothing out of the ordinary in his warmth."

Simhika insisted, "No! My hands are still flaming with his touch!"

Hearing her cry, Kasyapa came and felt his son's brow. Frowning, he said, "Aditi, Simhika is right – Surya's body is excessively hot. It must be a fever."

As the days passed, Surya's high temperature persisted, although he remained as active and cheerful as ever. Kasyapa and Aditi, worried over this abnormal development, were clueless as to its cause or remedy.

As they fretted one day, Vinata ran to them in excitement: "*Swami*, sage Narada is here!"

Kasyapa hurried out and greeted the distinguished visitor with folded hands.

"Narayana!" Narada blessed Kasyapa with his invocation of the Supreme God.

Kasyapa respectfully seated the sage on a mat of *darbha* grass and said, "*Maharshi*, we have missed your *darshan* these past months – you last blessed us with your presence at Surya's naming ceremony."

"Yes, Kasyapa, I have not passed this way for quite a while. By the way, how is the child?"

Kasyapa sighed heavily. "*Swami*, I must confess that I am very anxious about Surya. He has a persistent fever. In spite of all the remedies we have tried, his temperature remains abnormally high."

"Is that so? Take me to the boy." Sage Narada followed Kasyapa into the *ashram*, where he found Surya engaged in boisterous play, with Aditi panting to keep pace with her son's boundless energy.

Chuckling, Narada looked around him in surprise. He remarked, "The very air of the *ashram* seems to possess a strange sparkle!"

Kasyapa replied, "Yes, *Maharshi* – right from the day of his birth, Surya has been surrounded by a brilliant halo of light."

Narada gently picked up the lively child and gazed intently into his upturned face. To Kasyapa's surprise, the sage did not comment on the heat emanating from Surya. Narada seated himself on the raised dais in front of the house, holding the boy in his lap. He looked up at Kasyapa and Aditi and smiled, "So, our little beam of sunshine is spreading light everywhere, is he?"

Aditi said, "Yes, *Swami*. As he grows, his splendor increases in intensity."

"That is as it should be, Aditi. After all, the dissemination of light is Surya's innate trait."

Kasyapa agreed: "Yes, *Maharshi*, that's true."

"Narayana!" exclaimed the sage with a laugh. "Well, Kasyapa, if light is an inherent part of Surya, surely you will agree that heat is also an inseparable attribute of his being?"

Realization dawned on Kasyapa. "*Maharshi*, you mean..."

"Yes, Kasyapa, the heat which radiates from Surya is natural – not a fever, as you fear. Remember that Surya is the dispenser of heat and light, both essential for the survival of the universe."

Aditi and Kasyapa sighed in relief as the weight of anxiety lifted from their hearts. Narada handed the child to Aditi, who carried him into the house.

The sage turned to Kasyapa. "It is time to commence Surya's education. You will be his *guru*. Teach him the six *angas* – *siksha* (pronunciation), *vyaakarana* (grammar), *chandas* (prosody), *nirukta* (explanation of obscure terms), *jyothisham* (astronomy) and *kalpam* (religious rites)."

Kasyapa bowed in agreement.

Narada continued: "Let him learn the four *Vedas*. Impart to him the scriptural knowledge of *Meemansa, Nyaaya, Sabda, Dharma, Artha, Ayurveda* and *Dhanurveda,* and the *Puranas* as delineated in the *Sastras*."

Kasyapa could not hide his surprise.

Narada smiled at him and said, "Surya is destined to be the universal benefactor. Mastery of all the above eighteen *vidyas* is essential to equip him for this role. Kasyapa, your son will excel you in the acquisition, containment and dissemination of wisdom."

"So be it, *Maharshi*. Every father wishes to see the son to excel the parent."

Kasyapa fell silent and then heaved a sigh of remorse. "*Maharshi*, my heart continues to ache when I consider that I have failed in my duty as a father towards my other sons."

"Narayana!" Narada exclaimed. "Kasyapa, it was the will of my revered father, Brahma, that your sons establish the *deva* and *daanava* kingdoms. Although they are mutually antagonistic, they live happily in their independent realms."

"*Maharshi*, does this mean that you have visited my sons recently?"

"Yes, Kasyapa. In my role as celestial courier, I wander from one end of the cosmos to the other. Of course, keeping abreast of the workings of the rival factions is one of my priorities!"

"I am very happy to hear this, *Maharshi*. Please keep my sons in your care."

"Narayana! That is beyond my brief! Leave them to their own devices, Kasyapa. What must be, will be." Narada exhorted the dejected Kasyapa: "Come, Kasyapa, take heart from your good fortune in being Surya's *guru*. Better to impart wisdom to one worthy son than to educate a thousand undeserving ones."

Kasyapa, soothed by Narada's wise counsel, commenced Surya's education. With his vast intelligence and willingness to learn, Surya mastered the eighteen *vidyas* in an incredibly short period of time. The light of knowledge added extra luster to his naturally radiant countenance. His impartial treatment of all creatures earned him universal respect. As Surya reached adolescence, his statuesque physique, enhanced by his charming smile, endowed him with the exquisite beauty of the golden dawn.

One day, Aditi sat on the *ashram's* raised dais, watching her beloved son in the distance. Kasyapa, returning from the forest, emptied a basket of flowers and twigs on the *darbha* grass mat and sat beside her.

Looking at Surya in rapt adoration, Aditi said, "*Swami*, how handsome our son is!"

Kasyapa smiled fondly at the proud mother. "Yes, Aditi, Surya's beauty is indeed divine."

"I wonder which lucky girl is going to be his wife!"

Kasyapa started to reply, but stopped short as the lotus buds in the heap of flowers beside him suddenly unfurled their flushed petals and bloomed into renewed life. He looked up and smiled to see Surya standing before him.

"Father, give me the twigs. I will prepare them for the sacrificial fire." Surya took the sticks and went indoors, his parents' affectionate glances following him.

"Narayana! Narayana!"

They turned expectantly at the call. It was Narada, strumming his lute in accompaniment to his holy chant. Kasyapa and Aditi rose hurriedly and welcomed the sage with folded hands, pressing their warm hospitality on him.

Narada settled down on the dais and observed, "As I walked among the clouds, your son Surya was visible even from a great distance as a dazzling pillar of light. His beauty grows by the day!"

Kasyapa laughed with fatherly pride. "*Maharshi*, Aditi and I were just commenting on Surya's extraordinary good looks."

"Well, did you also discuss his coming marriage?" asked Narada.

Aditi replied, "*Swami*, that is not in our hands. God has to will it."

"God has already willed it, Aditi. A few days back, I saw a beautiful girl, suitable for Surya in every way."

"*Swami*! Really? Tell me all about her – who is she? Where did you see her?"

Narada laughed at Aditi's excitement and continued: "I suppose you know Viswakarma?"

Kasyapa nodded: "He is the divine architect Prabhaasavasu's son, right?"

"Correct, Kasyapa. Viswakarma is the son of Varastri and Prabhaasavasu, the last of the eight *Vasus*. Their eldest daughter, the beautiful Samjna, seems to be made for Surya."

Aditi turned to Kasyapa. "*Swami*, maybe you should approach Viswakarma and Varastri?"

Narada smiled. "I have already sounded them out in this matter, Aditi. Prabhaasavasu and his wife have heard glowing reports about Surya, not only from various individuals, but also from the four mouths of Lord Brahma himself. They are eager for this match."

Kasyapa said thoughtfully, "We will have to ascertain the girl's wishes."

Narada's eyes twinkled. "That too has been done, Kasyapa! I gave her parents an account of Surya's sterling character and beauty and then repeated it to Samjna in private. She did not have to utter a word – her glowing eyes said it all!"

Aditi laughed in merriment. "Oh, *Maharshi*! You have come to us with everything arranged!"

Kasyapa joined in her mirth. "Well, Aditi, that is sage Narada's inimitable style! He arranged our marriage in the same way." He smiled at his wife in fond remembrance.

"Kasyapa, if you want further assurance, let me tell you that I also overheard Samjna expressing her eagerness to wed Surya." A mischievous smile flitted across Narada's face. "Of course, I just happened to standing behind a hedge in the garden when she confided in her mother!"

Kasyapa chuckled in delight. "*Maharshi*, I think it would be best if you spoke to Surya about Samjna. After all, you are the one who can give him a first-hand account of the girl's charm and beauty."

Narada agreed saying, "Indeed, that is the very purpose of my visit. I will then arrange for Viswakarma to visit you."

With Surya's consent, arrangements for the marriage were made. Surya and Samjna were wed in a glittering ceremony at Viswakarma's palatial abode, in the presence of the *Trimurtis* – Brahma, Vishnu and Maheswara, and their consorts. All the attendant *devas, maanasaputras, prajapatis* and sages showered the new couple with blessings for long, happy lives and many children.

At Sri Mahavishnu's suggestion, Viswakarma built a beautiful palace for his beloved daughter and son-in-law. Made of pure gold, it emblazoned the vast reaches of outer space.

Surya and his new bride took their leave of Kasyapa and Aditi. Surya bid farewell to his aunts, assuring them that he would always answer their summons instantaneously.

Fondly embracing his weeping mother, Surya said in solace, "Mother, it is my duty to fulfill Sri Mahavishnu's will."

Kasyapa gently led Aditi away, reminding her: "Aditi, my dear, every circumstance of Surya's life has been ordained by the Lord. When you asked for a son who would be the universal benefactor, you put yourself above the natural self-interests of a mother. Wherever he may be, Surya's presence will always light up our lives."

<hr>

Surya and Samjna were flooded with an immeasurable tide of love for each other.

To Surya, every move of Samjna's lissome body was an enchanting dance; her doe-eyed glances became searing darts of love; the seductive swaying of her long, raven-black braid made his eyes light up in pleasure; her ruby lips smiled in tender promise of things to come.

Samjna entered the bed chamber with her graceful, swan-like gait. At every step, her anklets beat a sensuous tattoo on the gleaming floor. Seeing Surya reclining on the couch, her heart melted with affection and a shy smile played about her parted lips. She softly closed the golden doors and snuffed out the lamp on its stand: the brilliance which constantly emanated from Surya made its light redundant. She seated herself beside her husband.

Head bowed shyly, she said tremulously, "*Swami*, I want something from you. Will you grant my wish?"

Heart blazing with affection, Surya tilted up her chin with a tender hand and said, "Samjna, my beloved, all you have to do is ask. It will be yours."

She gazed adoringly into his radiant eyes. "*Swami*, I want three children from you – two boys and a girl."

Surya laughed: "So clear on that, my love?"

She flushed, but replied spiritedly: "Yes, my lord."

Surya gathered her into his arms.

Samjna caressed his broad chest and whispered, "*Swami*, I adore the touch of your body. Its intoxicating warmth kindles the fire of passion in my heart."

Surya held her close against him. "And you, my love, are a *varavarnini*."

"And what is that, my lord?"

Surya's lambent voice was a caress in itself. "A *varavarnini* is a beautiful woman whose precious body blesses her husband with life-giving warmth in winter and soothing coolness in summer."

An exquisite flush spread over Samjna's delicate cheeks.

Surya continued with a smile: "Samjna, you are not only my *varavarnini*, but also my *varaaroha*."

His wife looked up in mock sternness – "Yet another unknown term, my lord ... and what does this one mean?"

Surya erased the charming frown on her face with his gentle fingers and laughed. "This time, your long braid is best qualified to give you an answer – after all, it is more intimate with the contours of your beautiful hips than I am!"

In reply, Samjna hid her blushing face against her husband's chest.

THE BIRTH OF CHANDRA

Nirvikalpananda paused and looked at his disciples. They remained motionless, unwilling to stop the flow of their master's captivating chronicle.

Nirvikalpananda smiled and continued. "Well, my sons, I can see that you are ready to hear about the advent of the second of the *grahas* – Chandra."

"Yes, master," the four young men chorused eagerly.

"Chandra is also known as Aatreya, or son of Atri. Do you remember Sage Atri?"

Chidananda quickly replied, "Yes, master. You mentioned that he was one of Brahma's *maanasaputras*."

"Excellent! Then you will also recall that he married Anasuya. Who was Anasuya?"

Sadananda urged him on: "Please tell us, master."

"Anasuya was the daughter of Brahma's *maanasaputra*, Kardama, and his wife, Devahuti. Anasuya was a chaste and virtuous wife to sage Atri. For many years, they remained childless. The miraculous birth of Anasuya's sons is a wonderful tale."

So saying, Nirvikalpananda started on the second part of his narrative.

—⚬⚬⚬—

Sage Atri returned to his *ashram* with the grass and twigs necessary for his ritual worship. He gratefully accepted the cup of cool water Anasuya held out to him and smiled at his wife. No answering smile erased the lines of despair on her face.

"Anasuya, my dear, what's wrong?"

Anasuya looked up at him in sorrow. "*Swami*, you know my heart's desire."

Atri sighed helplessly and gazed into his wife's lovely face. The vermillion *tilak* was an autumn moon on the shapely crescent of her forehead. Her luminous eyes were dark pools under the delicately arched eyebrows. Her lips were tender, crimson petals. The gracefully draped *saree* emphasized her slim waist … Atri stopped short: the same slender waist reminded him that it was yet to bear the precious weight of pregnancy.

"*Swami*, what are you looking at?"

Atri emerged from his reverie and chuckled. "Now, Anasuya, as a faithful husband, which other woman can I look at, except my own wife? My dearest, you grow more beautiful by the day!"

A fleeting smile appeared on Anasuya's face, only to be engulfed by sorrow once more.

"*Swami*, without bearing fruit, beauty is but an empty husk." She paused. "I have faithfully performed every rite and propitiated all the gods in order to be blessed with children. Tell me … what more can I do?"

Atri reached out to her and held her close. "My love, now you can serve your husband."

She looked up at him questioningly.

Atri continued: "Anasuya, let me remind you: when Brahma created me as his *maanasaputra*, he decreed that we would have abundant progeny. His promise will not be in vain. We will be blessed with children when the time is ripe. Let us be patient."

Anasuya's eyes gleamed with the faint stirrings of hope. "*Swami*, do you believe this?"

"Of course, dearest," Atri said firmly. "Your virtue is peerless. God always grants a virtuous wife's wishes."

There was a trace of sarcasm in Anasuya's voice as she replied, "*Swami*, I sometimes fear that suffering is the only lot of a virtuous wife."

Atri exclaimed, "What makes you talk like this, Anasuya?"

"*Swami*, earlier this morning, Seelavathi was here."

"Ah ... you mean Ugrasravas' wife?"

"Yes, my lord. Seelavathi's virtue and loyalty to her husband are unmatched. She truly lives up to her name – the chaste one!"

"I have heard that Ugrasravas is a man corroded by evil in both body and soul."

Anasuya's voice trembled with pity. "Yes, *Swami*. Seelavathi is young and exceptionally beautiful. Her husband is an old man, afflicted by leprosy. Yet, she serves him as if he were god."

"The poor lady. It seems that Ugrasravas is possessed by the rage of despair. I was told that he is so eaten up with jealousy that he insists on accompanying his wife when she goes begging."

"Yes, *Swami* – she carries his rank-smelling body in a basket on her head and ekes out a living on the meagre alms she receives." Anasuya continued bitterly, "Now, *Swami*, I'm sure you will agree that virtuous wives get more than their fair share of trials and tribulations!"

Atri attempted to cheer up his wife. "Well, Anasuya. We know that precious gold must endure the heat of the furnace and the blows of the hammer before it is transformed into a beautiful ornament."

"So, do you think Seelavathi will become a lovely ornament?"

Atri smiled. "Not only Seelavathi, my dearest ... Anasuya too!"

———

Seelavathi draped a fresh *saree* around her thin body and applied the vermillion *tilak* on her forehead. She picked up the string of fragrant flowers a kind lady had given her earlier in the day and braided it into her long plait.

A coarse shout assaulted her ears. "Woman! Where are you?"

She hurried to her husband. "Here I am, *Swami*."

Seated on a rough hempen bedstead in a corner of the mean hut, Ugrasravas glared balefully at his wife. "And may I know whose eyes you seek to please with your fresh flowers and elegant *saree*?"

Seelavathi blanched at his tone. "*Swami*, we have been begging on the streets since dawn. My clothes were drenched with sweat and grime. You abhor bad odor. So, I took a bath and …"

Ugrasravas cut her off with a curt, "Enough of your stories! I'm starving. Will you give me my food or persist in wasting time with your blathering?"

"Just give me a moment, my lord." Seelavathi returned with a makeshift lamp – a rag wick floating is a small saucer of oil. As she used her hand to shield the feeble flame from the wind, the light illuminated her glowing face, highlighting its exquisite features. Ugrasravas drew in his breath sharply at this vision of his wife's ethereal beauty, as Seelavathi gracefully bent to light a larger lamp near the bed. Even devoid of any ornamentation, her loveliness shone through her like an inner flame.

Yes, his wife was indeed beautiful, Ugrasravas thought. An involuntary sigh escaped his lips. It was his misfortune that Seelavathi's very devotion had blighted any chance of his loving her. The extreme purity of her blind love, devoid of passion, had repelled him right from the start of their married life.

Ugrasravas shook his head and turned his greedy attention to the food Seelavathi placed before him. Helplessly dependent on his wife, he waited impatiently, scowling at her. As tenderly as she would a little child, Seelavathi fed him small mouthfuls from the plate.

Between bites, Ugrasravas shouted, "What is this, woman? Am I a baby to be fooled with tiny morsels of food? I suppose you are doing this deliberately to blunt the edge of my appetite: you sly creature – you plan to gorge on the remaining food yourself!"

Seelavathi calmly said, "Swami, you are teasing me – you know very well that I feel no hunger till you have eaten your fill."

Ugrasravas roared angrily, "Then feed me bigger portions." Continuing to scold his hapless wife between hungry mouthfuls, he soon finished his supper. He then asked, "Is there more food?"

Seelavathi sadly replied, "I'm afraid that is all the food we received as alms today, Swami."

Belching loudly, Ugrasravas shouted at her: "Ever since I had the misfortune of marrying you, I have been fated to endure the pangs of unappeased hunger. You disgust me!"

Seelavathi silently removed his plate. Coming back, she said: "Please lie down and rest, Swami. Let me massage your legs."

Ugrasravas looked up suspiciously. "Why such eagerness to put me to bed? Have you planned a little moonlight rendezvous after lulling me to sleep?"

"*Swami*! Please! You know that you are everything to me. And today is the night of the new moon ..."

Ugrasravas barked furiously. "Oh, shut up!" He continued thoughtfully: "By the way, I notice that you always hurry past a particular house without stopping to ask for alms. Why do you do that?"

"I prefer not to beg there," Seelavathi said quietly.

"Why, you fool – that is obviously the home of a wealthy person."

"*Swami*, that house belongs to a prostitute. It would be sinful to receive alms from her."

Ugrasravas sat up in excitement. "What! I have sometimes glimpsed a charming woman through the windows. Is she the prostitute you are talking about?"

"Yes, my lord ..."

Ugrasravas wondered aloud: "Oh, such a lovely face! And a body almost divine in its beauty!"

Seelavathi said soothingly, "*Swami*, you must rest. Forget about that woman."

But her husband was lost in a miasma of lust. He murmured softly, "My eyes are dazzled by her memory. I cannot close them in repose until I have drowned in the pleasure of her beautiful body."

Seelavathi cried out in alarm: "*Swami*, what are you saying?"

Ugrasravas turned to her angrily. "What's wrong in what I have said? It is no sin to visit prostitutes. These women only satisfy a natural, necessary craving in society."

Seelavathi protested in horror: "*Swami*, but ..."

Her husband exploded in rage: "No buts, woman! Do you think you can satisfy my body by constantly parroting '*Swami, Swami*' in my ears? Do you dare to disobey your husband? I command you to take me to her immediately!"

Controlling her tears, Seelavathi pleaded, "Please listen to me, my lord. Prostitutes must be paid for their services. You know we have no money ..."

Ugrasravas roared, "Don't I know that I am a pauper? Yet, we don't starve, do we? You don't mind cramming me into a basket, come rain or shine, and begging for alms, right? Well then, just do the same now – beg the prostitute to bestow alms of pleasurable delight on your husband."

Seelavathi was speechless in horror.

Ugrasravas continued to rave: "Fall at her gorgeous feet! Beg her to satisfy my passion! Tell her you will pay her fees by gathering alms from everyone."

"*Swami*, you are ill. Let me ..."

"Shut your mouth! It is the sight of your simpering face which paralyzes my limbs. The pleasures of her body will be a panacea for all my ills. Now, move! Get my basket!"

Like a maniac, Ugrasravas rolled about on the bed and struggled to come to his feet. Seelavathi sighed in resignation. Placing him in his customary position in the basket, she lifted her burden on to her head and walked towards the village with a heavy heart.

Ugrasravas, immersed in happy anticipation of the pleasures to come, luxuriously stretched out his legs. Suddenly, a cry of indescribable anguish rang out in the darkness of the new moon night, making Seelavathi stop short. As she strained her alarmed eyes, the vague outline of a human figure, impaled high up on the point of a vertical spike, was discernable in the gloom.

A hoarse male voice moaned, "Hear me – the thoughtless boor who kicked me will himself undergo excruciating torment. He will die when the sun rises. This is the immutable curse of Sage Mandavya!"

Ugrasravas murmured in fright, "My leg hit someone, I think."

Seelavathi's blood turned to ice in her veins. Who was Sage Mandavya? Would his curse come true?

⬦

Nirvikalpananda paused. His disciples waited in breathless anticipation, fascinated by the panorama unfolding before their mind's eye.

Vimalananda, unable to contain himself any longer, burst out: "Master, who was this Mandavya who cursed Ugrasravas?"

"My son, Mandavya was a great sage. One day, he was absorbed in deep meditation in his *ashram*, arms raised skywards in a yogic posture. A band of robbers, fleeing with their booty, stumbled upon his hermitage and concealed themselves there without his knowledge. The king's soldiers soon arrived there in hot pursuit, and urgently interrogated the sage. Mandavya, who was under a vow of silence, stoically ignored them. A systematic search of the *ashram* soon revealed the hidden culprits. Assuming that Mandavya was actually one of the band, and was hoping to evade capture by cleverly posing as a sage, the soldiers arrested him, along with the robbers.

"At the palace, the king sentenced the thieves to immediate death. In the case of Mandavya, the angry king ordered that he be impaled on the point of a spear thrust vertically into the ground. Since then, the sage had lingered on in prolonged anguish, to be further tormented by Ugrasravas' accidental kick."

———

'Hear me – the thoughtless boor who kicked me will himself undergo excruciating torment. He will die when the sun rises. This is the immutable curse of Sage Mandavya!'

The dark thunder of Mandavya's curse crashed repeatedly in Seelavathi's ears.

Her husband squealed like a frightened child: "Did you hear that? Someone has cursed me! I will die at sunrise. Take me home, take me home at once!"

As if in a trance, Seelavathi reflexively obeyed her husband and started walking home.

'He will die when the sun rises ... when the sun rises ... when the sun rises ...' the ominous words echoed in her heart, sounding the knell of doom.

On his part, Ugrasravas lamented loudly, tearing his hair: "Oh, what shall I do? When the sun rises, I will die! "

'When the sun rises ...' a strange thought surfaced in Seelavathi's mind: 'What if the sun did not rise?'

Seelavathi stood still. She straightened her statuesque figure. Her eyes gleamed resolutely. She held her head up high and proclaimed: "If it is true that I worshipped god alone as my husband before my marriage, and my husband alone as god after my marriage; if my chastity and virtue are truly beyond reproach – then, may the sun never rise again!" Seelavathi's voice resonated with bell-like clarity through the silent night. She then walked home with her husband.

The power of Seelavathi's incomparable chastity transformed her words into instant reality. The sun failed to rise and the cosmos was plunged into absolute darkness. Life everywhere came to a standstill. Sacred rituals could not be performed. The gleeful *rakshasas*, empowered by the absence of light, went on the rampage. Indra and the *devas* were unable to fathom the cause of this sudden calamity.

As they milled about in confusion, a blessed sound reached their ears: "Narayana! Narayana!"

It was sage Narada. As the gods milled round the sage, clamouring for an explanation, Narada narrated the story of Seelavathi.

Indra immediately set out for earth, declaring confidently, "I will make that woman lift her absurd curse at once!"

Narada stopped him. "Wait, Indra. That is easier said than done Ugrasravas is not only old and afflicted by leprosy, but also evil – yet, the chaste Seelavathi reveres him as god. She will never consent to let her husband die."

Indra asked anxiously, "What do we do, Narada?"

"Come, let us seek the counsel of Brahma, Vishnu and Maheswara."

The *devas*, accompanied by Narada, trooped to *Satyaloka* and explained their predicament to Brahma.

The Creator advised: "This is matter of such import that it requires the joint deliberation of the *Trimurti*. Let us all go to Sri Mahavishnu."

They reached *Vaikuntha*, along with Maheswara.

There, after a moment of thoughtful silence, Sri Mahavishnu said: "Mahendra, the formidable strength of Seelavathi's chastity and virtue renders us all powerless. Of course, if Mandavya withdraws his curse, Seelavathi will relent in her turn. However, the sage's curse is irrevocable."

Indra exclaimed in alarm: "My God, is there nothing we can do?"

Vishnu smiled and continued: "Anasuya, wife of Brahma's *maanasaputra*, Atri, is Seelavathi's equal in virtue. Your only recourse is to ask Anasuya to plead with Seelavathi to revoke her curse in order to preserve the universe. Go, Indra. May success be yours!"

Parameswara intervened: "Mahendra! Tell Anasuya from me that it is her duty to ensure that the sun rises for the well-being of all mankind. She must convince Seelavathi to withdraw her curse."

Brahma added his voice: "Yes, Mahendra. Tell Anasuya that this is the united command of the *Trimurti*."

Indra saluted the Holy Trinity and left on his mission, accompanied by Narada.

Atri and Anasuya warmly welcomed them into their *ashram* and listened gravely to their explanation for the sun's absence. The couple was astounded to learn that Seelavathi's curse was responsible for this cataclysmic disruption of the cosmic cycle.

Narada concluded saying, "Oh, Anasuya! It is your duty to persuade Seelavathi to retract her curse."

Indra added, "Yes, mother – this is not only our humble request, but also the *Trimurti's* command. We are but their messengers."

Atri turned to his wife: "Anasuya, my dear, will you try to convince Seelavathi to withdraw her curse for the universal good?"

Anasuya replied: "*Swami*, if the sun rises, Ugrasravas will die. Seelavathi would never consent to voluntarily bring about her own husband's death."

The anxious Indra said, "Oh, mother, can you not persuade Seelavathi to relent? The *Trimurti* assured us that you are the only one capable of accomplishing this task."

Anasuya remained immersed in deep reflection for a while. Then, she said: "I will convince her – but on one condition."

Indra eagerly asked, "What is your condition, mother?"

"Brahma, Vishnu and Maheswara must come in person to ask me to intervene in this matter."

Atri, Narada and Indra stood in perplexed silence at her unexpected request.

"Narayana!" Narada recovered first. "That's not a big deal! All we need is for Mahendra to pray to the Trinity for their presence."

Indra immediately looked skywards with hands raised in homage, calling out to the *Trimurti*.

Atri followed his wife indoors and said, "Anasuya, what is the meaning of this? Summoning the Supreme Gods here!! What do you plan to do?"

Anasuya smiled enigmatically: "*Swami*, I plan to make them play."

Before her puzzled husband could question her further, a strong wind gusted through the *ashram*, bringing in its wake a divine fragrance. The air shimmered with a corona of celestial light. From that splendid disc, the Trinity emerged and held out their hands in blessing to Atri and Anasuya.

The pious couple, speechless in awe, made humble obeisance to the *Trimurti* – they reverentially washed the gods' lotus-like feet in a basin and sprinkled the used water on their own heads as holy *teertham*.

Vishnu then addressed Indra: "Mahendra, why did you summon us here?"

"My Lord, Anasuya stipulated that the *Trimurti* must appear before her in person – only then will she intercede with Seelavathi on our behalf."

Brahma, Vishnu and Maheswara smiled and nodded benignly.

Sri Mahavishnu said, "Anasuya, you must persuade Seelavathi to rescind her oath."

Brahma added, "Yes, Anasuya, this is of utmost importance to the well-being of the entire cosmos."

Maheswara joined in with, "Convince Seelavathi to let the sun rise, Anasuya."

Anasuya bowed in deference and said, "My Lords, I will faithfully execute the task you have given me. In return, I beg you to grant me three boons."

Vishnu's eyes twinkled mischievously as he looked at his fellow-gods. "Of course, as Anasuya knows, everyone is powerless before a virtuous wife! Surya had to bow to Seelavathi's oath – now we three must accede to Anasuya's wishes!"

Parama Shiva smiled. "We will grant her the boons she desires."

Brahma agreed, "So be it!"

Vishnu turned to Anasuya: "Go to Seelavathi, my daughter. We will await your return and bestow three boons on you."

Thus did Anasuya, Atri's virtuous wife, bind the *Trimurti* with the indestructible bonds of devotion and chastity.

"Seelavathi! Seelavathi, my daughter!"

On hearing Anasuya's call, Seelavathi hurried out from her mean hut.

Touching Anasuya's feet in respect, she said, "Bless me, mother."

Anasuya replied, "Long may your husband live." Taking the young woman's hands in her own, Anasuya said, "Seelavathi, I come here to ask a favor of you."

"Mother, your wish is my command."

"My daughter, it is time to revoke your curse and release the sun from bondage. You must do this for the preservation of the universe."

Anxiety clouded Seelavathi's face. "Mother, if the sun rises, my husband will die."

"Seelavathi, you heard me give your husband the blessing of longevity. Believe in the power of my virtue."

"Mother!" Seelavathi cried out in anguished doubt.

Anasuya smiled at her reassuringly. "My daughter, tell me – would your own mother wish to see you a widow?"

Seelavathi hesitated. Then, folding her hands in respect, she resolutely said, 'Mother, I place my trust in you."

Turning to the east, Seelavathi closed her eyes in prayer for a moment and declared, "If I am indeed a chaste and virtuous wife, let the sun rise now!"

Even as her last word lingered in the air, a flare of red dispelled the darkness of the horizon. The sun had risen! Seeing the morning light, Seelavathi ran into the hut – Ugrasravas lay lifeless on the cot!

"*Swami!*" Seelavathi's anguished cry rang out in the silence. Ignoring the heart-rending wail of pain, Anasuya hurried back to the hermitage, which was now glowing in the flush of dawn. Atri embraced her with fond pride. The *Trimurti* extended their hands in blessing.

Lord Vishnu said, "Anasuya, you have removed the veil of darkness which shrouded the universe. We are indebted to you. Name your three boons, my daughter."

"*Bhagavan*, these are my first two wishes – they require instant gratification. Let Seelavathi's husband come back to life. Second, let him be a devoted husband, free from the blight of leprosy, and blessed with youth and good looks."

"Granted!" Vishnu responded immediately.

Indra chuckled in admiration. "Mother Anausya is indeed not only a virtuous wife, but also a woman of boundless wisdom!"

Brahma smiled and asked, "And what is your third wish, Anasuya?"

Anasuya walked forward slowly with a sober face. She stood before the Trinity and looked up at them with eyes brimming with emotion. Holding out the edge of her *saree* towards them, in the humble stance of a beggar asking for alms, Anasuya quietly said, "You, my Lords – Brahma, Vishnu and Maheswara – grant me the boon of residing in my womb and taking birth as my three sons."

For a moment the three gods remained completely nonplussed. Then they looked at each other and turned as one to Anasuya: "So be it!"

Anasuya's eyes overflowed with tears of joy. Along with her husband, now flooded with happiness himself, Anasuya paid grateful obeisance to the *Trimurti*.

Vishnu smiled at them, saying, "Anasuya, we will take birth as your sons and fill your home with play and laughter. As listed by you in your wish, Brahma will be your first-born, followed by me. Maheswara will be your third son."

Anasuya listened in joyful wonder.

Vishnu continued: "Atri, you and your wife are indeed fortunate. The beautiful moon which illuminates the night sky in its ethereal form will assume a gross body and become your eldest son. He will be Chandra – none other than Brahma, the Creator, himself!"

The Supreme Lord paused and then said: "In due course, I myself will take birth as Datta, your second son. I will also be called Dattatreya, or son of Atri. Finally, Parameswara will be born to you as Durvasa."

Voices trembling with joy, Atri and Anasuya said, "We are blessed, my Lord!"

Brahma turned fondly to his *maanasaputra*, Atri. "Dear son, at an auspicious place and time of your choosing, place your seed in Anasuya's womb – just as ghee is poured in libation into the pit of the sacrificial fire."

Atri humbly said, "I will follow your command, father."

As the pious couple bowed in reverence, Brahma blessed them: "May your three wishes be fulfilled!"

The other celestials chorused, "So be it!"

Atri and Anasuya raised their bent heads to find themselves alone.

Atri embraced Anasuya in joyous pride, saying, "Anasyua, you are truly blessed! Your fame will endure until the end of time." He chuckled. "Only now do I understand your words about making the *Trimurti* play! My beloved, the Holy Trinity will indeed play in our laps!"

Before his wife could reply, a cry was heard: "Mother!"

Anasuya and Atri turned to find Seelavathi at the threshold of the hermitage, hand in hand with a handsome young man. The beaming Seelavathi introduced her companion as her husband, Ugrasravas.

Seelavathi fell into Anasuya's arms with tears of joy. "Mother, I owe you my husband's life and my happiness. Due to your intercession, he is now free from the scourge of leprosy and is in the prime of youth. I can never repay my debt of gratitude to you!"

Anasuya embraced her and chided her tenderly: "There is no room for gratitude in a daughter's love for her mother! It is the *Trimurti* you should thank, Seelavathi. Your husband's rebirth is but the deserved fruit of your peerless chastity and the Gods' grace."

The young couple fell at the feet of Atri and Anasuya, invoking their blessing.

Anasuya advised Ugrasravas: "Seelavathi has remained your devoted wife, patiently enduring all the hardship of your former miserable existence. Be good to her, my son."

Atri added, "Ugrasravas, a husband can reciprocate his wife's precious gift of devotion only with own true affection."

Ugrasravas promised, "Father, we will strive to emulate you and Mother Anasuya in our marriage."

Affectionately holding hands, Seelavathi and Ugrasravas embarked on their new conjugal life. Atri and Anasuya exchanged contented smiles as they watched them leave.

———

Atri's eyes slowly took on a tender glow – fragments of Brahma's command wafted in his mind: 'the sacrificial fire ... place your seed ...' Atri turned and walked expectantly into the sleeping chamber.

He drew a sharp breath at the exquisite picture that met his eyes. Anasuya, her complexion glowing like ivory, lay on the spotless white sheets of their bed. Atri's heart quickened with passion. She was the lodestar of his life. To bear Brahma, Vishnu and Maheswara in her womb ... to suckle them, to raise them ... she was his goddess of good fortune. Through her, he would father the Holy Trinity!

Atri stepped forward silently. The bed was awash in silver. His wife was a voluptuous nymph floating on the softest of clouds. Atri gazed through the open window at the radiant full moon hanging low on the horizon. This celestial being was to be born as his son! The same iridescent moon which illuminated the skies would soon light up his home! He turned back to Anasuya's glowing face – had the moon already descended to earth?! Smiling tenderly, Atri reached the bed.

Anasuya stirred at his touch; her eyes were dark pools of desire. Coral-red lips parted in invitation, she melted into his arms.

———

Months later, Atri stood apart from the crowd of women who buzzed around his wife with their happy chatter, discussing her coming confinement. Anasuya sat in their midst, her face almost translucent with the glow of advanced pregnancy, softly thanking them for their good wishes. Seelavathi braided a string of flowers into Anasuya's lustrous, floor-length hair, while another sage's wife placed the vermillion *tilak* on her forehead. Anasuya smiled to herself and absently stroked her stomach.

Atri was lost in his wife's beauty – it seemed to him that Anasuya's full, radiant cheeks mirrored the moon cocooned in her womb.

"*Swami!*" Anasuya's call broke into his reverie. He blinked and looked about him. Anasuya's companions were gone.

"*Swami*, your eyes are on me, but your thoughts are far away!"

Atri smiled. "I lost myself in your beauty, dearest. I see the full moon shining in your face. I can hardly believe my good fortune! My father, Brahma, is going to be my son! Who could be luckier than I am?"

Anasuya asked mischievously. "Doesn't one half of your luck rightly belong to me, *Swami!*?"

Atri looked down at her in deep affection. "Anasuya, my dear, your good fortune is beyond mere luck. It is a divine gift – the rich reward of long years of prayer and sacrifice."

He placed his arm round her and gazed up at the moon outside their window. "When will the moon descend to the earth?" he teased her.

Anasuya smiled and leaned her head on his strong shoulder. "You won't have to wait much longer, my lord. He should be here in a matter of days."

———

In the year of *Soumya*, on the tenth day of the waxing moon, in the month of *Kaartik*, Anasuya gave birth to a beautiful baby boy: the physical manifestation of Brahma, brimming with the quality of *rajoguna*.

Atri held his infant son's naming ceremony at his *ashram*, in the presence of the *Trimurti* and their consorts. The host of *maanasaputras* and *devas,* along with sage Narada, showered their blessings on the baby.

Brahma cradled his own incarnation fondly in his arms and said, "This is Chandra."

Sri Mahavishnu stepped forward: "Chandra will refresh the worlds with the invigorating blessing of his innate coolness. He will be worshipped as one of the *Navagrahas.*"

———

Nirvikalpananda stopped, as Chidananda claimed his attention with a respectfully raised hand.

Eyes blazing in curiosity, the disciple said, "Master, we have seen the chaste Seelavathi freed from her misery. The virtuous Anasuya has realized her wish for progeny. Both these developments can be attributed to sage Mandavya's curse. But you have forgotten to tell us the sage's own fate: what happened to him?"

Nirvikalpananda replied, "My son, I have not elaborated on sage Mandavya's fate because it does not have much relevance to the story of the *Navagrahas*."

"But, master, we are on tenterhooks as to what befell him!" protested Vimalananda.

Nirvikalpananda gave his young acolytes an indulgent smile. "Very well. The king soon received proof of Mandavya's innocence. Filled with remorse, he ordered the sage's immediate release. However, as the guards lifted Mandavya's torso from the spike, the metal tip, or *ani*, broke off and remained lodged in his throat. Henceforth, the sage was known as 'Animandavya.' Since you are all interested in the strange circumstances of his life, I will add that this same sage was instrumental in Yamadharmaraja, the god of death, taking the *avatar* of Vidura in *Dwapara yuga*.

"And going back to Atri and Anasuya, in due course, Lord Vishnu and Lord Shiva were born to them as Dattatreya and Durvasa – their second and third sons, respectively."

He paused and teased them gently: "And now, my sons, may I proceed with the tale of the *Navagrahas*?"

His disciples smiled rather sheepishly.

Sadananda said, "Master are we going to hear about Kuja *graha* next?"

"Yes, my sons." He paused a moment. "Kuja's birth began with a discussion at *Satyaloka*."

The four disciples sat up straight in anticipation. They were all ears as Nirvikalpananda resumed his discourse.

THE BIRTH OF KUJA

Brahma sat on his pristine white lotus, with Saraswati beside him. They exchanged a knowing smile as the familiar chant, "Narayana!" reached their ears. Then, Narada stood before them, bowing in reverence to his parents.

Saraswati said, "Narada, you have arrived just in time!" She turned to Brahma: "*Swami*, why don't we ask Narada to be our referee?"

The curious sage asked, "What is this, mother?"

"Well, Narada, Chandra is none other than a part of Lord Brahma's essence, right?"

Narada nodded warily in agreement.

Saraswati continued, "But, I say that Chandra outshines Lord Brahma in good looks. Your father denies this. Now, we leave you to cast the deciding vote!"

Narada hesitated.

Hiding his smile, Brahma murmured, "Comparing me with an infant! Whatever next?"

Saraswati, looking at Brahma from the corner of her eyes, urged the sage: "Come, Narada! Who is handsomer: my Lord Brahma or the young Chandra?"

"Narayana!" the hapless Narada exclaimed. "I am caught in a dilemma! However, I must, at all costs, avoid falsehood in the presence of my mother, the goddess of speech. I must admit that Chandra is handsomer." Saying this, Narada anxiously scanned Lord Brahma's faces – to his great relief, all four were wreathed in smiles.

The Creator laughed aloud. "So, both of you have decided that I am blind to Chandra's beauty? It is I who willed that he be the handsomest of my creation!"

Saraswati's eyes sparkled in mischief, as she replied, "And all the trouble I had to take to make you declare the truth!"

Brahma and Narada joined in her laughter.

She then turned to the sage. "So, Narada, how is Chandra doing? Being suckled by Anasuya, I suppose?"

"Narayana!" Narada laughed. "Mother, you forget the passage of time. Chandra is no longer an infant feeding at Anasuya's breast. He now roams the forest, collecting *dharba* grass and twigs for the sacrificial fire. Atri has commenced his instruction in the *Vedas* and other scriptures."

Saraswati exclaimed in surprise: "Chandra is a young man? How time flies!" She paused. "In that case, I think it's time for the third *Navagraha* to make its manifestation."

Brahma nodded in thoughtful agreement. "Yes – and this time, it should happen through Parameswara."

"Parameswara, my Lord?" Saraswati wondered.

"My dear, Surya is Vishnu's incarnation, just as Chandra is mine. It is but right that the next *graha* is a manifestation of the third of the *Trimurti*."

Narada stepped in with a "Narayana!" He continued, "Is my father commanding me to pay a visit to Mount Kailash, by any chance?"

Brahma smiled: "Yes, Narada. Lord Vishnu and I speak in one voice. Be our messenger to Maha Shiva."

Narada bowed his head and set out joyfully on his mission.

———∞———

A hushed silence lay over Mount Kailash, Lord Shiva's sacred abode.

Narada wandered about the deserted landscape, wondering: 'Has everyone, including Lord Shiva, abandoned Kailash after Sati ended her life in the flames of the yogic fire?'

Then, abruptly, he came to a halt: there, before him, was Lord Shiva. Maheswara was seated in deep meditation, oblivious to his surroundings. His long, iridescent, copper colored tresses formed a nimbus about his head. His normally pale complexion blazed a deep red with the fierce intensity of his *tapas*. The very air round him pulsated with energy. The usually verbose Narada stood speechless before the *Mahayogi*, mesmerized by the awesome power and beauty of his divine penance.

A miracle unfolded before the sage's wonderstruck gaze. Lord Shiva's brow flushed a vivid crimson, as if anointed by a band of vermillion. A single tear-drop of perspiration formed at the center of the broad forehead, glistening like a precious pearl against the ruby-red skin. The bubble became a rivulet and flowed down the Lord's shapely nose. There it paused a moment, adorning Shiva like an exquisite nose ornament. Then, the pendant drop fell to the earth.

Narada's eyes widened in amazement as the bubble transformed into a beautiful baby boy with four arms. The infant's complexion mirrored the fiery red of Shiva's brow. The baby's loud wailing shattered the silence of the mountain. To Narada's surprise, Shiva remained immersed in his meditation, oblivious to the cry. The sage looked on helplessly. Then, as though in answer to the infant's call, an exquisite damsel materialized and gathered him tenderly into her arms.

Narada recognized her as Bhudevi, the goddess of earth. She pressed the baby warmly to her breast, hushing his tears.

Looking intently at Lord Shiva, she called out: "Parameswara!"

Lord Shiva slowly opened his half-closed eyes and looked serenely at Bhudevi and the infant cradled in her hands.

Bhudevi held out the boy to him, saying, "Parameswara, this is your son, who manifested from your perspiration. Take him."

Lord Shiva gazed with equanimity at the goddess and said, "Bhudevi, this infant has sought the shelter of your munificent lap. Raise him as your own child."

Bhudevi exclaimed: *"Bhagavan!"*

Shiva continued gravely: "Without my beloved Sati, I am but an orphan myself." Bhudevi's heart melted in sympathy at these words.

Shiva continued in a firm voice, "He is now your son. Feed him the sacred milk from your breast and cherish him. The boy is to be called Bhouma and Kuja, after your names, 'Bhumi' and 'Ku.' He will also be known as Angaaraka, for his fiery complexion."

Bhudevi nodded solemnly. "*Bhagavan*, I am honored that you have named the boy after me. Your wish is my command."

Before Lord Shiva could reply, Lord Vishnu and Brahma, accompanied by their consorts, appeared in Kailash. Bhudevi and Narada bowed in obeisance before the *Trimurti*.

Lord Shiva addressed his unexpected visitors: "It is good to see you all!"

Lord Brahma replied, "The pleasure is ours, Maheswara."

Lord Vishnu continued, "We come here with full hearts to felicitate you on your timely creation of the third of the *Navagrahas*."

Brahma turned to Bhudevi. "Goddess of the earth, as one of the *Navagrahas*, your son, Kuja, is destined for extraordinary things. Treasure him and raise him as your own."

Lord Vishnu in his turn said, "Bhudevi, this boy is a precious gift to you from your affectionate brother, Lord Shiva. As his mother, your name will live forever in the annals of cosmic history. Kuja will bestow the gift of land on all who seek his blessing on earth."

Mahalakshmi took the gurgling baby into her arms. Kissing his rosy cheeks, she exclaimed: "Kuja is as radiant as a lotus bud!"

Saraswati, in her turn, cradled the infant in her arms, saying, "I can see the extraordinary intelligence blazing from his countenance."

The pleased Bhudevi bowed in gratitude to Saraswati: "Goddess of wisdom, my Kuja is indeed fortunate to receive your blessing."

"You share his good fortune, Dharani. You have borne a son without enduring the natural rigors of pregnancy." Mahalakshmi smiled in agreement.

Narada stepped forward to say, "Above all, it is the human race which is fortunate. Due to the compassionate intercession of the earth goddess, they can now worship the first three of the *Navagrahas*, who are each a part of the *Trimurti* – Surya as Mahavishnu's vision in his right eye, Chandra as Brahma's incarnation and Kuja as Maheswara's essence."

"So be it!" said the gods and goddesses in happy unison, before making their departure from Mount Kailash. Lord Shiva raised his hand in benediction over Bhudevi and the gurgling Kuja, before they vanished.

Narada, now alone with Shiva, bowed in reverence and said, *"Bhagavan,* I ask your permission to leave so that I can spread the momentous tidings of Kuja's birth across the expanse of the cosmos."

Lord Shiva smiled in tranquil acquiescence and closed his eyes. Once more, the *Mahayogi* was immersed in his transcendental meditation.

⎯⎯∞⎯⎯

Nirvikalpananda stopped and looked at his spell-bound *sishyas.* "That was the birth of Kuja. Who can tell me whose story comes next?"

Chidananda replied eagerly: "I can, master! The fourth *graha,* Budha, is next."

"No, my boy." Nirvikalpananda laughed at Chidananda's crestfallen face. "We are familiar with the *Navagrahas* in this order: Surya, Chandra, Kuja, Budha, Brhaspati, Sukra, Sani, Rahu and Ketu. However, this particular order is based on their preponderance in terms of their respective merits and powers, as ordained by the *Trimurti.* It is not the actual order of their births. Kuja's manifestation was followed by that of Brhaspati and Sukra. Budha was born only after Brhaspati's marriage to Taara. Therefore, it is better to hear about Brhaspati and Sukra before proceeding to Budha's story."

The master paused for reflection. "In fact, my sons, both Brhaspati and Sukra were born prior to Chandra's manifestation. Since their births do not impinge on Chandra's story in any way, I chose to narrate Chandra's story before theirs."

"The correct order of the *Navagrahas* is clear to us now, master," Vimalananda said.

He was seconded by Sadananda: "Yes, master – your narration depicts the genealogy of the *grahas* in exhaustive detail."

Nirvikalpananda addressed his disciples: "My boys, clarity is of utmost importance in any treatise on mythology. There should be no room for misinterpretation – otherwise, there is danger of descending into the absurd."

With this caution, Nirvikalpananda resumed his discourse. "I hope you remember the name, Angiras: he was one of the *maanasaputras.* He had a number of wives and numerous progeny. But these are irrelevant to Brhaspati's birth. We need to know only about his wife, Sraddha, also known as Vasudha. Sraddha's eldest son was Utathya …"

THE BIRTH OF GURU

As the golden light of dawn flooded his *ashram*, Sage Angiras patiently quizzed Utathya on his *Vedic* knowledge. Utathya plodded along in his stolid way, answering his father's questions hesitantly and after much thought.

Angiras hid his disappointment and thought, 'A good student should have his answer ready even before the question has been posed! Alas! My son is slow to comprehend and slower yet to respond!'

He looked up in relief as Narada's chant, "Narayana!" reached his ears. Angiras dismissed Utathya and warmly welcomed the wandering sage.

Narada looked after the departing boy and asked: "So, Angiras, the son now excels the father in his knowledge of the scriptures – right?"

Angiras sighed in regret. "If only that were true, Narada. Utathya is undoubtedly a diligent and intelligent student. But he is rather slow on the uptake. I must admit that teaching him is a long- drawn out affair, often testing my fortitude. He even talks and walks slowly! How I wish I had a wise son who possessed an intellect with the speed of light!"

"Such a son will surely be yours one day, Angiras. Worship Agnideva, the god of fire. He will give you the child you desire."

Angiras exclaimed, "Agnideva?!"

Narada nodded vigorously. "Yes, Angiras. The god of fire holds you in high esteem. Earlier, when Agni renounced the world in a fit of anger, and left to do penance in the forest, it was you who stepped in voluntarily and performed his duties in his stead."

"Of course I remember, Narada. In fact, Agnideva asked me to continue to fulfill his role indefinitely. It was I who turned him down, telling him that I preferred to be considered his eldest son."

"Then, what are you waiting for, Angiras? Angideva would not hesitate to bless a wise man with a wiser son – all you have to do is ask!"

At Narada's suggestion, Angiras, along with his wife, Sraddha, devoutly performed the *Agnikaarya* – Agnideva's favored *homam*. As the flames of the sacrificial fire leaped high, the radiant Agni appeared before them in a dazzling shower of sparks. The enthralled Angiras folded his hands in salutation.

The god of fire smiled at him. "Angiras, I have waited long to grant you a boon. Tell me your desire." Agni's deep voice reverberated in the air, like shimmering columns of heat.

"Father, bless me with a son of extraordinary wisdom and intelligence."

"I cannot refuse your prayer, my son. Your wife Sraddha will bear a child of matchless intellect and exemplary oratorical skills. In time, his name will become a byword for wisdom in all the worlds. Through him, you and Sraddha will earn eternal fame."

Agnideva lifted his hand in blessing over the prostrate Angiras. The *yagna* fire flared brightly and the god merged into its flames once more.

Agni's promise soon bore fruit and Sraddha became pregnant. Angiras showered his wife with tender care as they awaited the birth of their much-anticipated son. One auspicious morning, Sraddha delivered a boy.

The infant's face glowed like a full-blown blossom and the radiant light of wisdom blazed from his eyes.

Angiras conducted his son's naming ceremony in the presence of his fellow *maanasaputras* and their families, in accordance with the prescribed *Vedic* rites.

At the end of the *Agnikaarya*, he pronounced his son's name: "This is Brhaspati."

Sage Narada, who graced the ceremony as the *Trimurti's* representative, proclaimed: "Angiras, your son will not only be a colossus of learning, he will also occupy a special place in the pantheon of the *Navagrahas*. This is the decree of the Holy Trinity."

Angiras and Sraddha exchanged looks of joy and kissed their son in fond pride.

Angiras said, "We are indeed blessed, Narada. The *Trimurti* have showered us with their grace."

Narada exhorted him: "Angiras, it is your paramount duty to carefully sculpt Brhaspati's intellect into realizing its full potential."

"Narada, rest assured that I will mould my son into a scholar past compare! He will be my superior in knowledge and surpass me in wisdom."

"Well said! This should be the rightful aim of every father – so be it, Angiras!"

Angiras eagerly commenced his son's education when he was yet a little child. To his father's delight, Brhaspati was an undoubted prodigy. The boy proved an adept scholar and his tiny mind absorbed the intricacies of the various arts and sciences as readily as a sponge. His family was awestruck by his brilliance. He soon excelled Angiras in his depth of knowledge and sharpness of intellect. Angiras and Sraddha, having arranged the marriage of their elder son, Utathya, now turned their attention to Brhaspati's matrimony.

Narada, in the course of his usual peregrination, visited Indra in *Swarga* and praised the glory of his reign over the *devas*. Although Indra was very pleased with the sage's commendation, there was one disappointment which continued to rankle in his mind.

He now confided, "Narada *Maharshi*, I strive to provide the gods with everything necessary for their welfare. But, to my great regret, we lack a *guru's* guidance. You are acquainted with everyone in the cosmos. I beg you – suggest a suitable person to be our preceptor."

"Narayana!" Narada exclaimed thoughtfully. "The preceptor of the gods must be a person of towering intellect and infinite wisdom. Hmm." He paused. Then, "Yes! Indra, there is one person who has the credentials to fill that unique position."

"Who is it, *Maharshi*?" Indra asked eagerly.

"Brhaspati, the son of Angiras and Sraddha. He has completed his instruction under his father and is an exemplary scholar. Under his guidance, the *devas* will undoubtedly go from strength to strength."

Indra immediately rose from this throne. "Let's not waste any time, *Maharshi*. Come with me to Angiras – he is one of the *maanasaputras*, right?"

Indra prostrated himself before Angiras and explained the objective of his visit. Angiras' spirits soared with justified pride at this open acknowledgement of his son's peerless scholarship.

"Indra, if Brhaspati's wisdom contributes to the gods' welfare, I am indeed the most fortunate of fathers. What more can I ask for? However, let's see what my son feels about this."

When Brhaspati answered his father's summons, Narada outlined their plans for his initiation as the preceptor of the gods.

Angiras urged his son to accept this offer: "Son, this is a unique opportunity to put your learning to optimum use."

Brhaspati reflected for a moment and then said humbly, "Father, your wish is my command. However, I do have one condition to make. You have given me the gift of knowledge. I wish to establish an independent *ashram*, where I can disseminate that knowledge to other disciples in my turn."

Indra immediately said, "We accept your stipulation. In fact, the *devas* themselves can be disciples at your *ashram*."

Indra went on to confirm Brhaspati as the *deva-guru* with his words: "Master, we will construct your *ashram* at a suitable location and present it to you as our *guru dakshina*."

Angiras said, "I am glad that has been settled satisfactorily." He paused. "On a different note, Sraddha and I have recently been considering Brhaspati's marriage."

Indra enthusiastically offered his help saying, "It will be my privilege to take on the task of finding a suitable bride for our preceptor. I will seek Lord Brahma's counsel in this regard."

Angiras expressed his approval: "My own father is to select my son's bride! What a blessing!"

Pleased with the developments, Narada asked, "Mahendra, when do you plan to hold Brhaspati's investiture at *Sudharma,* your court?"

"I leave it to my father, *Maharshi* Angiras, to decide the auspicious day and time for the initiation." Indra bowed respectfully in deference to the *maanasaputra.*

Accordingly, Brhaspati was installed as the *deva-guru* and commenced his chosen vocation of imparting knowledge to others. Residing at a beautiful hermitage, he visited *Swarga* as necessary to discharge his duties as the preceptor of the gods.

In due course, Indra introduced him to Lord Brahma. "Lord, this is Brhaspati, our preceptor. His parents desire his marriage at the earliest. We seek your valuable advice in this matter."

Brahma looked intently at the *deva-guru.* "Hmm. Brhaspati is indeed a handsome man! His wife should certainly be his equal in demeanour. Let's see."

Brahma closed his eyes in reflection. Indra and Brhaspati waited eagerly.

Then, the Creator said, "The beautiful young maiden, Taara, is at present performing penance to acquire a suitable husband. Brhaspati, you will soon be given the opportunity to make her acquaintance. She is fated to be your wife."

⚬⚬⚬

Brahma materialized on the banks of the pond where Taara was immersed in *tapas.* Her pristine white attire floated like delicate tendrils round her flushed, lotus-like face. Long, thick lashes emphasized her closed eyes. Her arms, as slim as lotus stems, were clasped gracefully in prayer. She stood like a lissome creeper, adorned with lotus buds.

With a sharp intake of breath, Brahma thought, 'What sublime beauty! My eight eyes can never have enough of this exquisite picture.' "Taara ..." he called aloud.

The large, limpid eyes opened and gazed at him in wonder.

"*Swami!*" Taara exclaimed, folding her hands in respect. Even to

Brahma, whose ears were long attuned to the magic of Vani's music, Taara's voice was a veritable symphony of divine lutes.

"Taara, I bear glad tidings. Your desire for a good husband will soon be fulfilled. Brhaspati, the preceptor of the *devas*, and a man of peerless intellect, is to be your husband."

"Your will be done, Lord," Taara bowed in obedience.

"Your one-fold marriage to Brhaspati will bring you two-fold happiness!" With this rather enigmatic blessing, Brahma disappeared, his eyes still dazzled by Taara's beauty.

Her face radiant with joy, Taara looked about with new eyes. The cool waves of the pond lapped at her feet in enticing invitation. Untying her long hair, Taara waded into its pellucid water – taking the ritual *avabridha snanam* which concludes a *yajna*. As Taara immersed herself in the water and came up gasping for air, the exquisite beauty of her face rivaled the charm of the lotus blossoms clustered around her.

———

The days passed. Taara waited in vain for Brhaspati. Yearning for his appearance, Taara wandered from one beautiful locale to another, constantly seeking the husband promised by Brahma. Brhaspati, in his turn, continued his duties at his *ashram*, all the while waiting impatiently for Brahma's boon to fructify.

One morning, leaving his disciples to revise their lessons, Brhaspati walked to the river to perform his ritual ablution. As he reached the shore, he stopped short: there, before him, was a beautiful maiden, emerging from the water. Her dripping clothes clung to the sensuous curves of her body, vainly attempting to curtain her loveliness from his eyes.

Brhaspati stood frozen by this vision of ethereal beauty: who could this be? Was she a river sprite? Or perhaps a *matsyakaantha* washed up from the depths of the ocean? Could she be a mermaid who had lost her way in the river? Under the spell of her golden body, Brhaspati walked towards her as if in a trance. A wave of excitement washed over him – for the first time in his life, he found himself staring with desire at a woman.

He thought, 'Oh, if only Brahma had ordained this maiden to be my wife, instead of the unknown Taara!' He gazed speechlessly into the depths of her fish-like eyes and struggled with the emotions crowding his mind. He wet his dry lips and tried to summon up his voice.

But the girl preempted him. "*Aarya* ... My name is Taara. Could you please help me? I come in search of the great Brhaspati."

Brhaspati's heart fluttered like the wings of a dove against his ribs. He could only stare at her in silence.

"Do you know him, by any chance? Where can I find him?" she continued. Her voice thrilled his ear with its sweet music.

He finally found his tongue and responded: "Taara – Brhaspati stands before you!"

"You?!" Taara exclaimed in joy.

Brhaspati held out his hand: "Come, Taara."

Brhaspati took his prospective bride to his parents for their approval. Angiras and Sraddha accepted Taara with joy and blessed their union. Brhaspati married Taara in the presence of the *devas*, sage Narada and the *maanasaputras*, in a grand ceremony arranged by Indra. With everyone's happy blessings ringing in their ears, the newlyweds took their leave of Angiras and Sraddha and reached their *ashram*, where they commenced their married life.

THE BIRTH OF SUKRA

Nirvikalpananda stopped and regarded his disciples. They remained in attentive silence, eager for him to continue.

"My sons, you have just heard the story of Brhaspati, the Guru. Now we will go on to the birth of Sukra, who was Brhaspati's contemporary." The master paused.

"Sukra is the sixth of the *Navagrahas,* and the son of sage Bhrgu, one of the salient Brahma *maanasaputras.* However, Sukra was not his given name – he acquired that moniker because of certain important reasons."

Sadananda spoke up in excitement: "Master, is that so? We were always under the impression that Sukra was his real name! Why did he change his name, master? What was his original name?"

Nirvikalpananda laughed gently at his disciple. "Now, now, Sadananda, let's not be in a hurry! We will come to each episode in its proper place."

He smiled at the four young men and continued. "Bhrgu married

Puloma, also called Poulomi, who belonged to the *rakshasa* clan. In due course, Puloma conceived. One day, when Bhrgu was away from their hermitage, a *rakshasa*, also bearing the name, Puloma, abducted her. This *asura*, who was an ardent past admirer of Puloma's, assumed the form of a hog and raced away with her. Being in an advanced stage of pregnancy, Puloma delivered a baby boy who fell to the ground from her womb in this mad rush. This was Chyavana ..."

Chidananda piped up excitedly: "Chyavana! That's Sukanya's husband – Chyavana *Maharshi*! Am I right, master?"

Nirvikalpananda smiled indulgently. "Yes, but let's keep Chyavana aside for the moment and focus on Puloma, shall we? Puloma was a woman of formidable character. Her chastity as Bhrgu's wife further enhanced her powers. In due course, Chyavana set out from home to undertake prolonged *tapas*. Subsequently, three more sons were born to Bhrgu and Puloma: Vajraseersha, Suchi and Ourva. Puloma, with her own prodigious strengths, could not hide her disappointment at the mediocrity of her sons, who were gentle and of average intelligence. She yearned for a son with a razor-sharp intellect, unshakeable determination and incomparable strength. Above all, she wanted a son who was single-mindedly dedicated to the cause of the *asuras*, Puloma's own beloved bloodline ..."

⌘

Sage Bhrgu sat under a tree, facing the east, concluding his morning rituals. Puloma emerged from the *ashram* and stood beside him. The sound of chatter and happy laughter reached their ears. They turned to watch their sons setting out to forage for the sacrificial twigs and grass required for the daily *yagnas*.

Bhrgu fondly remarked, "Your sons are on their way to the forest to collect *darbha* and *samidhas* without waiting to be told. You must be proud of them, Puloma."

"They are not my sons!" Puloma shot back. "They belong to you – in every respect!"

Bhrgu was flabbergasted at her sudden outburst. "Not your sons?! Whatever do you mean, Puloma?"

"Just what I say." Puloma looked unflinchingly into her husband's puzzled eyes. "I am distressed by their predominantly *saatwic* personality traits. They have inherited your gentle manner of thought, speech and action. Again, like you, they possess the tranquil disposition best suited to ascetics. So, I consider them to be your sons, not mine!"

Bhrgu frowned in bewilderment. "Are you disowning your sons, Puloma?"

Ignoring his accusatory tone, his wife continued firmly: "Tell me *Swami*, taking into consideration my own lineage, what do you think?"

Bhrgu remained speechless – Puloma's attitude was incomprehensible to him. It was clear that he and his wife were speaking on completely different wavelengths.

Puloma continued impatiently, "*Swami*, don't you understand? All our sons are purely *saatwic* in nature. None of them has the qualities I would prize in a son. They are a great disappointment to me."

Bhrgu, deeply disturbed by her words, beckoned her close. "Come, Puloma, sit beside me." He paused. "Now, tell me, what are these qualities you desire in our sons?"

"*Swami*, how naïve you are! Our sons, without exception, take after you in *saatwic* traits."

"That is as it should be, Puloma."

"Well, such soft-heartedness and diffidence does not appeal to me. I yearn to have a son of the sharpest intellect, brimming with self-confidence and pride. He should possess immense courage and fearlessness, making him a power to be reckoned with by all his adversaries."

Bhrgu looked at his wife with new eyes, giving her words serious consideration.

Puloma continued: "Do you understand now, *Swami*? I want a son endowed with the qualities I have listed."

Bhrgu spoke gravely. "Puloma, do you realize that you are asking for a son who is preponderantly *raajasic* and *taamasic* in nature? Such a combination of attributes is best avoided, my dear."

However, Puloma remained adamant. "*Swami*, I am indifferent to such niceties – all I know is what I want in a son. After all, you have four sons who conform to your expectations. Am I not, as a mother, entitled to one child of my own choice?" She gazed intently into her husband's eyes and touched his feet. "*Swami*, bless me with a son of my own preference."

Bhrgu remained for a moment in silent contemplation. Then, heaving a deep sigh, he placed his palm in blessing on Puloma's bowed head. "Yes, Puloma, every mother has the right to beget children of her own choice ..."

Late that evening, Bhrgu, the day's duties done, stood stroking his favorite deer in the *ashram* grounds. His gaze travelled contently round the garden and lighted on Puloma. Bhrgu froze into stillness, mesmerized by her exquisite loveliness. His wife moved swan-like among the profusion of flowering plants, watering them with infinitely graceful movements. Her face was suffused by the golden light of the setting sun. A gentle zephyr played with her flowing hair and ruffled her pale *saree*, outlining the shapely contours of her body, honed to supple perfection by hours of penance and rigorous discipline. Bhrgu could not tear his eyes away from this picture of youth and beauty. The neglected pet deer gently rubbed itself against his legs. Startled, Bhrgu looked down – the doe's large, limpid eyes but mirrored the beauty of his beloved wife's.

The garden slowly turned to silver under the light of the full moon. The heady fragrance of blossoms hung heavily on the night air. Puloma sat on a flat boulder, head tilted up at the radiant orb in the sky. Bhrgu walked towards her and gazed at her upturned face.

Puloma smiled up at him. "*Swami*, it is time you retired for the night. Come, let's go inside."

As she rose, Bhrgu reached out to take her hand in his. He lifted her chin with a gentle caress and gazed passionately into her dark, questioning eyes. He held her close for a breathless moment. Then, wordlessly, he guided her into a thick arbor of vines, covered with fragrant clusters of flowers.

The months passed. Puloma was in an advanced stage of pregnancy. A deeply contented Bhrgu watched his wife feeding the *ashram* cow with specially prepared fodder: the cow was also ready to deliver a calf.

Bhrgu thought: 'Puloma will soon have a son of her choice.' He smiled to himself. 'But the poor cow – she does not have any say in the attributes of her calf!'

He moved into the *ashram* to make the necessary arrangements for Puloma's confinement, including the *homam* to ensure an easy, painless labor. Puloma delivered a boy at an auspicious date and time.

With his inimitable sense of timing, sage Narada arrived at the *ashram* and congratulated the couple on the birth of their son. "Bhrgu, I come with glad tidings. The *Trimurti* and their consorts will grace your baby's naming ceremony."

The delighted Bhrgu exclaimed, "Lord Vishnu, ParamaShiva and Brahma – along with the *Devis* Mahalakshmi, Pravati and Saraswati! Really, Narada?"

Narada smiled at his excitement. "There is cause for their presence. You will hear it from them in person, Bhrgu. Make all the necessary arrangements and invite all your near and dear ones."

With the Holy Trinity as witness, Bhrgu celebrated his baby's naming ceremony and gave his newborn son the name Usana.

Brahma said, "Bhrgu, my son, Usana is a gift from the Supreme Lord. His will was the guiding force behind Puloma's request to beget a son of her choice."

Lord Vishnu declared, "Bhrgu, in due course, Usana will be elevated to the pantheon of the *Navagrahas* and will be an object of worship to the three worlds."

Shiva added, "Bhrgu, devote the greatest attention to your son's education. Make him a master of the arts of meditation, penance and *japa*."

Bhrgu folded his hands in reverence. "The *Trimurti*'s blessing is all my son needs to excel in every sphere."

Lord Vishnu turned to Puloma with a smile. "Puloma, your son will fulfill your expectations. You will not be disappointed in him."

<hr />

When Usana reached the age at which he could commence his education, Bhrgu was astounded by his son's keen intellect and instant grasp of the intricacies of the *Vedas*. The boy was an avid pupil, ready with probing questions and quick to express his considered opinions.

As Bhrgu instructed him in the arts and sciences, in her husband's absence, Puloma embarked on her own personal agenda. She availed of every opportunity to instill in her son an affinity for the *asuras*. Puloma gave Usana an account of the long-running rivalry between the *deva* and *daanava* factions, emphasizing the hardships endured by the *asuras*. She subtly suggested that the partisan support of the *Trimurti*, particularly Lord Vishnu, was responsible for her people's sufferings. Consequently, Usana grew up with a sense of outrage at the injustice meted out to his mother's clan, and viewed the *asuras* with great sympathy.

Usana completed his prescribed studies in record time. He continued to serve his parents and hone his skills at penance. As she observed the obvious differences between the dynamic Usana and his placid elder brothers, Puloma's heart was filled with a fierce pride: here indeed was the son she had long yearned for!

—✸—

The *rakshasa* king, Vrshaparva, sat on his throne, listening avidly to his spies' report on the doings of his arch rivals, the *devas*.

He was interrupted by a palace guard. "Hail, king of the *rakshasas*! The sage Narada waits outside. Shall I let him enter?"

Vrshaparva gave a snort of disgust. "Humph! Let him in! It's not as if we have any choice in the matter: that garrulous messenger of the cosmos will not leave without meeting me!"

The king turned to his espionage chief. "Soorpakarna, you can resume your report after Narada leaves."

"Narayana! Narayana!" Narada entered the court.

Vrshaparva nodded perfunctorily in his direction with a listless, "Narada."

"Narayana!" responded the irrepressible sage, as he seated himself comfortably near the king.

Vrshaparva frowned in annoyance. "Narada, your constant refrain is an assault upon my ears! Don't you know that Narayana is the *asuras'* sworn enemy?"

Narada looked up in mock horror. "I beg your pardon, Vrshaparva! My tongue is so accustomed to this beloved chant, that it sometimes forgets itself!"

The *asura* king shook his head impatiently. "Very well, Narada, come straight to the point: what is the purpose of your visit?" He added emphatically, "Uninvited, of course!"

"Nothing in particular, Vrshaparva. I am just going about my usual task – the collection and dissemination of information."

"So, you have come here to milk me for information, is it?"

"Now, now, Vrshaparva: why so cynical?! Perhaps I have come to give you tidings of great interest."

"Hah!" The *asura* king gave a sarcastic bark. "You can't fool me with your guile, Narada! Don't I know that you are a partisan of the *devas*, just like the person whose name you are so fond of parroting?"

Narada, not in the least bit perturbed, smiled. "How you misjudge me, Vrshaparva! Very well – here's a piece of information to prove my bonafides: Indra has appointed Brhaspati, Angiras' son, as the preceptor of the *devas*."

Vrshaparva frowned. "Brhaspati? Is he that qualified?"

"Yes, indeed. He possesses an extraordinary intellect. Soon his name will become a synonym for wisdom."

The *asura* king looked suspiciously at the beaming sage. "Going by your smug expression, Narada, I think it was you who manipulated this arrangement."

"Narayana!" The sage laughed. "How quick on the uptake you *asuras* are!"

Vrshaparva said accusingly, "Well, if you are truly impartial, why did it not occur to you to bring Brhaspati here?"

"Narayana!" Narada threw up his hands in consternation. "Who am I to take sides? Think, Vrshaparva: you are Brahma's great grandson, through his *maanasaputra*, Mareechi and his son, Kasyapa. I, on the other hand, am your grandfather Mareechi's brother. Unfortunately, the *suras* and the *asuras* are now adversaries, although you are brothers by blood. But, as far as I'm concerned, I, Narada, continue look upon the *devas* and the demons with strictly impartial eyes."

Vrshaparva gave him an amused glance. "Narada, you have an extraordinarily gifted tongue!"

The sage continued in an aggrieved voice: "I came here to tell you that you should emulate Indra and have a learned *guru* at your court ..."

Vrshaparva interrupted sarcastically: "Which is why you gifted Brhaspati to Indra, is it?"

"Narayana!" exclaimed Narada impatiently. "Forget Brhaspati: I have another person in mind for you. He has a razor-sharp intellect and excels Brhaspati in clarity of thought and firmness of action." Narada lowered his voice. "And now we come to the crux of the matter, Vrshaparva – he is also exceptionally sympathetic towards the *asuras*. He ..."

The *asura* king, all ears now, interrupted: "Who is this person?"

"I am coming to it, Vrshaparva." Narada chided. "You know Bhrgu *Maharshi*, pre-eminent among the Brahma *maanasaputras*? Well, he married Puloma, who belongs to your lineage ..."

Vrshaparva intervened impatiently, "All this is known to me – don't waste my time! Go on!"

"Very well. Bhrgu and Puloma's fifth son has completed his period of studies. He is a person of towering intelligence. In fact, he is more than equal to Brhaspati in all aspects. But the clinching factor in his favour is his obvious sympathy towards the *asuras*. Puloma has ensured that her favorite son has grown up to be a partisan of the demons."

Vrshaparva eyes glowered in excitement as Narada continued, "I suggest you engage Usana's services before he undertakes any other binding oath."

"Narada, why don't you intercede with Bhrgu on our behalf?"

"Narayana! That was indeed the purpose of my visit : now, do you concede that I am impartial?"

Vrshaparva laughed aloud. "Narada, I will do even better: I will now concede that you are partial towards the *asuras*!"

"Narayana!" Narada laughed. "I see that you *asuras* are definitely impetuous in nature! Come, let's not waste any time, but make at once for Bhrgu's hermitage."

Vrshaparva commanded: "Ugraa! Get the chariot ready at once!"

Soon they stood before Bhrgu with their proposal.

"Preceptor to the *asuras*?" the *Maharshi* pondered aloud.

"Yes," Vrshaparva urged. "We keenly feel the absence of a mentor and guide. Narada has given me glowing reports of Usana. I request you to bless our lineage by consenting to this appointment."

Narada added: "Say 'yes,' Bhrgu *rishi*. It is indeed a pity that the young *asuras* have no one to instruct them."

Puloma now spoke up. "*Swami*, please grant Vrshaparva's request."

At Bhrgu's surprise, Puloma explained, "Even when I asked you for the boon of a son like Usana, I had inklings of what was to come."

Usana, who had remained a silent spectator, now spoke up in his turn: "Father, let me fulfill my mother's wish."

Bhrgu shook his head and smiled. "It looks like I am outnumbered in this matter! Very well, Usana. May you garner great glory as the preceptor of the *asuras*."

"Father, rest assured that the knowledge you have imparted to me will be instrumental in earning that glory," Usana replied humbly.

The contented Vrshaparva respectfully touched Bhrgu and Puloma's feet saying, "The *asuras* are eternally indebted to you both for the blessing of your son."

Narada suggested, "Vrshaparva, tomorrow is an auspicious day. Why don't you anoint Usana as your *guru* then?" Bhrgu seconded the sage.

Vrshaparva declared proudly, "Usana's investiture shall outshine Brhaspati's in every way!"

True to his word, Vrshaparva inducted Usana into the preceptorship of the *asuras* with much pomp and ceremony. Usana immediately took on his appointed task of instructing the *asura* children and guiding the workings of Vrshapavra's court. Very soon, his sterling intellectual prowess, and overt hatred of the *devas*, earned him the *asuras*' respect. In time, Vrshapavra himself sought his counsel on matters of state and Usana firmly established his pre-eminence among the *asuras*.

———— ⌘ ————

Nirvikalpananda smiled at his spellbound disciples and continued his narrative.

"My sons, as I mentioned earlier, the story of Budha's birth is intertwined with that of Chandra, Brhaspati and Usana. Now that you are familiar with history of these three, you can easily comprehend Budha's origin."

The master paused to drink deeply of the water in the copper vessel on the floor.

"As you recall, Chandra was born to Atri and Anasuya. The couple lavished their love and care on their cherished son. Chandra pleased his father with his sterling character and intelligence. Anasuya, on her part, could not resist adoring her handsome son. In time, Anasuya brought up the question of Chandra's marriage. Atri replied that Chandra first needed to spend some time under the tutelage of an able *guru* ..."

Nirvikalpananda proceeded with his discourse.

———— ⌘ ————

Coming to the end of the day's lesson, Atri intoned, "*Om!*"

"*Om!*" Chandra echoed his father's concluding chant devoutly, with closed eyes. Father and son relaxed for a moment under the spreading branches of a tree in the *ashram*.

As Chandra rose to leave, Atri gestured to him to remain seated. "Chandra, I have something to say."

Chandra obediently waited to hear his father. "My son, the instruction you have imbibed from me is but a little drop in the vast ocean of knowledge. It is time you served a *guru* to further advance your education."

Hearing Atri's words, Anasuya, who happened to be passing by, said,

"*Swami*, what can Chandra learn from another *guru* that you yourself cannot teach him? Who is more knowledgeable than you?"

Atri smiled fondly at his wife. "My dear, you know Angiras, my fellow *maanasaputra*. His son, Brhaspati, is a powerhouse of knowledge and wisdom. His prodigious intellect has earned him the preceptorship of the *devas*."

Anasuya said, "Yes, I remember Brhaspati: we attended his wedding."

"Brihaspati has established an independent hermitage to impart knowledge to his disciples. I intend to send our Chandra to him."

With an affectionate look at her son, Anasuya said thoughtfully, "*Swami*, you are right. Brhaspati will be Chandra's ideal *guru*."

Atri gently corrected her: "Anasuya, Chandra will be Brhaspati's ideal disciple!" He smiled fondly at his son. "Chandra, you will leave tomorrow."

The next morning, Chandra prepared to set out for Brhaspati's *ashram*. Following the customary rite of departure, Anasuya served her son a sweet dish at the start of his journey.

Atri advised his son: "Chandra, you have thrived under my tutelage with your love, devotion and whole-hearted dedication. However, when you undertake your study under a *guru*, it is discipline and obedience which must take precedence. Above all, respect your teacher: remember, keep your head bowed when you address him." "Yes, father."

Anasuya added her counsel: "Son, you must also respect your master's wife. She stands in your mother's stead, and sees that you are fed. Make use of every opportunity to lend a hand in the daily chores of the hermitage."

"Mother, I will follow your advice," Chandra said. He touched his parents' feet in respect.

Atri blessed him with the words, "My son, may your praiseworthy behavior fill us with pride."

Anasuya embraced her boy and kissed him tenderly on his forehead. Her voice choked with emotion. "Chandra, my thoughts will always be with you. Take care of yourself, my son."

Atri and Anasuya watched Chandra leave. Anasuya remained standing on the threshold of the *ashram* until her son was lost to the view of her tear-filled eyes.

THE BIRTH OF BUDHA

The soothing cadence of *Vedic* hymns permeated the air of the *ashram*. Brhaspati's disciples, seated in sedate rows beneath the trees, recited their lessons under the watchful eye of their master. Multi hued parrots, hiding among the thick foliage of the branches, sweetly mimicked the *mantras*. The incessant chirruping of birds, punctuated by the occasional scream of peacocks, formed a pleasing background score to this serene symphony.

A sudden movement distracted Brhaspati, who looked up from his attentive focus on his pupils' recitation. He frowned, his thick brows almost meeting in surprise – a young man was silently making his way towards the hermitage on the grass-covered footpath. The *guru* marked the superbly sculpted torso and the glowing complexion. Here was a man endowed with incredible beauty: a beauty which would instantly cast its spell on all eyes, male or female.

'Who can this be?' wondered Brhaspati. 'Not even Indra's *Swarga* can boast of such breathtaking handsomeness!' The young stranger drew near. He stood behind the rows of disciples and waited respectfully.

Brhaspati, curiosity aroused, asked, "And who might you be, young man?"

"I am here to see you, master," replied Chandra courteously.

Brhaspati raised a hand to silence his pupils. The parrots followed suit and fell silent on their perches above. Brhaspati beckoned the newcomer forward. The young man stood before the *guru* and bowed his head. The disciples craned their necks to glimpse the unexpected stranger in their midst.

"I am Chandra, the son of sage Atri and Anasuya."

"Oh! Aatreya ..." Brhaspati acknowledged, as Chandra continued: "I am here to pursue my higher education under you, as commanded by my father."

"Is that so?" asked Brhaspati, again noting the extreme beauty of the new arrival.

Chandra prostrated himself at the *guru's* feet and said humbly, "Master, please accept me as your disciple and bless me with the gift of knowledge."

"May you be happy," Brhaspati replied.

Chandra looked up in surprise and exclaimed, "Master, I am here to be your student!"

Brhaspati's incipient frown turned into a smile. In effect, this young man had indicated that the *guru's* blessing was inappropriate to the situation.

"You are right, my boy – a disciple should not live in comfort." He lifted his right hand in benediction: "May all knowledge be yours!"

"I am truly blessed, master," Chandra saluted his new *guru*, who instructed:

"Chandra, go complete your morning rites and recover from the fatigue of your travel. Then ..."

Chandra interrupted: "Master, I performed the morning rituals on my way here." He paused to look around at the pleasant environs of the hermitage. "And my fatigue has vanished in this refreshing ambience."

Brhaspati smiled. "Very well, Chandra ... By the way, how is sage Atri?"

"He is fine, master."

"And Mother Anasuya?"

"She is fully occupied in catering to my father's needs."

Brhaspati smiled in approval. "Now, that is what I call an ideal couple! And you are fortunate to be their son." He pointed to the back row. "Sit there, Chandra. I will examine the depth of your knowledge this evening and then determine what course to follow with you – including any necessary corrections." He stopped as a young woman approached from the hermitage bearing a vessel of water, which she offered to Chandra.

Brhaspati made the introductions: "This is Punjikasthala, the hermitage maidservant. She tends to the disciples' dormitory and lends a helping hand round the *ashram.*"

Having drunk deeply of the cool water offered by the maid, Chandra made his way to the last row of disciples.

A pair of hungry eyes feasted unblinkingly on his broad, retreating shoulders. These large eyes peered furtively through an open window of the *ashram's* inner chamber. They did not belong to Brhaspati; nor to any of his disciples – no: these amorous eyes, limpid as lotus petals, belonged to Brhaspati's wife – to Taara.

⟶∞⟵

Late that evening, Brhaspati entered the bedroom. Taara sat statue-like on the bed, draped in a *saree* which fluttered tantalizingly in the breeze wafting in from the open window, redolent with the sweet fragrance of flowers.

The surprised Brhaspati exclaimed, "Taara! You are still awake!"

Taara jumped up at her husband's voice like a startled doe. "*Swami,* it's you!" She hurried on: "I am unable to sleep ..."

Brhaspati lay on the bed. Instinctively, his hand reached out for his wife.

Taara looked down at him. "Your new disciple ..." she swallowed with difficulty. Clearing her throat, she murmured indistinctly, "Chandra ..."

"Are you talking about Chandra, dear?"

"Yes, that's his name, right?" She paused. "I think he is much older than the other disciples – isn't he, *Swami?*"

"Not only is he senior in age, he is also miles ahead of the others in obedience, knowledge and wisdom." Brhaspati smiled approvingly.

"Is that so?"

"Taara, who do you think Chandra is? He is none other than the beloved son of Brahma *maanasaputra*, Atri, and his chaste wife, Anasuya."

"They are widely acknowledged to be an exemplary couple, *Swami.*"

"Yes, dear." Brhaspati continued with a note of pride. "Atri has particularly chosen me to be his son's *guru!*"

"That is indeed fortunate, *Swami*. It is good to have a young man among all these children – they cannot even carry water from the river for our use without spilling half of it on the way!" Taara waited for a moment and then asked, "*Swami*, could I ask Chandra to fetch water from the river daily?"

Brhaspati smiled indulgently. "Why, Taara, you don't need my permission for that! You know that, for every disciple, serving the *guru's* wife is tantamount to serving the master himself."

A deep sigh escaped Taara's lips.

Brhaspati gently pulled her towards him, saying, "Come, Taara, it's time you retired for the night. You are always up before dawn."

Taara deftly extricated her hand from her husband's clasp and came to her feet in one fluid movement. "You too need your rest, *Swami*. I am wide awake. I think I'll go for a stroll in the garden. I'll be back soon – don't wait up for me."

Without waiting for Brhaspati's response, Taara quickly walked out of the room.

⌘

The cool night breeze rippled through Taara's thick curls. A sudden gust blew her upper garment from her shoulders. As the wind played merrily with the truant cloth, Taara remained oblivious to her exposed body. Her *saree* fluttered in the breeze and then clung to her like a second skin, sculpting the contours of her sensuous figure. A torrent of dark longing rose from the depths of her being, flooding her with desire: well did she know the reason for her sleeplessness that night! She thought, 'Chandra pulls at me like an irresistible tide. I yearn for his touch.'

Brahma's words echoed in her mind: 'Brhaspati, the preceptor of the *devas*, and a man of peerless intellect, is to be your husband.'

Taara sighed. Could Brahma have been wrong? Perhaps it was Chandra who was destined to be her husband. Had she made a mistake?

Taara froze as someone tugged at her upper garment from behind! She gasped and turned slowly, expecting to see Chandra – but, no – with a sharp pang of disappointment, she saw that the cloth was merely tangled in the branch of a flowering plant. She freed the garment and threw it desultorily over her shoulders. Again, Taara drew up

short: there before her stood the disciples' cottages. In one of them
Chandra slept peacefully, blissfully oblivious to the tumultuous passion
which raged in her own sleepless heart! The intoxicating fragrance of
the flowers overwhelmed her senses. With a little cry of pain, Taara
ran back into the *ashram*. As she walked slowly towards her room,
Brhaspati's snores reached her ears.

It was the time of the noon meal. Brhaspati's disciples sat in two parallel
rows, facing each other, while their master took his place at their head,
commanding a view of both lines. Taara approached Brhaspati and served
his food on the banana leaf before him. Her husband suddenly frowned
and called out to one of his pupils: "Sanaathana! Where is Chandra?"

The boy replied, "Master, he has not come yet."

Taara intervened: "Who, Chandra? *Swami*, I sent him to fetch water
from the river. Unfortunately, I accidentally overturned the pot and spilled
all the water."

"But it is meal time, Taara ..." Brhaspati reproached his wife gently.

"*Swami*, I asked him to have his food first – it was he who insisted on
fetching the water immediately." She paused. "Carry on with your meal,
Swami. Chandra can eat with me."

Chandra stood hesitantly on the threshold of the dining hall. On the floor
before him were two banana leaves, one of which held a meal.

"Come, Chandra." He started at the voice. "Seat yourself at your leaf.
I have served your food."

Chandra turned round to see Taara, his master's wife, holding a bowl
of steaming rice in one hand and a spoon in the other. Chandra remained
standing by the door.

Taara laughed merrily. "So, what is it that fascinates you so? Me, or
the banana leaf?"

Chandra came to and bowed deferentially. "After you, madam."

"No, Chandra, I have told your *guru* that we will eat together. Come
join me!" she commanded him.

Chandra slowly walked towards the leaves. Taara gave an enigmatic
smile.

"Why the hesitation, Chandra? Are you not hungry? As for me, I am ravenous." She gestured invitingly towards his leaf. "Sit and eat."

Without removing her intent gaze from his face, Taara seated herself before him, saying, "Just give me a minute – I will serve myself."

As she bent over her plate, her upper garment dropped over the leaf. Chandra looked up at her sudden gasp and froze. He could not tear his eyes away from the startling beauty of her exposed breasts.

Taara gave a breathless laugh. "Oh! This garment refuses to stay put in its place!" She wryly held out her hands which were busy with the meal. "Chandra, could you please cover me?"

Chandra remained stock still, his eyes glued to her revealed body.

"Chandra!" Taara's insistent voice broke the spell.

Chandra jumped up. Picking up the cloth with a trembling hand, he gently draped it over her shoulders. Taara straightened up – the garment was now a curtain of snow over twin peaks. Taara nonchalantly commenced her meal. Chandra, on the other hand, had lost his appetite. The sharp pangs of hunger which gnawed at the pit of his stomach, and blazed from his eyes, had nothing to do with food.

Taara asked casually, "So, how is the food? Tasty?"

Coming to with a start, Chandra started on his own meal. A teasing smile played about Taara's lips. Chandra ate mechanically, his eyes straying constantly from his leaf to her face.

"Your *guru* says that your mother is a great woman." Taara remarked.

"Yes …" Chandra faltered.

Taara continued, "I also heard that she is very good looking." She stopped eating. "Is she really that beautiful?"

"Yes," Chandra's voice picked up assurance as Taara's questions gradually put him at ease. "My mother is indeed very beautiful."

Taara asked, "More beautiful than I am?"

Chandra looked into her mischievous eyes. Her teeth sparkled like jasmine buds through the parted, ruby-red lips.

Taara continued impishly: "Tell me, Chandra: who is more beautiful – your mother or I?"

Chandra remained speechless.

"Come now, Chandra: answer my question." She urged him on.

Chandra stammered, "Both … both of you are beautiful …"

Taara burst into laughter. "Poor Chandra!" She gestured towards his leaf. "Hmm … eat."

Closing his leaf abruptly, Chandra rose. "I have had my fill."

As Taara bent to pick up the leaves, her wayward upper garment again dropped from its place. Taara turned towards Chandra. "Ooops! Here we go again! This cloth seems to have a mind of its own today! Chandra …" She shrugged helplessly at him.

Standing close behind her, Chandra picked up the recalcitrant garment and covered her with it.

Taara's eyes twinkled. "My *sarees* are always like this – they insist on dropping down at the least provocation!"

Taara moved away, her swaying gait reminding Chandra of a swan gliding by on the surface of a crystalline lake. He stood mesmerized by her beauty. Was it possible that she could be even lovelier from the back? He thought of his mother – yes, Taara and Anasuya were both beautiful – but, each in her own way.

⸙

As darkness shrouded the *ashram* grounds, Chandra wandered sleeplessly beneath the trees. A muffled cry made him turn back and search anxiously among the foliage. Was she hiding in the concealing gloom? Was she abroad this night, wide awake like him? Was she also possessed by the tumultuous thoughts which lashed his heart with exquisite pain? Again and again, Chandra's mind replayed the tableau of Taara's upper garment dropping to reveal her breathtaking loveliness. The music of her lute-like voice haunted his ears.

Chandra wandered soundlessly about the garden, seeking Taara. Again, he heard a rustle in the bushes. He turned quickly – it was but the fluttering of wings. The bird flew away. Chandra sighed in remorse. Taara was his master's wife. Perhaps it was but commonplace for her upper garment to drop … maybe it was customary for whoever was near, master or disciple, to adjust the cloth. Was it his own inexperience with women which aroused such tumult in his heart? Chandra shook his head. Was he reading more into her enigmatic eyes than was warranted by the afternoon's events? He shrugged helplessly and walked towards his dormitory with a heavy heart.

As he moved away, a rustle was heard – a bush parted to reveal Punjikasthala. The maid smiled to herself and walked towards her own cottage. Punjikasthala was an *apsara*. To her resentment, Indra had ordered her to serve Brhaspati, effectively barring her from *Swarga*. The monotony of *ashram* life weighed heavily on the *apsara* – it was one boring, never-ending round of cleaning, gathering flowers for the daily worship and obediently carrying out the duties allotted to her by the master's wife. Here, there were no handsome young *devas* to compliment her on her beauty – no dance or song to enliven the long evenings. If only she possessed Urvasi or Menaka's extraordinary talent: Indra would never have cast her into this dull existence. Punjikasthala heaved a sigh: it was her unfortunate lot to live in the *ashram*, far from the excitement of *Swarga*.

Brihaspati's disciples devoutly recited the *Vedas* with closed eyes. Their master examined them meticulously. His gaze came to rest on Chandra. The young man sat detached from the classes' recitation, staring towards the hermitage, where Taara stood behind an open window, a lingering smile on her lips.

"Chandra!" Brhaspati's grave tone startled Chandra into attention. The *guru* continued seriously, "You are not concentrating."

Chandra flushed in shame. "Forgive me, master" he stammered.

Brhaspati admonished him: "Concentration is absolutely essential in order to master the *Vedas* – stay focused on your instruction."

Brhaspati completed his morning worship and prepared to set out for *Swarga*. After breakfasting on the offertory fruits, he turned to his wife. "Taara, my presence is needed at Indra's council today."

"When will you be back, *Swami*?"

"By tonight. I will leave Chandra in charge of the disciples."

"Yes," agreed Taara. "They require strict supervision if they are not to become boisterous in your absence."

Brhaspati looked intently at her face and said tenderly, "Let Punjikasthala take care of the chores, my dear. You look tired." His eyes mirrored his concern.

Taara nodded meekly in agreement.

Taara stood at the open window, watching Brhaspati's disciples seated in their orderly rows, reciting their *mantras*. Chandra had taken up his position before them, representing their master. A multitude of emotions buzzed through Taara's head like a hive of honeybees. Presently, she emerged from her reverie and turned resolutely from the window. A teasing smile played upon her lips.

She walked to the pots which stood ranged against a wall, filled to the brim with water. She carried a pot outside and poured its contents on the ground. Leaving the empty vessel there, she proceeded to repeat the procedure with the remaining pots. Once done, she looked at the row of empty vessels with a complacent smile.

"Punjika!" shouted Taara. "Punjikasthala! Where are you, girl? Come here."

The maidservant came running. "Mother, what is it?"

"The water was covered with dust – I have emptied the pots. Go and fetch fresh water from the river. The children need clean water to drink. Fill all the vessels."

"Yes, mother," Punjikasthala obediently picked up the pots and departed for the river.

Taara walked to the front of the class of disciples, studiedly ignoring Chandra. "The master has gone to Indra's court. I know that he has assigned lessons for the day, but the firewood is completely exhausted. Instead of studying, I want you all to go to the woods to collect kindling for the *ashram*. Sanaathana, you will be the leader of the foraging team." She turned to the other pupils. "I expect you all to obey Sanaathana …"

"But, mother," Sanaathana protested, "Master has appointed Chandra as our leader in his absence."

"I know that, Sanaathana." Taara's voice was tinged with impatience. "Chandra is needed here to perform a few tasks which are beyond you and me. So, go to the forest!"

The disciples needed no further urging – they willingly abandoned their lessons and set out for the woods in high spirits.

Chandra looked at Taara with doubtful eyes. "Master did order me to …"

Taara cut him off with a curt – "Chandra, I am aware of your *guru's* instructions." She continued on a softer note. "But, I hope you are aware that serving the master's wife is as important as obeying the master!"

Chandra marveled at her profile, as exquisite as every other part of her body. 'I have never addressed her as 'mother',' he thought. 'I wonder why.'

Taara turned to him and smiled, her pearl-like teeth gleaming between the coral of her lips. "Chandra, why is it that you alone among the disciples do not address me as 'mother'?"

Chandra's heart raced at the uncanny question. Could she read his thoughts?

"Come on, tell me why."

Chandra remained silent. He passed his tongue nervously over his dry lips.

"Come on, tell me why." Chandra jumped as her words echoed loudly from behind him. He turned quickly – there was no one there!

"Come on, tell me why." Again, her words reverberated in the silence. What sorcery was this? Then, the rustling of leaves pulled his startled gaze upwards: a parrot sat on the bough, fluttering its wings.

Taara burst into trills of merry laughter. "Until you answer, the parrot will repeat my words!" She drew near and placed her feather-light fingers over his parted lips for a fleeting second, saying, "But, not here – you will give me your answer in the garden."

"Come, Chandra," she clasped his hand and urged him on.

"Come, Chandra," the parrot repeated from the tree.

"Come, Chandra." Taara enticed him forward with her impish smile.

"Come, Chandra." The parrot reinforced her words from above.

Taara's hand, slim as a lotus stem, became a taut noose of desire – and he was its willing captive. Chandra gave a reckless laugh and staggered after the vision of loveliness moving ahead of him.

───⦅∞⦆───

Chandra tossed and turned restlessly on his mat. It was well past midnight, but sleep continued to elude him. Scenes from his afternoon tryst in the garden ran through his mind in a kaleidoscopic loop.

"Come on!" Taara gripped his hand and broke into a carefree run. She stopped, panting, in the thick undergrowth below the spreading branches of a tree. She smiled up at him. Chandra could not tear his fascinated eyes from the rise and fall of her breasts. Rivulets of perspiration ran down his face.

"You are sweating, Chandra. It must be all this running ..." remarked Taara.

He started as she reached up to dab at his face with the edge of her upper garment. He was intoxicated by the heady fragrance of pollen wafting from the cloth, blending seamlessly with the petal-soft touch of her hand.

"You are still sweating! Are you tired?" Taara looked at the beads of perspiration forming on his brow.

Chandra did not reply. Well did he know that fatigue was far removed from his mind and body!

"We are in the garden! Shall we pick flowers?" Taara asked vivaciously.

"If you want ..." Chandra managed to murmur the words.

"Very well – you take that side and I'll cover this one. Let's see who gathers more flowers." Taara laughed playfully as she added a condition. "And the collected flowers should be of different colours."

Chandra gathered flowers absently, his thoughts a riot of emotion. The touch of every flower was a caress from Taara's soft hand.

In a while, her sweet words carried to him on the breeze: "Chandra, where are you? Come here."

He walked slowly towards the melodious sound of her voice.

"Here I am." He could not see her. Was this to be a game of hide and seek?

"Chandra, here – in this bower!"

His blood sang in excited response to her lilting laugh. He walked slowly to the arbour, the fragrance-laden air pulling at him like a powerful aphrodisiac. He stooped to enter the thick canopy of climbing plants. The melodious tinkling of Taara's bangles greeted him in the subdued light of the leafy shelter. Suddenly, he was deluged by a shower of flowers.

As he gasped in surprise, her musical voice rang out in mocking laughter. "I gathered the flowers for you – not for god!" She paused. "Now, tell me – for whom are your flowers?"

He flinched, as her question hit him like a soft slap on the face.

"Come on, Chandra, tell me," her insistent voice refused to let him go.

Unsure as to how to address her, Chandra held out his flowers in mute offering.

"For me! Then, why don't you shower them on me?" Taara laughed. "But, wait ... no ... not like this ... not while I am standing ..." She lay back on the soft carpet of blossoms which covered the ground. Beauty personified, she reclined on her bed of flowers – one slender hand pillowed her head; the other encircled her waist; one leg was bent upright at the knee.

Chandra stared at her as if in a trance.

"Now, Chandra: bathe me in flowers!" She smiled sensuously. "Slowly,

slowly! Don't throw them – I want to be drenched in a gentle shower of blossoms."

Gathering his courage, Chandra rained flowers lightly on Taara. His trembling hand gradually steadied. He was a devotee at the altar of her beauty, worshipping her exquisite body with his blossoms.

"Chandra," her voice reached him softly from the depths of the bower. "Do you know whom you look like now?" She paused. "You are Vasantha, Manmatha's deputy – he who aids the god of love in adorning the virgin goddess of nature."

Chandra emptied his upper garment over her and gazed adoringly at Taara's flower-smothered body. She glowed like a lissome creeper bearing a profusion of multi hued blossoms along its curvaceous length. Her radiant face turned up towards him like a sunflower. Her pristine teeth sparkled like jasmine buds.

"You have not yet answered my two questions," she reminded him archly.

He looked down questioningly at her.

"It looks like I will first have to tutor you in the art of conversation!" Taara smiled indulgently and reached up to take his hand. "Come here, Chandra."

She pulled him down gently to sit close beside her. "Now, tell me: what is my name?"

"Taara ..."

"Very well. Now, tell me why you do not address me as 'mother,' as proper for a disciple?" She looked directly at him. "Tell me, Chandra. I will have an answer from you now."

"I dislike calling you so," he mumbled softly.

"Oh! Is that so?" She laughed. "Then, call me Taara!"

His eyes widened in surprise at her daring. Her own eyes wordlessly reinforced the command of her tender, leaf-like lips, tremulous in the cool breeze which reached into the bower.

As if of their own accord, his lips murmured, "Taara ..."

"Yes! Chandra, call me Taara!"

Had she not heard him? He repeated in a firmer voice, "Taara ..."

She laughed in undiluted pleasure. "There is something in the way you say my name ... I don't know what it is ... it makes my heart sing!" She paused. "I heard you the first time ... but I want to hear it again and again!" Her infectious smile was now mirrored in his own face.

"Do you know that you are even handsomer when you smile?" she asked. "Now, answer my second question: who is more beautiful – your mother or I?"

He had forgotten the question she had asked at their meal together: how long ago it seemed! He gazed into the bottomless pools of her eyes. Her garment of flowers rose and fell with each sweet breath, as if ruffled by a gentle zephyr. Her own glowing body highlighted the luster of the blossoms.

"Tell me, Chandra. Who is more beautiful – your mother or I?" She repeated her question with a mocking smile on her lips.

An image of his lovely mother flashed before his mind's eye and realization dawned at the same time: his mother's beauty was healing balm – Taara's was inciting flame; his mother's loveliness wrapped him in calm repose – Taara's banished sleep from his eyes.

She pressed his hand insistently. "If you don't answer, I will have to call my parrot." She laughed teasingly. "So, tell me now: who is more beautiful, your mother or I?"

"You ..." he murmured. "You are more beautiful." His eyes roved hungrily over her body, feasting on its lithe beauty.

"And do you know who is handsomer: you or my husband?" she asked.

He gasped at her presumption: "Taara!"

"Come on, ask me!" she urged. Her fingers stroked his hands, working their magic on his senses.

"Taara ..." was all that he could say.

She took his palm and placed it against her petal-soft cheek. "I will tell you even if you refuse to ask: you are handsomer than my husband." Her voice grew husky with desire. "Chandra, come close to me."

"Taara ..." again, it was the only word he could muster.

Her roving hand came to rest on his shoulder. "Closer ... closer! I want you close to my heart!"

Her voice rang with passion.

A last cry of sanity escaped his lips: "Master!?" only to be silenced by her own searching lips.

"I will not allow even a breath of air to intrude between us – leave alone your master!"

Her arms were unassailable creepers entwining his neck. He laid his cheek against hers. Like the river making its immutable way into the sea, Chandra melted into her exquisite loveliness.

―∞∞―

Chandra turned on his mat and smiled in recollected pleasure. He continued his musing. He had fallen under the spell of Taara's eyes right from the moment of his arrival at the hermitage. One look at her face through the window and he was lost! What was the secret of his instinctive cleaving to her? Could it be the strength of intimate bonds in their previous incarnations?

"Meet me at the river before sunrise. We will frolic in the cool water while the rest of the world still slumbers."

Taara's final words rang sweetly in his ears with their promise of pleasures to come.

He smiled once more and finally sank into sleep.

Chandra half-reclined on the grassy knoll, watching Taara sport in the river. She had the soul of a mermaid – her hands were golden creepers parting the water in clean strokes; now, she floated on her back in delicious lassitude; now, she flashed under the waves like a shoal of silver fish. Chandra drank in her loveliness. Treading water, she looked up at him. Her face was a lotus with its floating tendrils of moss-like hair.

She called out to him: "Come on, Chandra!"

He shook his head in refusal, preferring his grandstand view of her exquisite body. Taara quickly swam towards the shore and came to her feet in the shallows. The water lapped about her slender waist. Chandra felt the heat rise in him. She raised her arms to knot her long hair and then stretched her hand out to him. Chandra rose to help her out of the water. In a twinkling, he was thrashing in the water beside the triumphantly laughing Taara. As he came up for breath, her golden hands reached out for him, making him breathless once more.

Brhaspati was in the midst of a demanding lecture, as Chandra unobtrusively made his way towards the last row of attentive disciples. As he silently bent to sit,

"Chandra!" Brhaspati's voice cracked through the air like a whiplash.

Chandra froze.

"Where have you been?" The innocuous words were pregnant with dangerous undercurrents.

"To the river … master … for a bath …" He could not for the life of him conceal the guilty flush which suffused his face.

"Why did you not join your fellow-disciples in their morning ablutions?" The stern voice continued inexorably, "Why did you go to the river separately?"

Chandra thought for a moment. What if someone had noticed that he and Taara were absent from the hermitage at the same time? It would serve no purpose to be caught in a lie.

"Master, I accompanied the master's wife to the river – at her command." He bent his head.

Brhaspati admonished him gravely: "Chandra, your primary task here is to study. Your second duty is towards your master. There is absolutely no excuse for a disciple to serve the master's wife during study hours." He paused and continued seriously. "Focus on your study and prove yourself worthy of the name Aatreya – son of sage Atri."

"Yes, master," Chandra murmured.

"And one more thing. It has come to my attention that you are devoting a major part of your time towards carrying out your *gurupatni's* orders. Let me make it clear to you that the *ashram's* daily routine does not require your helping hand. I will inform my wife accordingly. From this moment, I expect you to dedicate yourself single-mindedly to your duties as a student."

"Yes, master."

Brhaspati signaled with his hand for Chandra to be seated and resumed his lesson. Chandra looked stealthily towards the *ashram*. His eyes caught the flutter of Taara's *saree* as she silently moved away from the open window.

<hr />

It was past midnight. Chandra wandered distractedly about the garden, coming back again and again to the hidden bower. Why was Taara not here? Would she come? Surely her signal meant that she would meet him here? Had Brhaspati delayed her? A spasm of rage rose in his breast against his master.

Coming to his senses with a start, Chandra realized the need to avoid the watchful eyes of the maidservant or an encounter with a sleepless disciple. He hurried into the concealment of the arbour. Suddenly, an invigorating fragrance wafted in on the breeze. In its wake came the mellifluous tinkling of anklets. Chandra's heart raced in excitement. Taara!

"Chandra ..." Her voice was low and seeking.

He hurried out of the bower. Taara rushed towards him in an agony of urgent longing. A sudden gust of wind blew her upper garment over Chandra's face: he was a willing fish caught in the net of desire. Taara fell into his arms. He clasped her tightly to his breast.

He pressed his ear against her lips which whispered, "Chandra!"

With one mind, they entered the bower and sat locked in a tight embrace.

"Taara," said Chandra with a heavy heart, "The last two days have been endless ..."

"For me too, my dearest. But, you know we have to be cautious. That's why I did not attempt to meet you."

"Taara ... Taara ... Taara ... I never tire of saying your beloved name."

Her hands were creepers of love entwined round his neck. She gently pulled his head down to rest on her lap.

"I want to shout your name out loud to the world – it is hard to be silent," he said.

She smiled down tenderly at him. "We are fated to love each other in secret, dearest." Her fingers stroked his hair.

Chandra sat up in a sudden burst of anger. "I refuse to accept that," he shot back at her. "I will not let the world come between us!"

"Chandra!" She hushed him, placing her fingertips against his lips.

He persisted: "We must be with each other through every moment of our lives. Just the two of us, living in ecstatic isolation in a world of our own."

Taara caressed his cheeks. "I too want to live with you forever, love."

"Then, come with me!" There was an urgent anxiety in his words.

"Where can we go, dearest?"

"To a place where none can intrude on our love."

"Is there such a place, Chandra?" She tenderly held his face between her two hands and sighed.

"Yes, there is – my personal abode."

"Your abode?" she asked in surprise. "You mean your parental home? The hermitage?"

"No! Viswakarma has built a palace for me: it awaits my coming once I am done with my education and am married."

"Really?"

Chandra smiled. "I was done with my education the very first day I glimpsed your beautiful eyes through the hermitage window!"

Taara caressed his arms.

Chandra continued: "As for my marriage, that has also taken place – with you! It was solemnized when I held your hand." He bent to place a gentle kiss on her palms. "It has the sanction of our scriptures as *paanigraham* – holding of the bride's hand." He continued resolutely. "Soon, I will take you away secretly. Again, this is in line with the scriptures, as ordained for the *asura* clan: *rakshas vivah.*"

"Chandra ... will all this really come to pass?" she asked wistfully.

He insisted firmly, "It will. You were born to be mine. Your marriage to Brhaspati was but a prelude to your life as my wife."

Taara pressed close to him. Her lips whispered into his ears: "Chandra, at first I tormented myself with the thought that you would run away from my grasp like a frightened child. But now, you are a man – and you are mine."

"And do you know when I became a man?" he whispered in his turn, caressing her ear with his lips. "I became a man when I first embraced the beautiful Taara."

She tore herself reluctantly from his arms and said, "Tomorrow morning, your master leaves for Indra's court."

Chandra gave a subdued laugh and clapped his hands soundlessly. "Good! The disciples will go to the woods to collect kindling and Punjikasthala will go to the river to fill the empty pots!"

"And we ...?" asked Taara.

"We will be together, my love. We will be together for all eternity."

———

Brhaspati sat on his customary dais under the tree, awaiting his disciples' arrival for their morning tuition.

"*Om! Om! Om!*"

The *guru* looked up in smiling approval as the primeval chant echoed from the boughs above his head: it was the *ashram* parrot, fluttering its wings among the foliage! It was a matter of pride to Brhaspati that his favorite parrot faithfully recited the chants which he taught his pupils. After all, it was generally acknowledged that, in a truly pious hermitage, parrots chanted *Vedic* hymns, while lions and deer lived in happy harmony.

The parrot's chant was a clarion call to the disciples, who were soon assembled before their master in orderly rows. Brhaspati took in the familiar faces – everyone was present ... no ... where was Chandra? Before he could question his students, Punjikasthala hurried to him.

"Master ..." the maidservant hesitated. Brhaspati urged her on with an impatient gesture of his hand.

"Your respected wife is not in the hermitage ..." she stood with downcast eyes.

"What! Taara is not at home?" Brhaspati blurted in surprise. "How can that be? She was here yesterday when I left for Indra's court!"

"She is not to be found, master," murmured Punjikasthala.

A murmur of excitement ran through the class.

"What is the meaning of this, Punjika?" Brhaspati frowned.

"I do not know, master. She vanished after your eminence left for *Swargaloka*. I assumed she had accompanied you ..."

A senior student stood up politely and seconded the girl: "Yes, *gurudev*, we also assumed that Mother Taaradevi and Chandra were with you ..."

Brhaspati's eyes narrowed. "I went alone." A note of criticism crept into his voice. "You should have kept an eye on Chandra ..."

"We last saw him near the river in the early hours of the morning, master," the disciple replied. "He did not join us in our ablutions."

Abandoning his class, Brhaspati paced thoughtfully aside for a few minutes. Then, he turned to the whispering disciples. "Perhaps they have gone to the woods to forage for sacrificial twigs and holy grass or kindling ..." He cleared his throat, attempting to rein in his galloping thoughts. "Sanaathana, take Suneeta and a few other senior disciples and go in search of them in the forest. I fear they may have met with some untoward accident."

He turned to Punjikasthala. "Punjika, prepare food for all."

He hushed the excited chattering of the class with a curt gesture. "The rest of you – recite yesterday's hymns."

In the intervening moment of silence, "Come on, Chandra!" The call rang merrily from above.

Brhaspati looked up in dismay at his clever parrot.

———∞∞∞———

"Come on, Chandra!" Taara's warm invitation reached out to caress Chandra's ears, as he stood on the threshold of his abode, gazing at the profusion of flowering plants which filled the garden with a riot of colour. He turned in obedience to her melodious call and returned to the bedchamber. Taara stood near the bed which was piled high with the softest of eiderdown mattresses. He came to stand beside her, encircling her slender waist with his hand.

She leaned back to rest her head on his broad shoulder. "What a beautiful bed!" she exclaimed.

"It was created by Viswakarma, the divine architect," Chandra added with a smile: "for you!"

Taara shook her head wryly. "No, Chandra, this palace and its contents were specifically created for you." She continued passionately. "But, now, I want everything! Forever! The feather-soft beds, the golden swings – everything is mine for all eternity! Will you let me have it all?"

Chandra smiled fondly. "Beloved, why such sudden vehemence?"

"I am sick and tired of the *ashram's* frugality. Coarse grass mats for beds, rough deerskin quilts, roots and leaves for meals … Ugh!" She snorted delicately in disgust. "I hate ugly things!"

She turned to face him. "Look at me, Chandra," she commanded.

Chandra obeyed her with pleasure, his eyes roving passionately over her lithe, exquisite body. She was beauty sublime. She had been created for him alone: not Brhaspati!

"How do I look?" she asked.

"You are a fragile, golden creeper …" he paused to draw her close. "And I am the pillar of support about which you will twine."

"Can a creeper be condemned to lie on coarse grass mats and animal skins?"

"Never again, my love," Chandra declared vehemently. "I will never allow that to happen. That is why I dared to bring you here to our Abode of Bliss!"

A teasing smile played about her lips. "Then, tell me, where should this beautiful creeper rest?"

Chandra pointed to the bed and whispered: "There, on the softest of beds."

She gazed into his eyes. "Not there, my Chandra," she laid her soft cheek against his broad chest, "But here!" Eyes melting in love, he looked into her upturned face. Her own eyes mirrored his emotion. He pressed her to him passionately.

"Chandra, can I ask you for something?"

"Anything, my love, anything!" he whispered against her hair.

"I want a son who reflects your beauty ..." her voice was a murmur against his breast.

Chandra tightened his embrace.

The extended search for Chandra and Taara led nowhere. Brhaspati was forced to admit that his wife, in the throes of infatuation, had eloped with his pupil. However, he held fast to the hope that she would soon realize her folly and return to him. After all, Taara was his adored wife, a gift from Brahma himself! He continued with the routine of the *ashram,* instructing his disciples and executing his duties at Indra's court. Punjikasthala managed the household chores.

Brhaspati did not confide in Indra: he was aware that the king of the *devas* accorded Taara the reverence due to a mother – as befitting the consort of their preceptor. He was unwilling to disabuse Indra of his good opinion, confident that Taara would soon be back and no one outside the *ashram* any the wiser.

The golden swing, carrying its precious burden, came flying towards Chandra. He extended his hands and gave it a gentle push. His heart clenched at Taara's sweet smile as the swing swept her away from him. As the swing carried her to him again, he was flooded with the fierce pride of possession. Just as the swing, which tried to carry her away, irresistibly brought her back to him again and again, so it would be with any opposing force in the world! She was his and his alone!

As the swing arched through the air and reached him, Taara jumped into his inviting arms. She rested her head against his shoulder and murmured, "I am tired."

"Tired of your favorite past time so soon this morning?!" He smiled down indulgently at her.

"The swing makes me giddy," she said softly.

"Yet, earlier, you could swing for hours with me pushing you!" he teased.

Taara looked enigmatically into his eyes. "Chandra," she said, "Look at me." He continued to gaze into her exquisite face.

She smiled at him. "Oh, your sweet innocence! What am I to do with you!" She paused and continued in a serious tone. "I no longer enjoy swinging because a little copy of you is swinging in my womb!"

"Really?" he was ecstatic. He pressed her tenderly to his chest and kissed the top of her head.

She murmured softly against him. "It is only now that I understand Brahma's blessing: 'Your one-fold marriage to Brhaspati will bring you two-fold happiness!'" She caressed his strong shoulders. "Truly my joy is multiplied many times over!"

❦

Brhaspati, coming to the end of his morning worship, folded his hands in silent prayer.

"Narayana! Narayana!" The familiar chant carried to him, announcing the arrival of sage Narada, the quintessential cosmic messenger.

Brhaspati hurried to welcome his guest. "*Pranam*, revered sage."

Brhaspati bowed to receive Narada's blessing. "May you soon be reconciled with your estranged wife!"

Brhaspati gave a startled gasp: "Narada!"

The sage smiled gently. "Brhaspati, why are you surprised at my knowledge of your wife's extended absence?" He paused. "After all, the dissemination of information is the purpose of my creation by my father, Brahma!"

Brhaspati remained speechless, with downcast eyes.

The sage continued, "Call off your disciples' futile search of the forest – Taara and Chandra are not there."

Brhaspati looked up in rising hope. "Narada, do you know Taara's whereabouts?"

"Of course, Brhaspati. Taara shares the beautiful abode constructed for Chandra by the inimitable Viswakarma."

The *deva-guru* flushed and asked haltingly, "Narada ... how ... how is Taara?"

"Oh, Taara is in the pink of health and spirits: in fact, she seems to be happier with your pupil than with you."

Brhaspati lowered his head.

"Chandra has established her there as his wife. Let me give you the location of his Abode of Bliss. Then, you can dispatch some of your disciples to him as emissaries."

❦

"Come on, Chandra!"

Brhaspati jumped as Taara's voice intruded on his dark thoughts. He looked up at the parrot preening itself among the foliage of the tree. That accursed bird! He would willingly wring its neck – or reduce it to cinders with a curse! He sighed and controlled his unreasonable rage: at least the faithful parrot had given him ample warning that his wife was enamored of Chandra. He continued to gaze at the spreading branches of the tree, where flowers had matured into fruits, marking the inexorable passage of time. He sighed. His hope that Taara would return had dimmed to the faintest, flickering ember.

Following Narada's counsel, Brhaspati had dispatched his senior disciples to Chandra's abode to fetch Taara, making Chandra see the error of his ways. The mission was a fiasco: Taara had lashed out viciously at them, while Chandra had intimidated them with threats and manhandled them out of his home.

Brhaspati himself, swallowing his self-respect, had personally gone to plead with the recalcitrant couple. He had excused himself, thinking, 'After all, Chandra is my disciple ... and Taara is my lawfully wedded wife ... she deserves my forgiveness.'

Even as he attempted to convince Chandra that sleeping with his preceptor's wife was one of the five cardinal sins, the arrogant young man shot back: "This is not your *ashram*: Let's not have any of your lectures on morality here!" Chandra looked down with disdain at his former *guru*. "And, for your information, it is also a cardinal sin to reject a lady who desires to be loved."

Brhaspati flushed at Chandra's vitriolic tone. Rubbing salt into his wounds, Taara gave a haughty toss of her head and burst into mocking laughter. He had endured a life-time of humiliation in that brief encounter.

"*Pranam, gurudev!*" Brhaspati looked up to find Indra before him.

"Mahendra!"

"You have abandoned my court, *gurudev!*" There was a note of reproach in his voice. "And you have failed to confide in me Mother Taara's elopement with that callow youth, Chandra."

"Yes, Indra – I foolishly convinced myself that it would all turn out well shortly." Brhaspati stood with downcast eyes.

"Take heart *gurudev*: you have also failed to take into consideration the depth of reverence in which the *devas* hold their preceptor." He sniffed in disdain. "Forget those foolish elopers – I assure you that I will find you a more beautiful and virtuous wife than the errant Taara."

"Mahendra!" Brhaspati gasped.

"Yes, *gurudev*," Indra continued staunchly. "By embracing her husband's disciple, Taara has forfeited both her chastity and her place as your wife."

Brhaspati addressed the king of the *devas* gravely: "Indra, let me tell you a little known fact of *dharma* – a woman is cleansed of the sin of adultery by her monthly curse. Her menstruation flushes her body of impurities and makes her chaste once more."

Indra listened attentively. To him, the *guru's* word was law. He bowed his head, acknowledging Brhaspati's vast wisdom. "*Gurudev*, as always, I defer to your wishes. In that case, I shall fetch Taaradevi and offer her at your holy feet as my *guru dakshina*!" He stood resolutely. "I will not hesitate to wage war against the feckless Chandra to gain my objective."

Brhaspati held out his hand in benediction. "May victory be yours, Indra!"

Vrshaparva ascended his throne, eager to deal with several pending affairs of state. *Acharya* Usana, the *rakshasa-guru*, was seated in his place of honor on the king's right. Just as the crowded assembly of *asuras* came to order, a stentorian voice rang through the vast hall:

"Victory to Emperor Vrshaparva!" It was Timiraasura: the king's trusted emissary and spy extraordinaire. All heads turned expectantly towards the new arrival, as he approached the throne and bowed in salutation.

"Ah, Timiraasura!" Vrshaparva boomed. "Your haste suggests that you come with information of great importance." He raised his bushy eyebrows in interrogation.

"Yes, my king. I bring you momentous tidings which will gladden your heart."

The *asuras* were now all ears. There was pin-drop silence in the court as the spy cleared this throat.

"My lord, you know that Brhaspati, the *deva-guru*, married Taara. Now, Taara has eloped with Chandra, one of Brhaspati's disciples. Chandra has established her as his own wife in his private abode and is reveling in her company day and night. Brhaspati, hopelessly infatuated with Taara, has made several futile attempts to reclaim his wife: both

personally and through his envoys." He gave a significant pause. "Now,
Indra, king of the *devas*, has given Brhaspati his sworn word that he will
reclaim Taara for him: even at the cost of waging war against the young
Chandra ..."

"Enough!" Vrshaparva thundered. "What a caboodle of nonsense!
Have you lost your mind, Timira?" He snorted in disgust. "What is it
to us if some besotted boy chooses to elope with his master's wife?" He
glowered at the spy. "If you have information of real import, let's hear
it, or else ..."

Usana intervened with a placatory gesture. "Just a moment,
Vrshaparva, just a moment." He continued thoughtfully. "There may be
more to this than meets the eye." `

He turned to the nervous spy. "Now, Timira, give us the other details
you have gathered."

The relieved spy continued: "Master, I have discovered that Indra is
ready to send an envoy to Chandra with an ultimatum: either return the
truant Taara to Brhaspati or face the devas' wrath."

Usana jumped up from his seat in excitement. "There is not a moment
to be lost! Vrshaparva, I must set out immediately!"

The *rakshasa* king looked at him in bewilderment. "Where to,
master?"

"To Chandra's abode."

"Master! To that feckless boy's residence?... You, in person? ... But,
why?" Vrshaparva was aghast.

Usana laughed. "To ensure that Chandra does not cave in to Indra's
ultimatum."

"But, why, master? Why do you want to get involved in this foolish
romantic caper?"

"Think, Vrshaparva," Usana urged. "If Chandra refuses to surrender
Taara, what will Indra's next move be?"

"To honor his ultimatum, Indra will be forced to declare war on
Chandra."

"Exactly! And what will happen if we in turn declare our support for
Chandra?" He paused to smile at the frowning *rakshasa* king. "Let me
tell you: once we have entered the fray, this little contretemps between
Indra and Chandra will explode into a full-scale war between the *devas*
and the *asuras*. The *devas* will be vanquished and the glory of *Swargaloka*
will be yours!"

Vrshaparva's face was wreathed in the broadest of smiles. He rose from his throne and saluted his mentor. *"Gurudev*, we *asuras* are indeed fortunate to have you as our preceptor! What guile! What brilliant strategy!"

Usana smiled and walked quickly to the hall's **main** exit.

Chandra gazed in perplexity at the majestic personage standing at his threshold. He bowed instinctively in deference. "Greetings, *Aarya*! May I know who you are?"

"Chandra, I am *Acharya* Usana, the preceptor of the *asuras*."

Chandra folded his hands in respect. "And to what do I owe the honor of your visit, revered *Acharya*?"

Usana looked earnestly at him and announced, "I am here to defend you against imminent peril."

"Peril?!" Chandra gasped.

"Yes." Usana paused for effect. "Taara and you face great danger." Usana's authoritarian tone captured Chandra's undivided attention. "Come, let us go inside and discuss these grave developments."

Seated closely side-by-side, Chandra and Taara waited anxiously on Usana's words.

"A sinister conspiracy has been hatched to separate you from each other -" the *rakshasa-guru* started somberly.

Chandra and Taara looked at each other in shocked surprise. Chandra tried to comment, but words failed him.

Usana continued inexorably: "Indra has given his word to his preceptor, Brhaspati, that he will present Taara to him as *guru-dakshina*. He has sworn to declare war on you if you remain intransigent."

Taara reached out to clasp Chandra's fingers with her own. Chandra patted her hand and turned anxious eyes towards Usana, who continued: "Indra's envoy is on his way here even as we speak. He will deliver an ultimatum to you: either surrender Taara to Brhaspati or confront the might of the *deva* army. He will threaten to lay siege to your abode ..."

Chandra blanched and put his arm protectively round Taara. He remained speechless.

Usana's strong voice brimmed with assurance, as his powerful gaze held Chandra's: "Chandra, do not fear. Your adored Taara will remain with you."

"But ... I ... I cannot face Indra's army ..." Chandra murmured with downcast eyes.

"You will not be called upon to confront the *devas*. The formidable *asura* army, under the able command of my disciple, King Vrshaparva, will be your bulwark against Indra's aggression. The *deva's* will taste defeat if they move against you. I give you my word that, henceforth, both of you will be under *asura* protection."

Chandra and Taara exchanged looks. The alarm in their eyes gave place to relief and growing confidence. They turned to Usana with one accord and touched his feet in respect.

"Master," said Chandra, "We are deeply touched by your affection for us and your compassionate understanding of our love for each other." He choked with emotion. "We are indeed blessed to have your friendship."

A sardonic smile flitted across Usana's face. He locked eyes with Chandra and declared proudly: "I, Usana, preceptor of the *asuras*, do not dissimulate! It is neither affection nor compassion which has earned you the *rakshasas'* support. We are willing to take up arms on your behalf for one reason alone: our all-consuming hatred for the *devas*."

He rose majestically and prepared to leave. As Chandra and Taara bowed in respect, he said, "Chandra, have faith in me. Do not be intimidated by Indra's threats. Challenge him to war!" He paused, his eyes on Taara. "Do not withdraw your protection from this innocent maid who trustingly placed her life in your care."

He lifted his hand in blessing. "May victory be yours!"

Usana's inspirational words, and promise of support, bolstered Chandra's confidence. Indra's envoy was confronted by a haughty Taara, and a belligerent Chandra, who defiantly threw Indra's ultimatum back in his face.

"I dare Indra to do his worst!" Chandra spat at the envoy.

Indra mounted his war chariot, driven by Maatali, and set out for Chandra's abode at the head of his army. Brhaspati accompanied him. As they reached the objective of their assault, the *devas* were shocked to find the *asura* army arrayed in a protective phalanx around the palace. Vrshaparva and Usana stood in the vanguard of this terrible force of demons. At the sight of the *devas*, the *rakshasas* raised blood curdling battle cries that shook the earth and the skies like the roar of thunder.

With a sinister clash, thousands of weapons sprang up from the massed body of aggressive demons.

"Naraya ..."

Sage Narada, travelling across the sky, bit off his sacred chant as the threatening rumble reached his ears. One startled look downward and he summed up the crises. In the blink of an eye, the sage stood before Brahma, explaining how Chandra's elopement with Taara had culminated in the *devas* and *asuras* confronting each other on the battlefield. The anxious Brahma jumped up from his lotus throne and hurried from *Satyaloka*.

Brahma, Narada by his side, stood between the two armies poised on the brink of war.

Brahma sternly confronted Usana and Vrshaparva: "I am amazed at your presence here! Surely, a trifling romantic misadventure cannot be the cause of war between you and the *devas*! Furthermore, Chandra's elopement is categorically a sin: it cannot be justified on any count. Reflect on your actions!"

He turned towards the *devas* and beckoned Brhaspati and Indra forward. "I trust that you will display the patience and fortitude which are in keeping with your nature," he said, a tinge of reproach in his voice.

Brahma made his way to Chandra's palatial residence, where Taara and Chandra saluted him with folded hands.

The Creator reprimanded them harshly: "You have both abandoned the path of *dharma* and succumbed to mere lust. Your double betrayal of Brhaspati, who is both husband and master, has caused him indescribable torment." His voice dripped with sarcasm as he continued: "Of course, it goes without saying that you have derived untold pleasure from your carnal sins – let that suffice!"

Brahma's words rang in the chamber with the relentless clarity of a bell. The Creator's penetrating glance bore into Chandra like a knife.

The youth thought in chagrin, 'This is what my own soul whispers to me.'

On her part, Taara conceded sadly, 'Brahma's words have the undeniable ring of truth.'

Brahma turned to look at Taara. Bearing the baby in her womb, she was a plump lotus bud. His gaze softened. "Taara. I hope you now understand the meaning of my blessing: 'Your one-fold marriage to Brhaspati will bring you two-fold happiness!'" He smiled gently at her. "Return to the husband decreed for you by fate. Be happy in his service!"

As Taara touched his feet in respect, Brahma blessed her: "Long may you live with your husband!"

He turned back to Chandra. "As for you, young Chandra, Taara rightfully belongs to your master. You will personally hand her over to your *guru* – that will be your expiation for your sin."

Chadra bowed in obedience to Brahma. Chandra then slowly turned to Taara with an aching smile and reached out to take her hand. Taara's fingers entwined his like a creeper seeking the blessed support of a sturdy branch. Their eyes locked in an agony of yearning. It seemed as though eons of unsaid endearments and affection were compressed into those fleeting moments. Taara blinked back her unshed tears and straightened her shoulders.

Brahma stood with a gentle smile on his face, watching Chandra and Taara walk away from him.

———— ❀ ————

A happy murmur ran through the waiting crowd of disciples as Brhaspati descended from Indra's chariot with Taara beside him. Refusing to acknowledge anyone, including Punjikasthala, Taara quickly followed her husband indoors.

Brhaspati made his way directly to the chamber of worship. He folded his hands in prayer and gave thanks to god. He then turned to his wife: Taara stood statue-like before him, her face devoid of expression.

Brhaspati said gently, "Welcome back home, Taara."

A faint tremor passed through her body. Her delicate lips were tender leaves ruffled by the breeze. A veil of tears shaded her lovely eyes. She started forward and bent to touch Brhaspati's feet, hampered by the weight of her pregnancy.

Brhaspati tenderly raised her up and gazed into her eyes. "I have regained my lost treasure," he whispered.

At these words, Taara burst into heaving sobs. Scalding tears coursed down her smooth cheeks.

"*Swami* … Forgive me … I have betrayed you …" She wept inconsolably.

Brhaspati wiped her tears with gentle fingers. "No, Taara, it is Chandra who has betrayed me." He tilted her chin up. "Look at me. We all have nightmares – we will consider this to be one such unpleasant dream and forget it."

"*Swami* ..." she whispered.

"Yes, Taara, we will move on." He stopped to look proudly at her swollen stomach. "Brhaspati's lineage – the Angiras *gothra* – will flourish through you!" His voice mellowed. "I cannot live without you, Taara."

She gazed up at him through tear-filled eyes.

———

Taara brought a baby boy into the world at an auspicious moment under the aegis of the *Poorvaabhaadra* star. Brhaspati's *ashram* resounded with joy. Narada spread the glad tidings far and wide. Indra and the *devas* celebrated the birth of their preceptor's son.

The boy's naming ceremony was held at the hermitage. Angiras and Sraddha were there to bless their grandson, while Brahma, Narada and the *devas* graced the occasion with their presence.

Angiras turned to his son: "Brhaspati, have you decided the boy's name?"

"Brhaspati does not have the right to name my son!"

All eyes turned in the direction of the angry voice – it was Chandra! Taara froze with the infant in her lap.

Brhaspati, seated beside her in the midst of the *jaatakarma* rites, jumped up in fury, his eyes blazing red. "You! ... you despicable betrayer of the sacred *guru-sishya* relationship!" He spat out his words in contempt. "You stole my wife – now you are here to steal my son. You will not escape retribution! Get out!" He moved threateningly forward.

Chandra stood his ground resolutely. "That boy is my son. If you choose to delude yourself otherwise, you are merely claiming my lineage as yours!" He laughed mockingly.

Brhaspati shouted, "Silence! It is my blood which runs in the boy's veins."

"You may continue to believe so. But, none can stop me from claiming my own son." Chandra moved towards the cowering Taara.

"Stop right there, Chandra!" Brhaspati thundered.

Indra jumped up. "*Gurudev*, stay calm." He turned angrily towards the intruder. "Let me deal with this turn-coat."

"Indra! Chandra!" Brahma's stern voice intervened, commanding their instant obedience. "Do not turn the *ashram* into a battlefield."

The Creator turned to Brhaspati. "Brhaspati, keep a tight rein on your emotions."

The *deva-guru* protested: "Grandsire, this concerns the crucial issue of my lineage. Chandra ..."

Brahma silenced him with a curt gesture. "Neither you nor Chandra can judge the baby's paternity. It is only the mother who can bear witness to the father's true identity. "

"I agree with Lord Brahma." It was sage Angiras.

Brahma turned to Taara. "Taara, take the child and come with me."

Taara followed him obediently with the baby in her arms. All eyes anxiously awaited their return. Brhaspati and Chandra smiled confidently at the guests, and glowered at each other, in turn.

After a few moments, Taara entered the room with downcast eyes. Her arms were empty. Then, Brahma followed, carrying the infant. There was pin drop silence in the hall.

The Creator mounted the dais and pronounced his judgement: "A child's lineage must be proven beyond the least doubt. It is the mother alone who can assert categorically from whose loins springs the child she bears. I have explained the crucial importance of this principle to Taara." He paused and held out the child. "Does he belong to Brhaspati? ... Does he belong to Chandra? ..." He paused again. "Taara has revealed the truth of the boy's paternity ..." He looked round at his attentive audience.

"Chandra is the boy's father!" Brahma's voice resounded across the chamber. "In your presence, I name the child, 'Budha,'and give him to his father, Chandra."

Brhaspati stood in speechless surprise. Chandra saluted Brahma and gently took the child into his arms.

Brahma advised, "Chandra, Budha is your son. Raise him well and devote the utmost attention to his education. Like yourself, he is to be anointed as one of the *Navagrahas*."

Chandra bowed in respect. "I beg your leave to hand Budha into the safekeeping of my father, sage Atri."

"You have my permission, Chandra – you may now leave."

Taara gazed yearningly at Chandra's receding figure through tear-filled eyes.

Brahma turned to Brhaspati. "Brhaspati, take heart: your lineage will endure and flourish. Taara will bear you many descendants."

The Creator held out his hand in benediction over the *deva-guru*. Brhaspati bowed his head in reverence.

—◦◦◦—

'*Aadityaaya cha Somaaya Mangalaaya Budhaayacha*
Guru Sukra Sanibhyascha Raahave Ketave....'

I offer my salutations to Aditya, Soma, Mangala, Budha, Guru, Sukra, Sani,
Rahu and Ketu

Nirvikalpananda recited the familiar chant to the *Navagrahas* and paused to consider his disciples. "And now, we come to the birth of the remaining *grahas* in their respective order."

A stir of excitement ran through his four *sishyas*.

Sadananda burst out: "Master, then it is time to hear about Sani!"

Nirvikalpananda smiled at his enthusiasm. "Yes, Sani is the seventh of the *Navagrahas*. The story of his birth is filled with extraordinary events and unexpected twists." He paused. "Sani is Surya's son. So, let's go back a little in our narrative – We know that Surya married Samjna, Viswakarma's daughter, and set up house in an isolated palace. Do you recall that Samjna asked Surya to bless her with two boys and a girl?"

The disciples nodded eagerly.

"Well, Surya did grant her wish …"

"Ah!" interjected Shivananda, "Sani was one of the three children!"

The master smiled indulgently. "No, Shivananda: the elder son was Vaivasvatha, the second was Yama and the daughter was Yami. Vivaswaan being one of Surya's twelve names, the elder son was called Vaivasvatha. He was in fact the Vaivasvatha *manu* who became the progenitor of the Surya dynasty. Ikshwaaku, Nagaa, Saryaathi, and other well-known personages, were his descendants."

He paused and looked at his attentive disciples. "Coming to the second son, Yama, he was none other than Yamadharmaraja: the god of death. The girl, Yami, took form as the river Yamuna …"

"Oh-ho, master," marveled Vimalananda, "So, Sani was born as their youngest brother?"

Nirvikalpananda gave a gentle laugh. "Now, now – let me tell you the story in its entirety!"

His voice grew serious again. "Vaivasvatha, Yama and Yami grew up under their parents' protection. At the time of our present tale, they were young children. One night …"

The master resumed his discourse.

THE BIRTH OF SANI

An uneasy silence lay over Surya's abode. The noise of children at play was conspicuously absent as Surya walked into the bed chamber.

Samjna stood motionless at the open window, gazing up at the sky. Her *saree* fluttered in the breeze, emphasizing the beauty of her body, silhouetted against the evening light. Surya came to stand close behind her and placed his hands gently on her slender shoulders.

Samjna flinched and jerked away from his touch. She gave him a fleeting glance before turning away quickly.

"Samjna, what are you afraid of?" Surya teased her affectionately.

To his astonishment, she admitted sombrely, "Yes, I am afraid ..."

A concerned Surya moved protectively close to his wife. "Dearest, what is it?"

Samjna moved away from him, shading her eyes with her trembling fingers. "Shall I tell you who it is who terrifies me?" she asked in tremulous tones.

"Tell me!" Surya said angrily. "Whoever it is, I will make him pay!"

His wife made a conciliatory gesture. "Please listen first -" She paused. "It is you I am afraid of!"

"Samjna!" Surya gasped at this bolt from the blue.

"Yes!" she reiterated. "I tremble at your presence ..."

Surya approached her with outstretched arms.

"*Swami*, please don't come any closer!" Samjna backed away from him. Surya froze in confused disbelief.

She continued: "Forgive me, my lord – I cannot help it: I am unable to bear the heat you emit."

Surya could not believe his ears. He stood speechless, staring at his wife, who continued to hide her eyes behind her outspread fingers. A faint hope dawned in his eyes – was this some kind of joke?

He asked, "*Devi*, are you making me pay for some transgression?" He smiled. "Are you angry, dearest? Is this love's penalty?"

Samjna gave an anguished cry. "No! It is not love's penalty – it is love's curse!" She continued her outburst: "I cannot bear the fierce heat from your body ... and my eyes are blinded by the harsh glare of your inner fire!" even as she spoke, she edged further away from him.

Surya's own eyes darkened in hurt. "Then, tell me: how did you manage to live with me all these years?" he asked quietly.

"I endured it ... what else could I do?" She appealed to him piteously. "Don't judge me harshly, *Swami*! I just cannot tolerate your fiery presence ... please stay away from me ... I am in agony!" She distanced herself from him, backing into a corner of the room.

Surya smiled gently. "Have you forgotten the days when you adored caressing my body?" he reminded her. "Days when you said my warmth kindled the fire of passion in your heart?"

"Those days are gone! That was in the first flush of our union – how can you expect the excitement of novelty and intimacy to endure? I was blind to all your faults then." She kept her face averted from him.

"Samjna!" a note of impatience crept into Surya's voice. "In effect, you are making me an untouchable with your unreasonable attitude."

She pleaded, "*Swami*, don't say that!" She finally turned to face him. "Will you do one thing for me?"

"What is it?" he asked.

"For my sake, will you reduce the intensity of your heat and radiance?"

"Impossible!" was his instinctive retort.

"*Swami*, I am your wife – the love of your life!" It was Samjna's turn to be hurt. "We are everything to each other!"

"Samjna, you are everything to me!" He continued gently. "But, I cannot grant your wish, dearest. It is beyond my power to reduce my heat and light."

"*Swami* ... but, why not?"

"Be reasonable, Samjna. Can you change the inherent temperature of your body?"

She hesitantly shook her head.

"No – in the same way, I cannot alter my own natural traits." He continued firmly. "You have to learn to tolerate my presence, as in the past." "*Swami* ..."

Surya brusquely brushed her hesitation aside and declared firmly: "Samjna, until you can arm yourself adequately with shields of affection and endurance as a protection against my innate qualities, I shall not trouble you with my presence."

He paused and his voice softened. "I shall wait for you to come to me."

He walked away from her.

Samjna sat helplessly on the bed, her face the picture of despair.

—⚬⚬⚬⚬—

"*Swami* ..."

Surya looked up at his wife's soft call and smiled encouragingly at her.

"I have thought hard about my predicament ... I ... I cannot bear to stay away from you ..." Surya's face lit up with radiant hope.

Samjna continued: "But, I need some time to fortify myself." She paused. "*Swami*, let me go to my father's house for a while. There I will have the leisure and space to introspect and strengthen my resilience. I will come back to you as the wife I ought to be."

Surya said gladly, "That's an excellent idea, my dear! Go ... and hurry back. I will wait eagerly for your return."

Samjna appealed to him in a tremulous voice: "*Swami*, until my return – promise me that you will take care of Vaivasvatha, Yama and Yami."

"Of course, dearest – but you must hurry back!" Samjna returned his tender smile.

———

Samjna had no intention of going to Vishwakarma's house. She was certain that it was impossible for her to ever again endure Surya's all-consuming heat and light. She needed to decide on her next course of action. She was running out of time: after a few days, Surya would go to her father's house in search of her: her absence would become known.

She walked towards the forest, where the blessed shade of trees wrapped her in cool benediction. She sank down beneath the spreading branches and pondered. She was needed as Surya's wife- what was even more essential, her dear children needed her as a mother. What was she to do?

Instinctively, Samjna slipped into a gradual, deep meditation. She remained utterly focused on her dilemma – her eyes closed; she was lost to the world. The hours passed. Then – a sudden tremor of excitement rippled through her still body. Her eyes widened in eager hope.

What if there was another woman who was a replica of her own self? A woman who was identical to her in appearance, speech and gesture: her double in every respect? Such a clone could easily pass herself off as Samjna and take on the role of Surya's wife and more importantly, be a mother to her little children! The exhilarating thought of being forever free from Surya's simmering presence brought Samjna to her feet. Oh for the liberty to spend the rest of her life in serene penance in these cool environs!

She paced in deep thought under the trees, as dusk fell and the shadows lengthened. It was essential to carefully fan the tiny spark of her idea into a steady flame ... she subsided on the ground once more and resumed her meditation.

———

The days sped past. Samjna persisted in her single-minded search for a solution to her predicament, using the laser-sharp light of meditation to show the way.

It was evening. Samjna walked to the lake and seated herself by the pellucid water. Her mind incessantly grappled with the all-important question: where could she find a woman who was her exact double? Her eyes were captivated by the lotus blossoms which clustered near the shore. She smiled at their beauty – her reflection smiled back at her from the mirror of the lake's surface. A gentle zephyr lifted her upper garment. Samjna held it back in place. Her shadow on the water replicated her demure gesture.

Samjna's heart raced in sudden excitement. There before her was her double! Her shadow was her clone in every way. But, it was just an adjunct to her own body – it had no individuality, no independent form. She frowned in thought.

Then – what if she could imbue it with a life apart from her own? What if she could fashion it into an entity in its own right? The frisson of discovery thrilled her being. Yes – she would fashion her replica from her shadow. She would endow it with every trait of her personality. Her shadow would become her doppelganger. She squared her shoulders in confidence.

This task was not beyond her: after all, she was Viswakarma's daughter! Right from birth, she had possessed unique powers, including the ability to assume any form at will. Imbuing her shadow with life should be simple enough!

Samjna quickly bathed in the lake. As she turned to make her way back to the forest, her shadow fell on the path before her. She stopped in abrupt thought. Then, scooping up some water in her cupped hands, she closed her eyes, softly murmured an incantation and sprinkled the water over the shadow. To her joy, in place of the shadow, there now stood her replica, distinct in its own right! Her doppelganger had a bewildered expression on its face.

Samjna gently said, "You are my double," and led it to the water. "Look at our reflections."

Her replica clapped its hands in childish glee: "We are copies of each other."

Samjna smiled and nodded in agreement.

"What is my name?" the clone suddenly asked. Samjna gasped at the sound of her own voice emanating uncannily from her double's mouth.

She considered a moment. "You are my shadow ... so, you are Chaaya." She paused and added, "And I am Samjna."

"Why did you bring me to life?" Chaaya asked curiously.

"I need a double to take my place as Surya's wife, and to be a mother to my children," Samjna explained gravely. "With you playing the role of wife and mother, I will be free to pursue my desired penance in the forest.

"I am your replica – so, playing your part should be easy enough!" Chaaya smiled. "For how long must I enact your role?"

"Forever," declared Samjna. "I give you leave to enjoy my husband's physical and intellectual companionship forever." She paused. "But only on one condition ..."

"And what is that?" Chaaya asked.

"Just as you accept my husband as your own, you must also wholeheartedly embrace my Vaivasvatha, Yama and Yami as your children – you must lavish your unstinting care and affection on them always."

Chaaya looked gravely at Samjna. "Samjna, you gave me life. My body and soul belong to you by right. Your wish is my command." She paused. "I give you my word: I will not just act – I will live the part! I will be a wife to your husband, and a mother to your children."

Deeply moved, Samjna, said: "Chaaya, your words warm my heart. Looking at you fills me with joy – we are so alike that I consider you my younger twin sister."

"I too feel that you are my dear elder sister," Chaaya replied. "We are identical twins!"

Samjna clasped Chaaya's hand affectionately and led her to her place of meditation.

Seated close to Chaaya, Samjna continued their conversation. "Chaaya, in order to carry off our deception, you have to know everything – and I mean everything! – about me."

"Just tell me once, Samjna: believe me, I am a fast learner." Chaaya smiled confidently.

Samjna was delighted with Chaaya's alacrity and quick intelligence. She started to fill Chaaya in on the myriad details of her life. "I am Viswakarma's daughter. My father is the son of a Vasu and is the divine architect ..."

"Samjna!" Chaaya interrupted with an impish smile. "I am Viswakarma's daughter – not you! Tell me about myself."

Samjna laughed at Chaaya's verve and continued. "Very well. You are married to Surya, the son of Kasyapa and Aditi. You have two sons, Vaivasvatha and Yama, and a daughter, Yami. A few days ago, unable to endure the intense warmth and light emitted constantly by your husband, you left on a sojourn to your father's house." She paused. "Are you clear on this?"

"Absolutely! So, I have left my husband's house. Carry on!"

"Now, you are returning to your husband, after arming yourself with the fortitude necessary to endure his radiant heat."

"I go in your place as Samjna – Surya's wife. " She smiled reassuringly at Samjna: "I will love your children as my own."

Samjna gave her a warm hug. "Let me tell you the intimate details of my private life with Surya. Then you will be ready."

―∞∞―

"Samjna!" Surya gasped in surprise at his wife's unexpected appearance at the door.

"*Swami,*" replied Chaaya, instinctively adhering to Samjna's instructions.

Surya walked eagerly towards her, hands outstretched in warm welcome. "Samjna, our home has been shrouded in darkness since your departure."

Chaaya smiled aside and thought, 'How naïve Surya is! He is the emitter of all light – and here he is saying that Samjna's absence banished the glow from his house!'

Aloud, she said: "*Swami,* I could not bear the separation from you and the children." Her voice choked with emotion. "I stand before you a new woman – I have renewed myself for you alone."

"Really?!" Surya was deeply moved. He held out his arms to her and Chaaya ran into his embrace. As he held her close, Surya was filled with overwhelming affection for his wife. Samjna was back: as she had promised, she had composed herself to endure his intense light and heat. Her body, trembling in his arms, was proof of her resolution.

"Samjna." Surya looked down at her face pressed against his chest.

"*Swami?*" she murmured.

"Never leave me again."

"Never again, *Swami.*"

"I will keep you close to me forever," Surya declared passionately.

She clung to his shoulders in reply.

"Mother!" a delighted child's voice rang out. Surya and Chaaya moved apart as Yami came hurtling towards them.

"Mother!" two other voices echoed Yami's glad cry. Chaaya embraced the girl and turned to the door. Vaivasvatha and Yama dashed into the room, close on the heels of their little sister.

'Just as you accept my husband as your own, you must also

wholeheartedly embrace my Vaivasvatha, Yama and Yami as your children' – Samjna's words resonated in her ears. Chaaya gathered the three children into her embrace and planted warm kisses on their plump cheeks. Her heart filled with gratitude to Samjna, her elder sister, for the gift of this life as Surya's beloved wife.

Time passed. Chaaya immersed herself in Samjna's persona, enjoying her physical intimacy with Surya as his wife, and also caring for Samjna's children as her own. Surya, on his part, gave Chaaya his unconditional love, never doubting for a moment that she was Samjna.

<hr />

"Narayana!" Sage Narada saluted Sri Mahavishnu and Lakshmi.

"Why, Narada," Vishnu smiled in blessing. "I was just thinking it would be nice to have you here!"

"And here I am!" Narada exclaimed. "As I am here in answer to your thoughts, *Bhagavan*, am I right in guessing that you have a commission for me?"

"It is time for the incarnation of the seventh of the *Navagrahas*, Narada." Vishnu smiled at the sage. "It looks like that cannot happen without your intercession."

"Narayana! Narayana!" laughed Narada. "If you will it, who can prevent it from happening?"

"No, Narada," Vishnu said gravely. "Your intercession is needed. The seventh *graha* is to be Surya's son."

"Narayana!" Narada said in surprise. "Surya's son, my Lord? Surya already has two sons."

"Narada, those two sons were begotten by his wife." Vishnu continued enigmatically. "Now, our seventh *graha* will be born to the wife who is not his real wife."

"Narayana!" Narada's voice mirrored his bewilderment. "The wife who is not his real wife?!"

"Unable to endure Surya's intense heat and radiance any longer, Samjna breathed life into her own shadow, Chaaya, and deputed her to Surya's abode in her stead. Chaaya now lives there as Surya's wife and the mother of Samjna's children, impersonating Samjna flawlessly."

Vishnu pointed out: "Chaaya is absorbed in Samjna's children: so much so that the thought has never crossed her mind to have children of her own." He looked gravely at Narada. "It is here that you come into the picture, Narada – it is up to you to instigate Chaaya into having children of her own. Suggest that she pray to Surya for this favor: only then can the seventh of the *Navagrahas* take birth."

"As you command, my Lord!" Narada automatically bowed to Vishnu's wish. "But, one small doubt – where is Samjna? Is she with her father?"

"Oh no, Narada! Surely you can see that her presence in Viswakarma's house would reveal her secret?! ... She is engaged in penance in the forest."

He raised his hand in benediction. "Go to Surya's abode, Narada."

<hr />

"Chaaya!" Narada called out. He smiled when she turned to him. "You are indeed Samjna's double!"

Chaaya, alone at home in Surya's absence, gasped and stammered, "I ... I ... I am Samjna." She recovered her poise. "And who might you be?" she asked haughtily.

"Narayana!" Narada said serenely. "I am Narada – and I am privy to the secret of your impersonation." He continued reassuringly. "Don't worry, Chaaya – I have your welfare at heart. Are you aware that you are an innocent victim in this drama choreographed by Samjna?"

"*Maharshi* ..." said the bewildered Chaaya.

"Yes, consider your position. Regardless of the care you lavish on them, Samjna's children can never be your own." He paused for effect. He now had her complete attention. "You are a woman in your own right. Only when you bear Surya's children can you consolidate your relationship with him. It is children who make a marriage truly meaningful."

"But ... Samjna's children ..." Chaaya frowned thoughtfully.

"Of course, they will remain here and continue to enjoy your care." He cannily pointed out: "Moreover, did Samjna tell you not to have children of your own?" Chaaya shook her head. "So, you are not betraying Samjna in any way." He spoke firmly: "Chaaya, put aside your reservations and ask your husband to bless you with children – at least three. You will then be Surya's wife in every way."

Narada extended his arm in blessing. "Narayana!" His job done, the satisfied sage made his departure.

Narada had skillfully sowed the seeds of dissension in Chaaya's receptive mind.

<hr />

'Samjna's children can never be your own.'

'It is children who make a marriage truly meaningful.'

'Ask your husband to bless you with children.'

Narada's words beat an incessant tattoo in Chaaya's heart. She pondered darkly. Her impersonation was no longer a secret. How long would it be before it became public knowledge? If Surya came to know of her deceit, he would surely abandon her. She must take pre-emptive measures before it was too late. Narada was right – the only way to consolidate her position was to bear Surya's children.

After all, she had sacrificed her own individuality by assuming Samjna's persona. She had given her unconditional love to her elder sister's husband. She lived with the constant fear of discovery, playing a dangerous game of duplicity. Her courage certainly deserved a reward – and that reward would be her own children.

Chaaya came to a decision: Yes, Narada was right. She squared her shoulders and walked resolutely to her bed chamber.

***

Chaaya plaited her long, lustrous hair before the mirror. Surya came to stand close behind her. She adjusted the string of flowers adorning her braid and smiled at his reflection in the glass. Surya placed his hands on her shoulders.

"Samjna ... your beauty never ceases to work its magic on me." He rested his chin gently on her head.

"Ready with compliments – as always!" she smiled seductively into the mirror. "But not so ready with gifts!"

"I have gifted my entire being to you!" Surya smiled back. "What more can I give you, dearest?"

"What about a homecoming present on my return from my father's house? Surely I deserve one!" Chaaya smiled mischievously.

"Yes, my dear – you are right." He caressed her shoulders. "I should have given you a gift then, or on some other occasion." He paused and smiled at her reflection in the glass. "Well, it's never too late to remedy a wrong. Choose your gift now, Samjna."

"Really?" Chaaya asked.

"Yes: tell me what you desire. Whatever it be, it shall be yours."

"I want children," Chaaya said.

Surya's reflection mirrored his surprise. "Children?! Samjna, we have children: ask for something you lack."

Chaaya insisted: "The only gift I desire from you is children."

Surya gently turned her round so that she faced him. He looked down into her eyes, drowning in their dark pools of desire.

"Very well!" He laughed softly and teased: "You made your wish to my reflection, but I am ready to grant it to you in person!"

Chaaya's arms tightened around his broad chest. Her eyes shone in triumph. "Three children, *Swami*: two boys and a girl. Agreed?" Her coral lips parted in delicious invitation.

"Agreed, dearest. How can I refuse such a charming request?!"

In the mirror behind them, their reflections merged to become one.

A fond smile played on Surya's lips as he watched Chaaya walk towards him. Her pregnancy weighed on her, slowing her gait.

"Samjna, pregnancy suits you: how your body glows!" he said.

Chaaya smiled back at him. "*Swami*, it is but the reflection of your own radiance."

Surya shook his head. "The inner light which makes you shine belongs to neither of us, my dear. It comes from the son in your womb."

"So, tell me, *Swami*: will my son's complexion match my golden skin, or will it reflect your flaming hue?"

"Why, dearest, his fresh, ocher radiance will combine all our yellows and oranges in a unique palette of his own!"

Chaaya glowed with pride. "Yes, he will reflect the best of both his parents!"

It was the eighth day of *Pushya* in the year *Pramodootha*. With the star, *Swaathi*, in the ascendant, and the *Ashtami* moon waning in the sky, Chaaya gave birth to a baby boy. Contrary to his mother's expectations, the infant's skin tone was far removed from vibrant gold: in fact, he had the darkest of complexions!

Chaaya looked askance at the weakly mewling infant with the dark, thin, ill-proportioned body and strange, tawny eyes. She turned to Surya in bewilderment.

"What is it, Samjna?" Surya smiled gently. " Is it the boy's complexion?"

"*Swami*, I expected him to be like you ..."

"My son is like me, dear: he is my alter ego. My own golden body has its indivisible, dark shadow. My son is my shadow: naturally, his complexion is dark."

Aditi and Kasyapa, along with Viswakarma and his wife, were proud grandparents at the baby's naming ceremony. To their delight, the *Trimurti* and Narada made their unexpected appearance on the occasion.

Sri Mahavishnu addressed Surya: "Your son will always walk with a measured tread. Restraint will be the hallmark of all his actions. The name I have chosen for him will reflect these traits -"

Surya intervened devoutly: "Lord, our son is indeed fortunate to receive his name from you!"

Vishnu smiled. "Your son is Sanaischara," he said.

The *Trimurti* blessed the infant. Shiva and Brahma advised Surya to devote the greatest care to his education and upbringing, as the boy was destined to attain eminence as one of the *Navagrahas*.

Kasyapa was delighted to hear that his lineage was now elevated to include two of the *Navagrahas*.

Sanaischara flourished under Chaaya's special care. In due course, Chaaya gave birth to a second boy. Surya named him Saavarni, in recognition of his flaming complexion – a faithful reflection of his father's radiance. Lastly, Chaaya delivered a baby girl, whom Surya named Tapati.

Chaaya reared her own three children along with Samjna's trio. As she delighted in Sanaischara, Saavarni and Tapati, Chaaya's former affection for the others gradually dimmed.

"And now we come to the birth of Rahu, the eighth of the *Navagrahas*." Nirvikalpananda paused to look at his disciples. "Listen carefully," he exhorted.

"Master, Rahu is also known as Simhikaagarbhasambhoota, isn't he?"

Shivananda interrupted. "Does this mean that he is the son of Simhika, Kasyapa's wife?"

"Excellent, Shivananda!" the master smiled approvingly. "You are right. Rahu is the son of Simhika – Kasyapa's wife and Daksha *prajapati's* daughter." He paused. "The story of Rahu, the *graha* who is powerful enough to swallow both Surya and Chandra, is simple enough. It begins in Kasyapa's hermitage ..."

Nirvikalpananda continued his narration.

THE BIRTH OF RAHU

Kasyapa's wives sat companionably together at the hermitage, passing the time of day in pleasant chatter.

Danu remarked: "We are all mothers – except Simhika."

"Danu, how can she have children? She is too slow!" Diti laughed mockingly. "She neither prays to god for progeny – as Aditi did – nor does she appeal to our husband – as the rest of us did!"

Riled by the amusement which greeted Diti's word, Simhika cried: "Oh, please! I may be slow, but I am certainly not dumb!" She looked steadily at each woman in turn. "Tell me, whom should I approach: god, or husband?" Her voice was determined. "I will ask for progeny and prove my worth to your satisfaction."

"If you pray to god, he will advise you to turn to your husband. So, you might as well save time and approach our husband, the visible and merciful god!" Kaala joked. The other women laughed knowingly.

Aditi, always gentle, turned to Simhika with a smile. "Our husband possesses great power, Simhika. Go to him: he will advise you as to the proper course of action. Pray to him – you will certainly be blessed with motherhood."

———

Kasyapa sat in deep meditation under a tree on the bank of the river. Simhika seated herself before him and waited. Kasyapa remained oblivious to her presence, his eyes closed.

Unable to contain her impatience any longer, Simhika said: "*Swami!*"

Kasyapa slowly opened his eyes. He looked interrogatively at his wife. "Simhika, why are you here?"

Now alarmed at her own temerity, Simhika stammered: "I ... I ... I am here to ask a boon from you ..."

"A boon?" Kasyapa smiled indulgently. "Very well, Simhika. What do you want?"

"I want a son."

"That's certainly a meritorious desire," Kasyapa said encouragingly.

"My son should possess great power and prodigious strength." She paused and then rushed on excitedly. "Everyone should look on him with fear."

Kasyapa grew serious. "A son who is feared by all?!" He cautioned her. "Think carefully before you define your boon, my dear."

Simhika remained intransigent. "I do not need to reconsider. I know what I want: and that is a son who fills every heart with dread. He should be held in the deepest awe by all."

Kasyapa sighed. "Very well, Simhika – come here." He beckoned her close and laid his palm on her head. "I grant you the boon you seek: soon, a son who possesses the traits you specified will frolic in your lap."

———

"*Swami,*" Aditi conveyed the glad tidings to Kasyapa: "Simhika is going to become a mother." She continued. "She is so eager to bear a son – I do hope you blessed her with the beautiful son she desires."

"Aditi, your younger sister did not ask for a handsome boy." Kasyapa laughed wryly. "In fact, she was insistent that her son inspire fear in all onlookers." He sighed. "It was a case of asking for the wrong boon at the wrong time! She will give birth to a hideous son with the complexion of raging fire."

"*Swami!*" Aditi was aghast at his words.

"Don't worry, Aditi." Kasyapa reassured his wife. "Remember that all things come to pass as ordained by God's will. I am confident that Simhika's wish was also instigated by God."

At the end of nine months, Simhika gave birth to a baby boy whose skin glowed a deep red. Daksha and his wife, accompanied by Brahma, Narada and Indra, graced the naming ceremony of Simhika's son.

Brahma informed Kasyapa that his youngest child was ordained to take his place in the pantheon of the *Navagrahas*. He advised the sage to devote great care to the boy's education, saying: "The child will grow to be universally worshipped and influence the lives of all living creatures. He will come to receive and renounce. In line with his traits, he is to be named Rahu."

Rahu grew up in the care of Simhika and Kasyapa's other twelve wives. In due course, Kasyapa commenced the boy's education.

"We have heard the antecedents of eight *grahas*," Nirvikalpananda told his disciples. "Now, we come to the birth of the ninth *graha* – Ketu."

"Master, Ketu is almost always mentioned in conjunction with Rahu: there seems to a close relationship between them." Vimalananda asked: "Like Rahu, was Ketu also Kasyapa's son?"

"That's a very pertinent question, Vimalananda," the master said. "But it cannot be answered with a categorical 'yes' or 'no.' The epics give us several versions of Ketu's birth."

He paused to collect his thoughts. "In one version, Kasyapa and his wife, Danu, had a son called Ketumantha. It is believed that this Ketumantha is the Kethu *graha* – here, the fact that they are siblings explains the intimate bond shared by Raahu and Ketu. Ketumantha is also reported to have taken the later incarnation of Amithouja during the age of the *Mahabharatha*."

Nirvikalpananda continued: "However, the *Vishnudharmotthara Purana*, one of the eighteen *Puranas*, gives a different account of Ketu's origin. According to this epic, Brahma was deeply concerned as the earth groaned under the weight of the insupportable burden of life. In order to give the earth relief, he created Mrthyu – the goddess of death – and ordered her to destroy all living beings. The tender-hearted Mrthyu shed tears at his ruthless command and refused to comply. When Brahma demanded her obedience, the goddess heaved a fierce sigh; this sigh metamorphosed into a pennant of fire, from whose flames emerged the infant Ketu. Brahma declared that the boy would achieve fame as Ketu and Dhooma Ketu."

Nirvikalpanand paused to give his disciples time to digest this lengthy explanation. "A third narrative revolves round the familiar Churning of the Ocean of Milk. One account holds that an *asura*, Rahu, in the guise of a *deva*, managed to partake of the *amrita* distributed by Mohini to the gods. However, the *Skandha Mahapurana* gives an alternative version: '*Tadaa Raahuscha Kethuscha Dwaavethaa Dhaithya Pungvou, Devaanaam roopamaasthaaya Amrthaartham twaraanvitou upavishtou tadaa pankthyaam Devaanaam amruthaarthinou*' –. meaning that two *rakshasas*, named Rahu and Ketu, adopted the disguise of gods in order to share the *amrita*."

He paused questioningly as Chidaananda raised his hand. "Yes?"

"Master, which version do we accept?"

"Any version we choose," suggested Shivananada.

Nirvikalpananda smiled and shook his head. "No, Shivananda. If each of us chooses the version we personally prefer, there will never be a convergence of opposing claims." He urged them: "We must subject the different versions to strict analysis, find the common denominator which runs through them all and then reach a conclusion." He paused for effect. "And that conclusion should adhere faithfully to age-old beliefs." He smiled at their puzzled countenances. "Come, let us subject the different versions to an equity of treatment."

"But, master ... how do we arrive at such an objective stance?" It was the puzzled Vimalananda.

"Let us first hear the version of Ketu's birth which connects Kasyapa and Mrthyu. That may answer your question."

Nirvikalpananda voice assumed its narrative tone. "In ages past, the earth groaned under the unbearable weight of rapidly multiplying living beings, who were yet to come under the ambit of death. Bhudevi, the earth goddess, saw a calamity in the making ..."

THE BIRTH OF KETU

Narada, flying across the sky in the course of his routine peregrinations, came down to earth to rest momentarily near the Himalayas. Instantaneously, Bhudevi appeared before him.

"Narayana!" gasped the startled sage. "Mother! It's you!"

"Narada, I have watched you crisscrossing the sky and waited anxiously for you to descend to earth."

"Narayana!" exclaimed the sage in concern. "Mother, I have never before seen such abject woe on your countenance!"

Bhudevi said dejectedly: "Narada, I am weighed down by despair. Brahma continues to go about his task of creation, ensuring that the children of Manu proliferate exponentially. The entire burden of his creation falls on me. It is becoming insupportable! I fear that I may collapse under the intolerable weight at any moment!"

She turned her pleading eyes to him and continued urgently, "Narada, convey my agony to your father, Brahma. Intercede with him on my behalf and ask him to find a way to reduce my burden."

"Narayana!" Narada rose to the emergency. "I recall my father, and his father, agreeing that it would be dangerous to increase the earth's burden beyond a certain point. I will go to *Satyaloka* immediately!"

He flashed into the sky.

Narada stood before Brahma and Saraswati, giving his account of his meeting with Bhudevi. He emphasized that the massive explosion in population had brought the earth to the brink of imminent catastrophe.

"Son, this is indeed a grave matter," Brahma pondered.

"Father, suppose you take a break from creation ..." Narada suggested.

Saraswati smiled gently. "That would be futile, Narada. The earth is unable to bear the weight of its present burden of living things."

Brahma nodded in agreement. "Yes, son. Maintaining the population at its present level is not the solution – a definite decrease in numbers is the need of the hour." He frowned in thought. "I must give this deep consideration."

He turned to his son. "Narada, give Bhudevi my assurance that her burden will soon be reduced."

"Yes, father," said the sage with alacrity and hurried on his mission.

Brahma pondered on the menace looming over the earth. Time passed but a solution continued to evade him. His increasing impatience and irritability fanned the smoldering embers of rage within him – tongues of flame roared from his four heads and spread through the cosmos, posing a grave threat to the animate and inanimate world. Oblivious to the inferno he had unwittingly ignited, Brahma remained immersed in deep cogitation.

Parameswara, keenly aware that the universe was in jeopardy, appeared before Brahma and caught his attention: "My dear Brahma, the intensity of your thought process has pushed the cosmos to the brink of disaster. Come, come: calm yourself – after all, your task is creation, not destruction!"

He continued, "I suggest that you create a power tasked explicitly with death – this is the sole means of relieving the earth of its insupportable burden." He paused. "As for me, I am the god of destruction: my duty is not to take lives, but to grant peace to the dead."

Brahma nodded in agreement. Shiva was right: The very purpose of his genesis by Lord Vishnu was creation. Creating life was his only duty – not death. As Brahma ceased his relentless quest for a solution, a woman emerged from his body, sporting a mottled red, black and yellow complexion. She stood facing the south and raised bewildered eyes to Brahma.

"Who am I?" she asked.

"You are Mrthyu, the goddess of death. I have created you to perform a crucial task: bringing death to all the creatures of the cosmos. Commence your duty at once!" commanded Brahma. Mrthyu immediately dissolved into abject grief. The surprised Creator reached out his cupped palm to catch the tears coursing down her cheeks.

The goddess sobbed: "Forgive me, Lord. Bringing death to innocent creatures is blatant injustice: it is beyond me to perform this task. I abdicate my responsibility and leave at once to undertake rigorous penance."

Shiva looked thoughtfully after the departing goddess and advised Brahma: "Mrthyu's tenderness is an integral part of her femininity. Be patient and gentle with her: you can persuade her to execute her duty in due course."

⁂

Mrthyu took her leave of Brahma and commenced her penance at Dhenukaasrama. Suddenly, a grave voice cut through her meditation.

"Mrthyu!" It was Brahma.

"*Swami!*" exclaimed the startled Mrthyu.

"Mrthyu, I will persist in reminding you of your ordained duty. You are destined to fulfill the purpose of your creation – and that is the destruction of living beings. You cannot evade your fate. Accept the inevitable,"

Brahma smiled gently at the worried goddess and continued in softer tones: "Mrthyu, listen to me: I will explain your brief. I do not require you to be a hands-on, cold-blooded killer. When I explained the purpose of your creation, I gathered the tears of sorrow which you shed. Each teardrop will metamorphose into a fatal disease and death will come as a natural consequence to living beings. All you have to do is oversee the process."

He urged her: "Accept your fate with grace, Mrthyu. Commence your ordained task."

Mrthyu reluctantly acknowledged her helplessness in the face of fate. Realizing that her hands were effectively tied, she heaved a searing breath of surrender which became a streaming banner of heat. It shimmered in the air ... then, in its place, there appeared an infant boy!

Brahma smiled at the astonished goddess and said: "It was in expectation of this birth that I let you walk away on the day of your creation. This is your son, Mrthyu."

The goddess instinctively gathered the boy into her warm embrace.

Brahma continued: "As he emerged from a pennant of heat, he is Ketu – the flag. He is yours to nurture and rear."

Mrthyu shook her head in reluctant denial. "Lord, you have assigned me a mammoth task which will consume all my time and energy. I will be unable to give the baby the care he requires. Please accept the boy as your own."

"No, Mrthyu: however, there is a perfect solution to your problem. Your son has the innate traits of a *rakshasa*. As such, Kasyapa, who is the progenitor of the *rakshasa* lineage, is the most suitable person to entrust with your child's upbringing." He continued: "I will ensure that Kasyapa accepts Ketu as a part of his family."

Mrthyu tenderly kissed the infant. "I am indeed blessed, Lord," she said.

"*Swami! Swami!*" Kasyapa's wife called urgently as she rushed into the hermitage.

Kasyapa looked up from his meditation. "What is it, Danu?"

She held out the infant in her arms. "Look – a baby boy! I found him playing happily among the bushes at the rear of our *ashram*."

Kasyapa looked thoughtfully at the bundle in her arms. "He must belong to someone ..."

Dhanu interrupted excitedly: "He is my son – I found him!" She thrust the child under her husband's nose. "Look: his face ... his eyes ... they are exact replicas of my own children's!"

As Kasyapa remained silent, her impassioned voice rose. "Isn't that proof enough that he is mine? He is my son – I will adopt him!" She fiercely hugged the baby to her breast.

Kasyapa smiled indulgently. "Very well, Danu. You may keep him: I don't see anyone objecting to that. After all, God's will reigns supreme!"

Danu gave a contented smile. Then, "*Swami*, what shall we call our son?"

Kasyapa pondered. "What name do you suggest, Danu?"

Before his wife could respond, a voice was heard: "Brahma has already given the boy the name Ketu." It was Narada.

Kasyapa exclaimed in surprise: "*Maharshi*! It is you!"

"Nayayana!" Narada smiled. "I came explicitly to explain that my father named the boy and sent him to you. He requests you to accept him as your son and devote yourself to his upbringing."

Kasyapa folded his hands in respectful acceptance. "It will be our pleasure," he said.

Danu's eyes melted with affection as she looked down at the boy. "Perhaps this explains why my breasts swelled with milk the moment my eyes fell on the baby."

She murmured tenderly, "My son."

<hr>

Ketu, Danu's adopted son, and Rahu, Simhika's child, developed the strongest of bonds which was further strengthened by the inexorable march of time. Even as infants, they were inseparable – they crawled at the same time, moving side by side on chubby hands and knees. They went on to toddle together on unsteady legs, holding each other for support. As they grew old enough to commence their education, Kasyapa found, to his amazement, that one could absorb the knowledge imparted by him to the other.

Danu was rather suspicious of this extraordinary bond.

She said: "*Swami*, I suckled Ketu just as I did my other children – but, instead of cleaving to his own siblings, he prefers Rahu's company." She frowned anxiously. "What does this unusual behavior portend?"

Kasyapa smiled indulgently at her. "Who knows what runs in Ketu's little head?! And that applies to Rahu also – he follows Ketu like a shadow!" He paused thoughtfully. "Maybe they share a relationship of which we are not aware."

Danu nodded slowly in agreement.

Kasyapa reassured his wife: "Perhaps it is Lord Brahma's will that Rahu and Ketu grow up together, sharing the strongest bonds of affection." He pointed out: "Danu, Brahma could easily have entrusted Ketu to the care of some other *maanasaputra* and his family: however, he particularly chose us to be Ketu's parents." He paused. "I think the Supreme God has ordained that Rahu and Ketu are to grow up together, as inseparable as twins."

Danu shrugged aside her misgivings and said: "Whatever be the reason, I am indeed fortunate to be Ketu's mother."

Rahu and Ketu entered manhood. Kasyapa arranged the former's wedding with Simhidevi, while Ketu was married to Chitralekha. In due course, Rahu and Simhidevi had a son called Meghahasa.

The passage of time did but reinforce Rahu and Ketu's strong bond of affection.

Nirvikalpananda came to the end of his narration delineating the genesis of the *Navagrahas*. He pointed out: "We have heard the genealogies of the *Navagrahas* as per the timeline of their incarnations – not in the order in which we recite their names in our daily prayers, or follow in astrology: 'Surya, Chandra, Budha, Guru, Sukra, Sani, Rahu and Ketu.'"

He considered his disciples, engrossed in the fascinating discourse. "Like their births, the lives and times of the *Navagrahas* are of extraordinary interest. Here, we will follow the familiar order of their names: commencing with Surya and ending with Ketu."

He paused and smiled at his four students. "So, now we go back to Surya's background." He turned to Shivananada. "Can you tell me who Surya's parents are?"

"Aditi and Kasyapa, master!" Shivananda answered eagerly.

"And you, Chidananda: who is Surya's wife?"

"Samjna, Viswakarma's daughter, master," said Chidananda. "Later, Samjna deputed her shadow, Chaaya, to impersonate her."

Nirvikalpananda said, "Excellent!"

He turned to the other two disciples. "And now you will tell us the names of Samjna's and Chaaya's children."

"Vaivasvatha, Yama and Yami are Samjna's children, master," Sadanand said promptly.

"Master, Chaaya is the mother of Sanaischara, Saavarni and Tapati," Vimalananda said in his turn.

"I am pleased that you can recall these details." Nirvikalpananda smiled in approval. "As I recounted, Surya's six children were growing up in Chaaya's care. As time passed, Chaaya's love for her own three children stifled her former affection for Vaivasvatha, Yama and Yami. One day ..."

The master picked up the threads of his discourse.

PART 2

THE LIFE OF THE NAVAGRAHAS

THE LIFE OF SURYA

Chaaya's dislike of Samjna's children festered like a hidden sore until it burst into active hatred. She soon found herself unable to bear the very sight of Vaivasvatha, Yama and Yami. One day, Chaaya gathered her three children together in a secluded room and addressed them gravely:

"My dearest children, listen carefully to what I have to say. Vaivasvata, Yama and Yami are wicked – they are a very bad influence on you. Henceforth, I want you to avoid their company. Understand? You are not to play with them or associate with them in any way."

Sanaischara, Saavarni and Tapati exchanged surprised glances.

Saavarni protested: "But, mother, our brothers, Vaivasvata and Yama, and sister, Yami, are good ..."

Sanaischara admitted grudgingly: "Yes, mother, they are always kind to us."

Tapati added her voice to the childish chorus: "Mother, they never quarrel with us. We play together happily and they love us very much."

Chaaya admonished them: "You are too young to understand their underhanded ways and great cunning. They ..."

Tapati's eyes widened in surprise at this. She said, "But, mother: Sister Yami likes me very much. She always lets me win the games we play and never refuses me anything I want from her!"

Chaaya looked at her protesting children in exasperation. Keeping a tight lid on her rising temper, she said softly: "My darlings, there is one immutable truth which you must know – good people's eyes will project their own decency on everyone they look at. As you are good children, Vaivasvata, Yama, Yami mistakenly appear to be virtuous in your eyes."

Sanaischara asked eagerly: "Mother, we are good and decent – unlike the others!" His voice throbbed with pride. "We are superior to them, right?"

Chaaya patted him approvingly on his back and smiled complacently. "Yes, my son. It is only because you are good that you are misled into thinking that those three are also good." She lowered her voice to a conspiratorial whisper. "Do you know what those wicked children told me?" She paused for effect. "They said that you are bad children who get into all kinds of mischief behind my back."

To her satisfaction, Sanaischara, Saavarni and Tapati gasped and looked at each other in righteous indignation.

She reassured them: "Of course, I don't believe a single word said by those liars! I know what good, obedient children you are." She added: "You always follow my advice."

Sanaischara broke the uneasy silence which followed: "Mother, you are right. I don't know why – but, whenever I see them, a flood of rage rises in me! I have to hide the instinctive glare of hatred sparking from my eyes."

Chaaya smiled triumphantly and encouraged her eldest son: "That is the normal reaction of all good children who are confronted by the wicked." She warned him: "Henceforth, beware of them. Be careful not to let them make you as wicked as they are."

Tapati's anxious eyes searched her mother's face. "But, mother, how can we be careful?"

Chaaya reassured her daughter. "Don't worry, darling. All you have to do is close ranks with your brothers." She addressed them as a group. "Stay away from them. Be a tight-knit threesome and don't let them interact with you."

Sanaischara was elated at the turn of events. "Mother, I am the leader of this group, right?"

"Of course, Sanaischara: as the eldest you are naturally the leader."

Chaaya looked at them gravely. "Now, children, you must remember one thing: this is a secret among us. You must not tell Vaivasvata, Yama, or Yami what I have said. Above all, you must not let your father know what we have discussed today."

"Why should we keep this a secret from father?" Sanaischara asked curiously.

"Because I am telling you to!" Chaaya shot back heatedly.

"But why?" Sanaischara insisted.

Chaaya heaved an impatient sigh. "Sanaischara, your father will not recognize the truth in this. His fondness for those children makes him blind to their wickedness." She paused to get their undivided attention. "You know, he loves them more than he loves you."

The children were aghast at her words. Tapati's eyes filled with hot tears.

Saavarni asked: "Really, mother?" He murmured sadly, "We did not know that father loves them more ..."

"Now you know that it is your mother who loves you most and always puts your welfare above all else," she smiled down at them. "So, it is your mother whom you must always obey!"

Chaaya's brainwashing had its required effect on her three children. They deliberately ignored Samjna's children and spurned their friendly advances. The first overt rift occurred between Yami and Tapati, who was most inclined to blindly accept her mother's advice. Tapati's love for Yami now metamorphosed into an intense hatred of her older sister.

In her turn, Chaaya let the mask slip from her face and openly exhibited her dislike for Samjna's children. Vaivasvata and Yama were bewildered by her sudden change in attitude, while the soft- hearted Yami was broken-hearted.

Yama brought the issue into the open with his elder brother. "Mother no longer treats us with affection, Vaivasvata. She openly shows her preference for Sani, Saavarni and Tapati....."

Vaivasvata agreed sadly, "Yes, Yama, I am also aware of this."

"Mother's change in attitude is deeply wounding. Let's take it up with father," Yama suggested.

Vaivasvata placed a restraining arm on his brother's shoulder. "Yama, it would not be right on our part to complain about mother to father. It is wrong."

Yama shook his head in vehement protest and exclaimed passionately: "No, it is not wrong! It is never wrong to point out another's offence. Be it one's father or mother, justice is justice! Our mother cannot be exonerated of wrongdoing just because of her position and age. The path of righteous *dharma* is uncompromisingly straight and true!"

Vaivasvata smiled indulgently at his younger brother. "You are very preoccupied with *dharma* these days, Yama!"

"Yes," Yama said gravely. "I believe that *dharma* is the very foundation of all creation. This precept has slowly taken strong root in my mind." He paused in deliberation. "Brother, it may have escaped your notice, but mother's attitude towards us began to change subtly right from the time of Sani's birth. It became progressively negative with the arrival of Saavarni and then Tapati."

Yami raised her puzzled gaze to Yama's face. "I don't think I ever noticed this change, brother."

"Nor did I, Yama," added Vaivasvata. "I cannot comprehend how it was discernible to you alone!"

"The change was increasingly obvious in mother's eyes," Yama observed sadly. "When she looks at them, her eyes fill with a tender glow. But, the same eyes burn with a red-hot flame when they fall on us." He sighed. "Now, even her voice openly reflects her hatred for us."

"Why does mother hate us?" Yami asked innocently. "Now that you have pointed it out, I too recall mother's partiality towards the others. She always breaks into smiles when she sees Tapati and is ever ready to praise her." Her eyes filled with tears again. "But ... when I go to her, she scowls and chastises me for no fault of mine!"

"It is the parent's righteous duty to treat all their children with impartial affection. It is against the code of *dharma* for a mother to discriminate against any of her off-spring. I will no longer tolerate this injustice from mother!" With this impassioned declaration, Yama walked out resolutely. The others looked after him thoughtfully.

"*Dharma, dharma, dharma* ..." Vaivasvata chanted softly. "This has become Yama's constant refrain! I wonder what it portends."

Yami smiled in understanding. "He who recites the word, *dharma*, will act in accordance with its dictates."

Chaaya smiled fondly at Sani, Saavarni and Tapati, as they relished the *ksheeraanna* she had prepared specially for them. "Eat, my children. Let me refill your bowls."

Sani paused with a spoonful of the rice and milk pudding raised halfway to his lips. He stared unblinkingly at his mother and then looked meaningfully towards the door. In silent comprehension, Chaaya followed his gaze: Vaivasvata, Yama and Yami stood at the entrance.

Chaaya glared at the trio and scolded angrily: "Why are you here? Go to the garden and wait until you are called."

Yama moved forward resolutely, accompanied by the others. "Mother, we are hungry," he declared.

"Stop right there!" Chaaya's voice cracked through the air like a whiplash. "Didn't you hear me? Go to the garden at once!"

Yami froze in mid-stride, her startled eyes wide with fear. Yama stepped forward fearlessly to stand shoulder-to-shoulder with his little sister. He locked eyes with Chaaya. "We are hungry, mother. Give us some of the pudding. Now, if you please!"

Chaaya's eyes reddened in anger. "Yama!" she thundered. "Be careful: your behavior borders on disrespect!"

"My lack of respect is not towards you, mother." Yama stood his ground. "It is the injustice meted out to us which I hold in contempt." He continued determinedly. "I will oppose injustice whenever and wherever I encounter it. I will not tolerate your unfair discrimination against us. We deserve our fair share of your love and of the *ksheeraanna*."

He turned towards his siblings and held out his hands to them. "Come, brother. Come, Yami. Let's eat our share of the pudding."

Chaaya glared at Yama in fierce loathing.

Sani's face mirrored her emotions, as he complained: "Yama always behaves like this, mother. Even when we play our games, he constantly chants, 'Dharma, dharma,' and uses it as a pretext to defeat us."

Chaaya looked angrily at the standing trio and declared: "I refuse to serve you now. Let Sani, Saavarni and Tapati have their fill." Her voice dripped with contempt. "Whatever remains will be yours."

Sani exhorted the others: "Saavarni! Tapati! Eat quickly: we must finish it all! Don't let a drop remain in the bowl!" He started to gorge himself on the pudding, hurriedly gulping down large mouthfuls.

Chaaya calmed him with a gesture and said, "No hurry, my son. Take your time and savour the pudding: it's all yours!"

Yama addressed Chaaya gravely: "Mother, this is base injustice. We are all your children and are equally deserving of your care. It is your ordained duty as a mother to treat us with impartial affection." He straightened his shoulders and declared: "We will not accept leftovers! If you refuse to serve us, we will help ourselves to our fair share of the pudding!"

"Stay where you are, Yama!" Chaaya thundered. "You demand equal care from me?" She paused and spat out at him: "Well, let me make it clear to you: I refuse to treat you on par with Sani, Saavarni and Tapati. Understand?" She sniffed in disdain. "Like it or lump it – there is nothing you can do about it! Now, go!" She challenged him with an icy glance.

Yama glared defiantly back at her with angry, red-rimmed eyes. He raised his foot to step forward.

Chaaya exploded in a frenzy of rage: "You insolent, spoilt child! How dare you raise your foot against me! Is it to kick me?" She pointed to the offending foot. "Well, you can reap the consequence of your stubborn defiance!" Her voice resounded harshly in the silence. "May your foot fall from your body and provide fodder for worms!"

Yama froze in disbelief. The other children gaped with open mouths at Chaaya's face which was a white-hot orb of fire.

The shocked Yama stammered: "Mother ... you have cursed me! ... how could you?! ... mother!"

The unrelenting Chaaya shouted: "Yes, I have cursed you! I will see you dead! Now, get out of my sight: you are not my son!"

Yama's stared fearlessly into Chaaya's hate-filled eyes. Slowly, he bent to look at his foot: hot tears welled up in his own eyes. Wordlessly, he turned and made for the door.

Vaivasvata and Yami followed him as if in a trance...

⌘

"What?!" the astonished Surya gaped at his three eldest children. "Did you hear her correctly? You may have misinterpreted her words!" He frowned in disbelief. "No, this is impossible! No mother would curse her own child!"

Vaivasvata stepped forward and locked eyes with his father. "What Yama says is absolutely true, father. Mother cursed him, saying that his foot will fall off and become fodder for worms."

"Father," Yami brushed the hot tears from her cheeks. "Mother has been ill-treating us right from the time of brother Sani's birth."

Surya looked silently at the grief-stricken trio.

"Father," Yama's voice was a tremulous whisper. "What will happen to my foot? How can I walk if it –"

Surya moved swiftly to interrupt his son. "Do not fear, my boy. I cannot revoke your mother's curse, but I can amend it."

He placed his right hand gently on his son's head. "Some flakes of flesh from your foot will fall painlessly to the ground and the worms will feed on them. In this way, your mother's curse will take effect and, at the same time, you will not lose your foot." He paused to stroke his son's hair. "Cheer up, Yama. Forget the curse!"

Yama's eyes filled with tears of relief as he looked up at his father's loving face. Surya bent to wipe the tears from his son's cheeks and turned to his eldest son. "Vaivasvata, I want you to tell me the truth: is your mother ill-treating the three of you?"

"Yes, father," Vaivasvata said firmly. "We concealed this from you as it did not seem right to complain about mother." He ordered his chaotic thoughts and continued. "After the birth of Sani, Saavarni and Tapati, a marked change crept into her attitude towards us. She looks fondly on them, but her eyes are filled with hatred towards us. Today, she refused to serve us *ksheeraanna*, telling us that we could make do with the leftovers."

"Mother always praises Tapati but constantly criticizes me using harsh words." Yami piped up timidly.

"Father," Yama asked, "Can I tell you something?"

Surya bent his head towards his son. "What is it, Yama? Speak out, my boy."

"The other day, I overheard mother advising Sani, Saavarni and little sister, Tapati, to keep away from us. She told them that we are wicked children. And ... and ..." his voice choked with emotion. He swallowed and continued: "And today ... after cursing me ... she shouted: 'You are not my son – get out of my sight!'"

"Mother also threatened to see Yama dead, father," Vaivasvata added gravely.

"Father, will mother really do that?" a tremor of fear underlined Yama's words.

Surya looked speechlessly at the three forlorn children standing before him. A frisson of rage coursed through his body. Then, he turned abruptly and walked swiftly towards Chaaya's chamber. Vaivasvata, Yama and Yami followed close on his heels, running to keep up with his long, angry strides.

"Samjna!" Surya's voice thundered across the vast palace.

Chaaya jumped up in surprised alarm. Her husband had never raised his voice at her in all these years! One look at their father's crimson face and Sani, Saavarni and Tapati took refuge behind their mother. Surya strode up furiously to confront his wife. His burning eyes bored into her own. In contrast to his flaming glare, his voice was as cold as naked steel.

"Did you curse Yama?"

A shiver of fear pulsated through Chaaya. For the first time in her life, she was unable to bear the intense heat emanating from Surya's body. She moved back, hugging herself protectively. She feared that she would be burnt to ashes by his white-hot anger.

"How could you possibly have the heart to pronounce such a terrible curse on your own son?" Surya hissed at her through clenched teeth. "You call yourself a mother? You are a disgrace to motherhood!" His eyes blazed in contempt. He brought his face close to hers. "And what do you mean by telling Yama that he is not your son? Are you not his mother?"

For the life of her, Chaaya could not stop trembling like a storm-tossed leaf. She was transfixed by the frenzied fire which swirled in the golden hollows of Surya's eyes. His violent rage battered her like a thousand brutal rays of unendurable heat. Beads of sweat formed on her forehead. Her eyes brimmed with hot tears.

'Are you not his mother?' Surya's accusation reverberated in her ears. Unable to meet his eyes, Chaaya bowed her head in surrender. She realized that she could no longer maintain her impersonation and conceal her pact with Samjna. Her lips trembled as she struggled to speak.

"I ... I am ... I am not the mother of Vaivasvata, Yama and Yami," she managed to blurt the truth.

"Samjna!" Surya shouted. "Have you lost your mind?"

"*Swami*, I am not Samjna!" There – it was said! Chaaya pleaded: "Please forgive me, *Swami* – I am not your Samjna."

Surya eyed her in suspicious disbelief. "What?! What do you mean?" His voice was troubled.

Chaaya lifted her head and locked eyes with him. "I swear I am not

Samjna." Her voice strengthened. "I am Chaaya – Samjna's shadow. Samjna used her divine power to make me come alive in the flesh and imbued me with her personality ... she commanded me to impersonate her as your wife and as the mother of her children ..."

Surya stood speechless, spell-bound by Chaaya's incredible narrative. Beside him, his six children listened with wide eyes and gaping mouths.

⌘

"Father," Yami gave an agonized cry and clasped Surya's legs. "Will mother never come back to us?"

In reply, Surya hugged his daughter tight. His heart ached at his children's grief-stricken faces. He had not entertained the least suspicion about Samjna's innocuous request to visit her father's house. His mind was flooded with regret: he had left his precious children under the care of a woman who was not their mother; he had foolishly fallen for the drama enacted by Chaaya; the physical intimacy and happiness he had experienced with her was but a shadow of the real thing; his very life over the past years had been one long falsehood!

"Father, we want our mother!" Vaivasvata and Yama pleaded in one voice.

Surya looked at their woebegone faces and bent to plant a kiss on his daughter's head. Gently pushing her close to her brothers, Surya said, "Vaivasvata and Yama, take care of your sister." He warned: "Stay away from Chaaya."

"Father ... what about mother?" Yami's eyes brimmed with tears.

"Don't worry, darling." His voice rang with the decisive clarity of a bell. "I will come back with your mother."

⌘

Based on Chaaya's testimony, Surya made his way straight to the forest. His heart ached with the sorrow of his long separation from his adored Samjna. His soul was a conflagration of agonized pain: its fire even exceeded his inherent physical heat! Although he sought Samjna with single-minded determination, the forest was strangely quiet and bereft of life: not a single wild animal or bird crossed his path; no secluded *ashram* or meditating ascetic appeared among the dense foliage.

Suddenly, the loud neighing of a horse shattered the eerie silence of the woods. Surya quickly set out in the direction of the sound, hoping to gather some useful information from the horse's rider. A whinny reached his ears – he thrust aside the brambles and thick bushes and hurried forward. He burst into a clearing and stopped short. There before him was a large pond whose pellucid water reflected the emerald green and cerulean blue of forest and sky. But it was not the water which caught his attention: it was a pristine white horse, standing still on the further bank of the pond. Surya approached slowly – it was a mare.

The mare stood motionless, her large, limpid eyes gazing unblinkingly at him. Her long tail swayed gently in the wind like a damsel's braid. Her radiant body was dappled silver in the rays of the sun.

Surya was drawn towards the mare by some irresistible force. The lovely animal kept her fearless gaze on him as he moved closer. When he locked eyes with the mare, a pronounced tremor ran through her body. Slowly, her fore legs began a rhythmic tapping on the ground. She continued to hold his gaze. The mesmerized Surya gave a gasp of surprise – those eyes ... where had he seen them before? Surely, the message lurking in them was familiar to him!?

Suddenly, the realization hit him; his entire body was covered with goosebumps – these were Samjna's eyes! Yes, the beautiful mare was none other than his Samjna! And her beloved eyes invited him to become one with her.

In a trice, Surya assumed the form of a tall, majestic stallion.

The mare rubbed her cheek against the stallion's muscular flank. In his turn, the stallion gave a soft nicker and bent his head to gently nuzzle her lovely neck...

The secluded forest was the lone witness to Surya and Samjna's poignant reunion with each other as stallion and mare. Free from all inhibitions and restraints, they resumed their conjugal life in those sylvan surroundings, making up for their long period of separation. Subsequent to their passionate mating, the mare miraculously delivered three sons through her flaring nostrils. Immediately, both Surya and Samjna resumed their original forms and gazed fondly at their offspring: a boy with normal features, and a pair of twins, sporting equine faces on human torsos.

Bowing to Samjna's wishes, Surya named the horse-faced twins Naasatya and Dasra, while the third boy was given the name Revanth.

To Samjna's anxious query as to the fate of her sons, Surya said reassuringly: "Our three miraculously born sons are not ordinary beings. They are *devas*. Naasatya and Dasra will become divine physicians and earn universal renown as the Aswinikumaras. Revanth will achieve fame as the doyen of equestrian science." Samjna smiled in satisfaction.

Surya gazed lovingly into her eyes and said: "Samjna, I know all the details of your pact with Chaaya. Your beloved children, Vaivasvata, Yama and Yami, yearn for their mother. Come, let us go home."

Wordlessly, Samjna lowered her eyes. Beads of sweat shimmered on her face and body.

Surya tilted her chin up with gentle fingers and said softly: "Yes, dearest, I understand your predicament. I am now aware that my unyielding attitude was largely to blame for our separation." He smiled tenderly. "For your sake, I shall reduce the intensity of my heat and light. But, first, let us go home."

Samjna broke into a delighted smile. "*Swami*, I am fortunate indeed!" She paused. "But what about the Aswins and Revanth? – are we taking them with us?"

"No, my dear. Their rightful place is Amaravati. The Aswins will be divine physicians, while Revanth will serve as the equestrian expert of Indra's court."

"But, father," Revanth asked, "How will we go to Amaravati?"

Surya smiled and pointed skywards. "Look, son. Sage Narada is here."

"Narayana!" Narada said with a happy smile, as he came to stand beside them. "My father, Brahma, has entrusted me with the mission of escorting the Aswins and Revanth to Indra's court." He turned to Surya. "Your sons will achieve great eminence there."

"They are indeed blessed, Sage Narada," Surya said.

"Yes, they have received the blessings of the Creator." Narada beckoned to the boys. "Come, young men. Let's be on our way!"

The Aswins and Revanth prostrated themselves at their parent's feet. Samjna raised them up one by one and planted a tender kiss on their foreheads. Surya gathered them into his fond embrace and bid them farewell.

He had a parting word of advice for the Aswins. "My boys, do not confine your skills as divine physicians to the *devas* alone. Let the human race also experience the balm of your healing hands."

"Your wish is our command, father," the twins said in unison.

Sage Narada turned to Samjna: "Samjna, be aware that your adventures were ordained by the Supreme God, Lord Vishnu. Chaaya's impersonation of you, and your assumption of a mare's form, have both borne precious fruit: Chaaya has given birth to Sani, Saavarni and Tapati, while you have brought forth the Aswinkumaras and Revanth." He paused and said: "Sani's incarnation was the main objective of Chaaya's creation." He smiled at her. "Now, you can contentedly resume your life with Surya."

"Narada!" exclaimed the surprised Surya. "You have been aware of Chaaya's charade all this while?!"

"Narayana!" the sage chanted. "It was God's will, Surya." He turned briskly to his young charges. "And now, Indra's court awaits our arrival."

Surya and Samjna gazed skywards as their sons followed Sage Narada and were soon lost to view. Samjna's eyes were moist.

Surya placed a consoling arm on her shoulders and said: "Come, Samjna: Vaivasvata, Yama and Yami eagerly await their mother's return."

Samjna blinked away her tears and smiled up at him.

⁖⁘⁖

"Mother!" The delighted chorus reached Samjna's ears as soon as she entered Surya's palace.

Vaivasvata, Yama and Yami came running into her outstretched arms. Samjna hugged them close, lavishing her kisses on their bent heads. Her eyes brimmed with tears of joy. Surya smiled fondly at the poignant scene of Samjna's reunion with her children after long years of separation.

The sound of hesitant feet at the door caught their attention: Sani, Saavarni and Tapati edged slowly into the room with anxious eyes. They stopped some distance away from Samjna and gaped at her in astonishment – she was a mirror-image of their mother, Chaaya!

"Mother ..." Tapati's quavering voice broke the momentary silence. She took a tentative step forward. Samjna smiled encouragingly at the three children and beckoned them to her.

"Come here, darlings! I am your mother."

Pushing Vaivasvata, Yama and Yami gently aside, Samjna now gathered Sani, Saavarni and Tapati into her open arms and embraced them.

Sani looked up at her. "Mother ... that mother ...?" he questioned, looking back uncertainly at the door.

Samjna raised her voice and called, "Chaaya!"

Chaaya slowly entered the room and stood by the door, doubt clouding her face. At Samjna's warm smile, she lowered her head guiltily.

"Chaaya, come here!" Samjna commanded her shadow.

Chaaya approached Samjna with reluctant feet – her eyes were fixed on her three children.

"Chaaya, look at me!" Samjna insisted.

When Chaaya finally met her gaze, Samjna continued: "Chaaya, your mission is complete. It is time for you to forget your individuality and renounce your motherhood." Her voice became gentler. "Chaaya, you know that you are merely my shadow and there is no reality to your existence. Come, merge with me – it is time for us to become one again."

Chaaya gazed speechlessly at Samjna, who urged her: "Come on, Chaaya, I'm waiting for you!"

As Surya and the children looked on in awe, Chaaya silently moved to Samjna. She hovered beside her for a second – then, she fused into Samjna.

For a moment, Samjna stood still and sighed, gazing at her shadow which was now silhouetted on the golden wall. She then turned to her children with a reassuring smile.

"My dear children, don't worry. Chaaya and I are one and the same. You are all my very own children." She reached out to caress them all in turn.

Surya smiled fondly at the happy tableaux before him: his family was now truly complete!

"Unbelievable!" Viswakarma exclaimed. He listened in astonishment as Surya gave him an account of his family's incredible experience in the recent past.

Viswakarma sympathized with his son-in-law: "But, I must say that Samjna was content enough with your radiance when she consented to marry you!"

Surya nodded and then said: "Father, I am determined to reduce the intensity of my heat and light. This is the only way Samjna and I can live together." He pleaded with Viswakarma. "I need your help. You must find a means to cut down my inherent warmth and radiance."

Viswakarma pondered long on this and then addressed his son-in-law: "Surya, it is practically impossible to reduce your light and heat as long as you remain in your present form. It is essential that you resume your original orb shape. This will enable me to use a circular file to reduce the size of the disc. The orb will automatically lose heat and light in correspondence with its size – and your present figure will also lose its equivalent volume of heat and light."

Bowing to Viswakarma's counsel, Surya assumed a yogic posture and took on the configuration of an orb. The divine architect took up his special file and carefully shaved away an eighth portion of the disc. Once he was done, Surya resumed his form. He gazed in surprise at the large quantity of gold dust heaped on the ground.

Viswakarma remarked: "These gold shavings possess considerable power. They should be put to good use." He paused thoughtfully. "Yes, I shall fashion four objects of immeasurable value from this accumulated gold dust."

"Four objects?" Surya asked.

"Yes, four priceless objects: the discus – *Sudarsanam*, the trident – *Trisul*, the spear – *Sakti*, and finally, the flying vehicle – the *Pushpaka Vimana*, which will wing across the sky like a bird."

Surya smiled at the architect in deep admiration. "Father, the *Sudarsanam*, the *Trisul*, the *Sakti* and the *Pushpaka Vimana* are indeed divine objects!" He asked curiously, "What will you do with them?"

"Surya, let me explain," Viswakarma voice was grave. "The force which emanates from you when you assume the shape of an orb is in fact Lord Vishnu's glorious power. I will offer the four divine objects fashioned from your form to his son, Brahma. Let the Creator decide what to do with them."

Surya bowed in gratitude to Viswakarma: "I am eternally grateful to you for your help, father-in-law." He paused. "And now, tell me – has my innate brilliance and heat indeed been reduced?"

Viswakarma smiled. "Samjna, your wife, and my daughter, is the one who is best qualified to answer that question!"

Surya touched Viswakarma's feet in respect and took his leave.

Samjna was delighted to see Surya return with his heat and light dimmed to bearable proportions. She gladly devoted herself to the role of wife and mother once again.

As time passed, Surya could not fail to notice Yama's extraordinarily staunch discrimination between *dharma* and *adharma*: right and wrong. He recognized that Yama's unique trait was a harbinger of great things to come.

After much thought, he summoned Yama. "My son, I perceive great, latent stores of wisdom and leadership in you. You must concentrate on developing your individuality and intelligence. Brahma, the Creator, is best suited to guide you on the right path." He paused and looked gravely at his son. "Yama, in order to propitiate Brahma, you must undertake rigorous penance. Go and commence your *tapas* in a secluded place of your choice."

"I bow to your wishes, father," Yama humbly said.

With his parent's blessings, Yama bid farewell to his brothers and sisters and set out on his mission.

"And that brings us to the end of our chronicle of Surya's life," Nirvikalpananda concluded.

Vimalananda raised a hand to catch his *guru's* attention. "Master, I have a doubt."

Nirvikalpananda smiled indulgently. "What is it, my boy?"

"Did Viswakarma manage to fashion those four divine objects from the gold shavings from Surya's orb?"

"Undoubtedly, Vimalananda. We do know for a fact that the *Sudarsanam* discus is Lord Vishnu's weapon, Lord Shiva carries the *Trisul* and the *Sakti* is Lord Subrhmanya's weapon of choice. Brahma distributed these arms to them."

"And what about the *Pushpak Vimana*, master?" Chidananda asked eagerly.

"Brahma gifted the *Pushpak Vimana* to his friend, Kubera, the god of wealth. Later, Ravana, the king of Lanka, forcibly took it from Kubera," Nirvikalpananda explained. "Let's leave it at that and take up Chandra's life story, which is the subject of our next discourse."

He considered his disciples in turn and said: "We know that Taara returned to her husband Brhaspati, leaving Chandra. Brahma gave Taara's son, Budha, to Chandra after attesting that the boy sprang from Chandra's loins. Chandra entrusted his parents, Sage Atri and Anasuya, with Budha's care and lived a life of solitude in his isolated abode."

He paused. "Chandra passed the time in nostalgic reminiscence of the halcyon days spent in Taara's company. One day, Sage Narada came to visit Chandra ..."

THE LIFE OF CHANDRA

"Narayana!" Narada stood at the threshold of Chandra's palatial abode. Hearing the familiar chant, Chandra rose reluctantly to receive his guest. "Welcome, Sage Narada," he said, hands folded in respect.

"May good fortune come your way!" Narada blessed him. The sage's keen eyes noted Chandra's listless eyes and lethargic gait. "So, Chandra: it looks like you continue to wallow in sad nostalgia!"

Chandra heaved a deep sigh. "I must confess that my heart still aches with memories of the past."

Narada gave a wry smile. "I can well understand that an illicit relationship with one's master's wife will cause heartache." His mocking tone became gentle. "Chandra, Taara has departed from your home – it is not right to let her memories continue to dwell in your heart."

"That's easier said than done!" Chandra remarked with a scornful curl of his lips.

"Narayana!" Narada settled himself in a comfortable chair. "Well, it was easy enough for Taara!"

Chandra eyes asked a question.

"Yes, Chandra," Narada smiled complacently. "Unlike you, Taara has erased the past from her heart and mind. She is now content to be a devoted wife."

Chandra bowed his head in sorrow.

Narada continued more sympathetically: "Taara has managed to put her past misadventure behind her because she could count on her husband's unconditional support." He paused meaningfully.

Chandra's eyes darkened with an undecipherable grief.

Narada's voice assumed a persuasive tone. "Chandra, you are young. You are punishing yourself needlessly by living here in self-imposed solitude, without a woman's companionship." He urged: "Think, Chandra: Brhaspati's unstinting affection and concern were instrumental in erasing the lingering shadow of your memory from Taara's heart. In the same way, a woman's loving companionship will free you from Taara's stubborn hold."

Chandra nodded his head in half-hearted agreement.

"You must get married, Chandra," Narada stated firmly. "Marriage is the most reliable remedy for love-sickness!" An impish smile lit his face.

Chandra turned his back to Narada and stood stiffly, staring at the wall.

The sage continued: "If it is the difficulty of finding a bride, after the debacle of your elopement, which worries you – let your mind rest easy! Your extraordinary good looks and youth are reason enough for everyone to assume that it was your master's wife who seduced you."

Narada paused a moment. Then, "I'm sure you are familiar with Daksha *prajapati:* at present, his palace is bursting at the seams with lovely maidens!" He lowered his voice suggestively. "In fact, right now, there are twenty-seven girls, shining like beauteous stars, who are ready to get married." His keen eyes noted that Chandra's shoulders relaxed fractionally.

Narada continued: "Daksha knows me well – if I were to go to him with a proposal ..."

Chandra turned to face Narada. There was a new animation in his face.

Narada smiled in satisfaction. "So, Chandra, shall I approach Daksha and his wife on your behalf?"

"No," Chandra said quickly. "I would prefer to ask my parent's permission before making any move."

"Take it from me – you can safely leave it to Daksha to obtain your parent's consent. He is a go-getter beyond compare!"

For the first time since Narada's arrival, Chandra smiled.

Narada rose and locked eyes with Chandra: "Listen to me, Chandra. Taara is no longer the Taara of old. She has willed herself to become Brhaspati's true-hearted wife. You must not entertain fantasies about another man's staunch, wedded consort."

With this grave warning, the sage made his departure.

Daksha *prajapati* frowned in deep thought, as he considered Narada's proposal. He remarked discontentedly: "Narada, Aatreya is notorious for taking his master's wife to bed!"

"Narayana!" exclaimed the sage. "Once she fell in love with him, Taara used her irresistible beauty as bait to trap the naïve Chandra. He was but a callow youth whom she enticed into her bed." He paused and pointed out: "Anyway, Brhaspati himself has conceded that their sins have been purged."

Daksha murmured uncertainly, "You are right, but ..."

His wife interrupted: "Narada, tell me what you think – is Chandra a suitable groom for my daughter?"

Narada turned to Prasootidevi. "Not daughter – daughters!" He smiled at the bewildered expression on her face. "This is not my proposal: it comes from my father, Brahma. I am only the executor of his will." He continued reassuringly. "As to whether Chandra is worthy of your daughters, remember that his handsomeness captivated Taara and she was willing to have a child by him." Narada smiled. "Your twenty-seven daughters are glowing beauties. Let Chandra be surrounded by these lovely stars."

"So, this has been ordained by Lord Brahma. Very well," Daksha made up his mind. "Let us obtain permission from Atri and Anasuya to make Chandra our son-in-law." The *prajapati* stood up decisively.

"Fortune will smile on us!" Narada pronounced his benediction on their cause. "I will accompany you to Atri's *ashram*."

Atri and Anasuya extended a warm welcome to their unexpected guests. When Daksha explained the purpose of their visit, Atri and Anasuya exchanged astonished glances – a marriage proposal for their errant son?!

Atri bowed his head in sorrow. "Our Chandra sinned grievously by sleeping with his master's wife: his action has brought great dishonor to us, his parents." He sighed. "We were obliged to take on the responsibility of bringing up his son through Taara."

Narada brushed aside his recriminations. "Sage Atri, forget the past. Budha's birth as Chandra and Taara's son happened by divine decree." He argued, "The time is now ripe to accept Daksha's daughters as Chandra's wives."

Atri smilingly pointed out: "Narada, you are using the plural form."

Narada said serenely, "My choice of the plural was deliberate, *Maharshi*." He elucidated with a smile: "Lord Brahma has made it explicit that Chandra is destined to have a large number of wives!"

"It is becomingly increasingly clear that Lord Brahma himself firmly holds the reins of our Chandra's past, present and future!" Atri exclaimed.

"I can readily accept that," Anasuya said aside to Prasooti. "You must be aware that Chandra was born to me as part of Lord Brahma's essence."

"Yes, Anasuya, it is Lord Brahma who sent Narada with the proposal to make our daughters your daughters-in-law," Prasooti replied in calm resignation.

"Twenty-seven girls ..." Anasuya said thoughtfully. Then, she shrugged aside her misgivings and smiled mischievously. "Well, I must say that, with this veritable army of wives standing guard, our Chandra will definitely not have the time or inclination to think about another man's wife."

The others laughed aloud at Anasuya's light-hearted repartee.

Still chuckling, Atri turned to Daksha. "Daksha *prajapati*, Anasuya and I accept this proposal. You may make arrangements for the marriage."

"Narayana!" Narada exclaimed in satisfaction. As the assembly discussed the coming marriage with mounting excitement, Budha approached them with an armful of sacrificial wood and grass.

Atri beckoned the boy forward. "Budha, my son, come and offer your respects to Daksha *prajapati,* his wife, Prasooti, and sage Narada."

Budha obediently paid obeisance to them all and received their blessings.

Narada smiled at the boy. "Budha is a replica of Chandra as a boy. Taara but admitted the truth when she acknowledged that Budha was Chandra's son."

Atri and Daksha, with Narada's counsel, fixed an auspicious date for the marriage.

—∞∞—

Chandra's marriage was solemnized on schedule. The groom stood in the midst of a circle of twenty-seven radiant brides, each of whom held a sparkling *diya* in her hand. Under Prasooti's direction, her daughters – Aswini, Bharani, Krthika, Rohini, Mrgasira, Aardra, Punarvasu, Pushyami, Aaslesha, Makha, Purva Phalguni, Uttara Phalguni, Hastha, Chitta, Swathi, Visakha, Anuradha, Jyeshta, Moola, Poorvaashaada, Uttaraashaada, Sravana, Dhanishta, Sathabhisha, Poorvaabhaadra, Uttaraabhaadra and Revathi – gracefully held out their clay lamps towards their husband. The handsome Chandra glowed in the mesmerizing flicker of the golden flames.

"Behold the handsome Chandra among his beautiful stars!" exclaimed the appreciative Narada to Daksha *prajapati*.

Chandra slowly turned to look at each of his brides in turn. His eyes shone with the reflected light of the *diyas*. Suddenly, he came to a standstill: his eyes were arrested by one face whose radiance seemed to outdo the combined luster of the other twenty-six.

'Hmmm,' Chandra thought, 'I know her name ... yes, Rohini!' He turned away with difficulty.

'She pulls at me like an irresistible magnet!'

—∞∞—

Chandra and his brides arrived at his palatial abode. The air was thick with palpable excitement, as the girls prepared themselves for their roles as dutiful wives, as advised by their mother. The three eldest, Aswini, Bharani and Krthika, prepared the first meal at their new home. The chattering group laid the dining table and waited expectantly for their husband's entrance. Suddenly, Aswini realized that Rohini was nowhere to be seen! She turned to Moola and said, "Sister, go and see what Rohini is up to."

The others laughed at this.

Moola remarked jocularly, "As if she has worked any harder than the rest of us!" and prepared to go in search of her sister. But, before she crossed the room, the door opened and Rohini entered in their husband's company.

Rohini leaned on Chandra's arm which encircled her slender waist like a belt of gold. Laughing at some shared joke, they were oblivious to the presence of the other twenty-six sisters. Chandra and Rohini blithely seated themselves side by side at the table. As the others debated as to who should join them, Chandra firmly resolved the issue, by declaring unequivocally: "Rohini and I will eat first and then spend some time enjoying the breeze in the garden. The rest of you can eat together after we leave the hall."

He paused and looked expectantly at them. "Come, now – who is going to serve us?"

Once Chandra and Rohini left for the garden, an uneasy silence prevailed in the hall. The other twenty-six sisters sat down to a meal which seemed to have turned into ashes in their mouths. After hurriedly swallowing a few mouthfuls, they followed in the couple's wake. To their surprise, not a trace of the two was to be found! After a futile search of every nook and corner of the garden, they held an anxious consultation.

"Perhaps they have returned to his chamber while we were having our meal," said Aswini thoughtfully.

Bharani agreed and said, "Yes, that must be it! Come, let us join them at once ... otherwise our husband will be angry!"

The girls hurried indoors again.

Aswini and her younger sisters came to a sudden standstill outside Chandra's room as Rohini's voice pealed in laughter from within.

"What will my sisters think?!" they heard her exclaim.

"Who cares?" Chandra replied flippantly. He paused and continued playfully: "Tell me something – at our recent meal, did you eat all the items served on your plate, or only those which you liked?"

"Only the ones I liked, of course," Rohini said.

"There you are!" laughed Chandra. "Just as we cannot eat all the items served at a meal, we cannot enjoy the company of all the inhabitants of an abode. Just as we choose what we like to eat, we also choose the company of those we like!"

In agreement, Rohini added her merry laughter to Chandra's deep guffaws.

Aswini soundlessly moved away from the taunting door and made her way to a distant room. Her younger sisters followed sadly. They silently lay down in a row on the floor and settled down to their first night as brides in their new home.

'Aswini,' Prasooti's voice reverberated hollowly in her ears. 'You will be your husband's senior wife. Chandra will first seek your intimacy. Act in accordance with his wishes and gladden his heart. Also ensure that your younger sisters please him in every way.' Aswini's eyes filled with unshed tears.

Krthika, lying stiffly awake beside her, whispered: "Sister, why are things going wrong? Didn't mother say that our husband would give you precedence?"

Brushing her own doubts aside, Aswini consoled her younger sister. "Who knows? Maybe he assumed that Rohini is the eldest among us." She whispered, "Don't worry, everything will work out."

The atmosphere in the room was oppressive with the heavy sighs of the twenty-six forlorn new brides.

⸺∞⸺

As the days passed, Aswini's hope that Chandra and Rohini would come to see the error of their ways gradually dimmed. Chandra ceased to look at, let alone talk with, any of his wives, except Rohini. He was completely immune to their overtures. They were no longer allowed to even wait on him at his meals. Rohini alone served his food, with Chandra tenderly feeding her the choicest morsels from his own plate.

Rohini's indifference to their plight deeply wounded her sisters. They had grown up together, sharing their childhood song and dance and happy play. Now, the same sister who had enjoyed their warm companionship and intimate confidences, studiedly ignored their very presence. She looked on them as if they were twenty-six strangers in her home: not just strangers, but servants who were duty-bound to obey her every command.

The days merged into weeks and the weeks into months. Chandra continued to keep the sisters at an ever-growing distance, treating them with icy indifference.

One day, Mrgasira declared: "Enough is enough, sisters!" Her voice was resolute. "It is time we took a stand against this injustice and asserted ourselves." She looked at the others in turn. "Today, when our husband and Rohini go for their customary swim in the pond, we will insist on accompanying them."

Aardra spoke up in agreement. "Yes, we must show some spirit if we are to be given consideration. I propose that we join them in the pond – even if it is over our husband's objection."

The other sisters silently nodded their approval.

Chandra and Rohini, hands clasped affectionately, walked through the door leading to the garden. Rohini's sisters, adhering to their plan, followed close behind them. Chandra, descending the steps to the pond, paused and looked back in irritation. He frowned darkly.

"Stop right there!" His voice was harsh. "Where do you think you are going? Return indoors at once and go about your assigned tasks!"

Mrgasira and Aardra resolutely ignored his words, and continued their descent towards the pond.

"I said stop!" Chandra's voice was white-hot with fury. "What is your name?"

"Mrgasira ..."

"Mrga – how very appropriate your name is!" Chandra's voice dripped with sarcasm. "It explains why you are behaving like an animal!"

He turned angrily to the others. "Go in, at once: all of you!"

Mrgasira, deeply wounded by her husband's words, dissolved into tears and ran indoors, accompanied by a trembling Aardra. Their other sisters followed them with downcast eyes and heavy hearts.

Chandra and Rohini's jeering laughter hounded them into the palace.

———

A pall of collective gloom descended on Aswini and her twenty-five younger sisters. Far from the comfort and security of their childhood home, and bereft of their parent's affection, the girls wilted under the humiliation and insults meted out to them on a daily basis. The husband whom they had joyfully followed to their new home treated them with utter disdain, and a cold indifference, which cut them to the quick.

Chandra's harshness was compounded by Rohini's selfishness and overbearing manner. Spurned by their husband, and constantly goaded by their sister, Daksha's twenty-six daughters sank into despair.

One afternoon, the despondent girls sat in abject misery, exchanging a few desultory words.

"Narayana!" They looked up to see Sage Narada standing before them.

They quickly rose to welcome him with respectfully folded hands.

The perceptive sage took one look at their woebegone countenances and exclaimed in surprise: "Aswini! What is the matter? Where is Chandra? Is he away from home?"

"He is at home, *Maharshi*," Aswini said softly, "But we do not know where."

"And what does that mean?" Narada questioned her sharply.

Bharani spoke up. "We are always in the dark as to where he and our sister, Rohini, may be ..." she broke off sadly.

Narada looked intently at the group. The sisters sported a uniformly forlorn look: disheveled hair, carelessly arranged attire, red-rimmed eyes and grief-stricken faces, with *kohl*-smudged cheeks marking the track of hot tears.

The sage addressed the eldest girl. "Aswini, the anguish in your hearts is reflected clearly on your faces. As the person instrumental in your marriage to Chandra, your happiness is my responsibility. Tell me: what is the matter?"

Daksha's daughters gazed speechlessly at his concerned face, unable to meet his eyes.

Narada continued: "Your father and I are both Brahma's *maanasaputras*: this makes us brothers. So, I am also your father." He paused. "Your forlorn looks are far removed from the customary joy of new brides. What is the reason for this?"

Her younger sisters turned expectantly to Aswini, letting her take the lead.

Narada addressed her: "Come, Aswini, my daughter: confide in me as you would in your father."

Narada's kindness finally broke down her wall of reserve and Aswini dissolved into wracking sobs. Her sisters wiped their own tears as she gave Narada a painful account of the indifference and humiliation Chandra and Rohini had subjected them to over the past months.

Narada listened attentively to their tale of woe. He then gathered them together and said: "So, this is the issue! Let us see what is to be done ..." He pondered for a few moments. "You are innocent girls. You must now make a deliberate effort to attract your husband and secure his love, like Rohini."

"And how do we go about that, *Maharshi*?" Bharani mustered the courage to ask.

Narada smiled gently at them. "You are all soft-natured and benign:

these *saatvic* traits have their own merit, but much more is needed to attract a man. Wallowing in sorrow and patiently waiting for your husband's attention will get you nowhere." Narada paused meaningfully. "Action is called for. It is time you learnt to add the passion of *rajas* to the tenderness of *satva*." He looked at their attentive faces: "Devotion and respect alone will not win your husband's affection. Passion and charm are also essential to gain his love: do you understand?"

Daksha's daughters exchanged looks of dawning comprehension.

Narada continued: "Let's translate this into practical terms: you must be better groomed and ornamented than Rohini. You must bubble with high spirits and scintillating conversation." He smiled at them. "Surround Chandra with an effervescence of happiness – smother him with joy!"

Aswini nodded her head in eager agreement. Her sisters shared her rising excitement.

"Narayana!" Narada stood up. "I will return in four days. I am confident that your faces will be glowing with happiness when I see you again."

It was dusk. Aswini and her younger sisters stood in the corridor outside Chandra's room, waiting expectantly for their husband's arrival. They were attractively decked out like new brides: from their exquisite *sarees* to the fragrant braids of flowers in their hair. They had made impeccable preparations for his reception.

'Here he comes!' Their palpable excitement throbbed in the air.

Chandra strode towards them. The sisters fell smoothly into their well-rehearsed moves. As he crossed the threshold, Punarvasu and Pushyami placed a golden platter on the floor before him. Aslesha and Makha each took a hand and guided him to stand on the plate. Aswini came forward to tenderly wash his feet with the cool, scented water which Bharani poured from a golden ewer. Hastha sprinkled the residual water in the plate on her own head and on the heads of all her sisters. Aswini then garlanded her husband with colourful, fragrant blossoms.

Chandra frowned in bemusement and absently removed the garland from his shoulders. Bharani immediately stepped in with another garland. As he walked forward, Daksha's daughters gently showered Chandra with flowers. Ignoring all this paraphernalia, Chandra's restless eyes, ablaze with desire, incessantly sought Rohini.

He turned crossly to Aswini, who stood beside him, and demanded: "Where is Rohini?"

Before Aswini could find her voice, the door of the bedchamber was flung open and Rohini stood before them. Chandra's face was immediately wreathed in tender smiles. He gazed adoringly at Rohini: then, as his eyes took in her disheveled attire and unadorned hair, he frowned in disapproval – not at her but at her hapless sisters!

"You call yourselves women?!" he spat at them. "Shamelessly decking yourselves in gaudy finery!" He paused to glare at them in contempt. "Did none of you think to offer my Rohini some flowers for her hair?" He hissed, "You are disgusting!"

Before the shell-shocked eyes of Aswini and her sisters, Chandra removed the garland from his shoulders and tenderly draped it over Rohini. Placing his arms round her, her drew her close and walked into the bedroom.

The door slammed shut behind them.

Aswini's doe-like eyes hardened into adamantine stone. Her younger sisters flinched at the sparks of rage which flashed from them. She remained frozen in statuesque stillness, oblivious to their soft calls of entreaty. The humiliation meted out to them the previous evening was an all-consuming inferno in her soul.

"Sister ..." Krthika hesitantly reached out to touch her shoulder.

Coming to startled animation, Aswini jumped up and declared resolutely: "I will no longer tolerate this gross injustice!"

She stormed past her siblings and angrily strode to Chandra's bedchamber. Her twenty-five younger sisters milled about in confusion for a moment and then followed in her wake like churning waves after a ship.

Aswini stood defiantly before the closed door and loudly called: "Rohini!"

Her summons echoed angrily through the long corridor.

"Rohini!" the word rang out yet again in challenge. The younger girls exchanged anxious looks.

"Rohini!" Aswini's insistent call hung in the air. The bedroom door was flung open: Rohini stood before them, face crimson with rage.

"Shh!" she hissed at them through clenched teeth. "What is the meaning of this ruckus? Don't you know that he is sleeping?"

"Yes, we do!" spat Aswini. "I am here for the express purpose of awakening him from his slumber!"

She locked eyes with her sister. "Rohini, snap out of your delusion: are you not aware of the damage you are causing? Do you realize that you are instrumental in the humiliation and injustice being meted out to us?" She struggled to control her rage. "Open your eyes to the circumstances of our marriage, sister. Chandra does not belong exclusively to you: we are all his wives. Admit the error of your ways and give way!"

Rohini's lips curled into a cruel sneer. She held out her hands in sarcastic parody. "Look, sister: I have not forcibly tied him to me with the edge of my *saree*! If he voluntarily chooses to hover round me like a honeybee poised over a flower, what can I do?" She gave an elaborate shrug. "You are welcome to entice him in any way you like – rest assured I will not stand in your way."

"It is your bounden duty to remind him of his obligation towards us," insisted Aswini.

Rohini looked haughtily at her sister. "Aswini, let me make one thing clear: on the day of our marriage, I did not ask him to take me alone into his embrace and spurn the rest of you. And now, I will not spurn his advances and ask him to embrace you instead!" She continued on a mocking note. "Shall we just say that I am lucky ... and you are not?!"

Aswini raised her voice in angry accusation. "Rohini, shame on you – you are behaving like a harlot! One last time, let me warn you: you had better accept that we too have our claim on him as his wives. Don't you dare ..."

"What? – steal your rights?" Rohini interrupted with a sniff of disdain. "I am sick of your mealy-mouthed platitudes and tears. Leave me alone!" She slammed the door in their faces.

"That's the last straw!" Aswini shook in uncontrollable rage. She moved angrily towards the closed door – only to come to a sudden halt. The door flew open on its own accord – Chandra stood before them, his eyes blazing with temper.

"So, you are ready for a confrontation, is it?" He gave a snort of disgust. "Well, let me spell it out for you once and for all: Rohini is the love of my life. She is the only reason I have given you access to this palace. Don't waste your petty wiles with flowers and scented water on me!" His mocking voice lacerated their sensibilities like a whipcord.

He turned angrily toward Aswini: "And, as for you, I heard every word
you said about my Rohini. Now, just get this into your thick head: Rohini
is my queen. If you wish to remain in this palace, you may do so only as
her servant – and mine. Understand? Now, go!" He barked his dismissal
at them and turned away with a withering look of contempt.

As Chandra moved back into the bedroom, Rohini came forward
to close the door. Chandra placed his hands possessively on her slender
shoulders. Rohini gave her sisters a triumphant smile as she shut the door
in their faces.

Aswini, head held high, walked out of Chandra's palace, followed by
her sisters.

Daksha *prajapati* seethed with indignation as he listened to his daughter's
tale of woe. Prasooti's eyes misted at the sight of their grief-stricken faces.

"Leave aside our son-in-law: he is a stranger," she paused in pained
disbelief. "How could Rohini do this to her own sisters? Her behavior
is inexcusable: she has ruthlessly discarded the relationships lovingly
nurtured over the years!"

"You did not send us to Chandra's palace to be servants!" Aswini
declared passionately. "Why should we submit to that selfish couple's
authority? We would rather stay here and serve our parents." Her sisters
chorused their agreement.

Prasooti turned to her husband. "*Swami*, what shall we do?"

"I burn with anger at the humiliation meted out to my beloved
daughters." Daksha controlled his temper with difficulty. "But this is
not the time to let emotion cloud my thinking. Understanding and
compassion are called for now, more than ever." He paused and smiled at
his daughters: "You are exhausted by the ordeal of the past months. Stay
here for a few days in your mother's loving care."

He addressed his wife: "Prasooti, I will personally meet Chandra and
Rohini and resolve this issue."

"Narayana!" Narada extended his hand in blessing towards Rohini, who
welcomed him to Chandra's palace.

He asked casually: "Where are your sisters, daughter?" Narada was
quick to note the flash of disquiet in her eyes.

"They have gone to my father's house," Rohini murmured.

"Leaving you alone?" Narada persisted in his interrogation. "Why did they go? Were they, by any chance, goaded by anger or pique?"

Rohini's eyes shifted uneasily at Narada's inconvenient questions. To her relief, Chandra made his timely appearance.

"*Pranam*, Sage Narada," Chandra greeted their visitor. "Maidens love to adorn themselves with anger and pique, don't they?" His voice was studiedly careless. "Daksha's daughters have gone on a brief visit to their parents."

"What a witty answer, Chandra!" The sage's eyes twinkled in wry amusement. "I must say that you are indeed fortunate to enjoy the anger and pique of twenty-seven maidens!" He paused meaningfully. "As it was I who arranged your marriage, I take a personal interest in your welfare."

Chandra remained stubbornly silent.

Narada shouldered his lute and rose saying, "I dropped in here on my way to Brhaspati's *ashram*. I will be on my way, now."

'Narayana! Narayana!' his chant receded as he disappeared into the distance.

Chandra and Rohini heaved sighs of relief at his departure.

<hr />

Chandra looked up in startled alarm as Daksha *prajapati* made his sudden appearance, accompanied by his twenty-six daughters. Rohini's eyes clouded with anxiety.

Daksha seated himself majestically on a chair, his daughters ranged behind him. Rohini alone stood beside Chandra.

The *prajapati's* commanding voice filled the hall. "Chandra, I married ten of my daughters to Dharma, and gave another thirteen as wives to Kasyapa. In both cases, my girls are leading lives of fulfillment as wives and mothers. Out of respect for your parents, and in appreciation of your radiant good looks, I bestowed my twenty-seven beautiful stars on you." He looked sternly at his son-in-law. "But you have sinned – just as stealing another's wife is a crime, spurning one's own wife is also a serious offence."

Daksha paused, giving Chandra time to digest his criticism. Chandra averted his eyes at this overt reference to his misadventure with Taara.

Daksha continued: "You sinned in the past when you eloped with your master's wife. By humiliating and rejecting Aswini and her twenty-five younger sisters, you are sinning yet again." His voice lost its severity. "Chandra, as your father-in-law, I am also your parent. I forgive your transgression and give you a chance to redeem yourself. Treat all my daughters with impartial affection. Do not lavish your attention on Rohini alone and discriminate against the others."

Daksha rose and addressed Aswini: "Aswini, my daughter, take your sisters and go to your rooms. From today, your husband will keep you all in his tender care."

The girls obeyed him with rising hope dawning in their faces.

Daksha turned back to Chandra who remained silent. "Aatreya!" Daksha chided him. "I am waiting to hear your response."

Chandra slowly looked up to meet his father-in-law's intent gaze.

Daksha reiterated: "I am willing to overlook your offence this time." His voice hardened in warning: "I will not be so magnanimous in the future. If you continue to sin, rest assured that you will receive a curse from me: you may consider it to be your dowry from your father-in-law. Is that understood?"

Chandra nodded perfunctorily.

Daksha addressed Rohini: "As for you, Rohini, go to your room at once: I wish to speak with you in private."

Rohini quickly made her way to her room, followed by her father. She closed the door and stood waiting in silence, her head bent in contrition.

"Rohini!" Daksha's voice was stern. "Your mother and I never dreamt of the selfishness lying dormant in you all these years! Are you aware that you are casting a blight on the lives of your twenty-six sisters? You are not Chandra's senior wife – you have usurped Aswini's rightful position with your guile." His voice grew gentle. "Remember that, like you, your sisters too cherished a thousand tender hopes when they entered this house as new brides."

His penetrating gaze brought a flush to her face, as he continued: "Rohini, I expect you to make amends for your unacceptable behavior, examine your conscience and do your duty. It is your obligation to make your husband see the error of his ways. Apologize to your sisters and live amicably with them."

"As you command, father ..." Rohini murmured.

"I go now – but, rest assured, I will be back if further injustice is done to your sisters!"

Daksha *prajapati* stalked out of her room.

Rohini collapsed weakly on the bed.

—❧—

Aswini and her younger sisters waited expectantly in their chamber, but their hopes were dashed yet again: Chandra did not summon them.

Seeing their chagrined faces, Awini assumed a cheerful tone and said: "Sisters, I'm certain that our husband is finding it awkward to make the first overture towards us. Consider his sensibilities and pride – he would not want us to think that his actions are dictated by fear of our father."

She smiled encouragingly at them. "Let's be patient. He will come to us in his own time."

Her sisters struggled to convince themselves of the truth of her argument.

Rohini sat hidden among the shadows of the bedchamber, lines of anxiety marking her brow. Her father's words echoed ominously in her ear.

Chandra set a lighted lamp beside her and tilted her chin up with gentle hands. His smile was tender as he reassured her. "My darling, pay no heed to your father's threats. He fails to see that I am absolutely unsusceptible to curses." He looked into her eyes. "Now, tell me: is Daksha *prajapati* greater than Brhaspati, the preceptor of the gods? Is he more powerful that Mahendra, the king of the *devas*?" He paused and gave a defiant smile: "Even when I made love to his wife and begat a son through her, did the great Brhaspati dare to curse me? Did Indra, his staunch adherent, think to pronounce a malediction on me?"

"Why not, *Swami*?" ventured Rohini, timidly.

Chandra gave a proud laugh and declared: "The handsome Chandra, beloved son of Atri and Anasuya, is immune to curses!"

Rohini said hesitantly, "My sisters ..."

Chandra gave an impatient shrug. "Oh, they can go to the dogs, for all I care." He caressed her cheeks and said: "Rohini, I swear I belong to you alone – Rohini's lover ... Rohini's servant ... Rohini's husband! Your sisters will remain Daksha's daughters: they can never be Chandra's wives." His voice was softly cajoling. "Come, give me a smile, dearest!"

"*Swami*," Rohini murmured.

His eyes blazed in sudden rage. He hissed through clenched teeth: "What insolence! To go to their father's house without my permission – to make false accusations against me – to hide behind Daksha's threats!"

Chandra's face was dark with ominous fury. "Let the new day dawn: I will show them who I am!"

Rohini snuggled up to Chandra and rested her cheek against his broad chest. She gazed adoringly into his angry eyes. "*Swami* ... your anger ..."

Chandra looked down at her, the glow of love banishing the darkness in his eyes. "Rohini, one touch from you is all it takes to convert my anger into affection."

His arms tightened round her.

———⊶⊷———

Aswini and her sisters jumped up in glad surprise as Chandra entered their room unannounced.

One thought flashed through all their minds: 'He has seen the error of his ways!'

Chandra looked at each of them in turn. "Yes, I have come for you."

Twenty-six faces glowed in rising hope.

"Just as I drew Rohini close to my heart ..." he paused deliberately: "I will not do the same with you!"

He laughed cruelly, as the incipient light of happiness was snuffed from their eyes. "How dare you go to your father's house without my permission? You had the temerity to make false accusations against me and my beloved Rohini! You even had the gumption to instigate your father to threaten me!" He sneered at them. "Is that how you prove your loyalty to your wedded husband?"

He glared at them defiantly. "Do you think I can be intimidated that easily?" He gave a sniff of disdain. "I give a fig for your father's curses! No one – neither your father, nor mine – can force me to accept you as my wives!" His voice assumed a decisive tone. "Get this clear in your wooly-headed minds: Rohini is my only wife. You are her servants – and mine. This is the immutable truth!"

The sisters stood still in stunned disbelief. The only sign of life in their frozen bodies was the tears which coursed down their pale cheeks.

Rohini took up her position close beside her husband. Their arms entwined in a snake-like embrace. A triumphant smile lit up her eyes.

She glared haughtily at her sisters and said: "I hope that has made things clear to you all. You know your position here. It's up to you to take it or leave it!" She gave an elaborate, indifferent shrug.

Sparks of rage banished the tears from the eyes of Daksha's other daughters, which now flashed fire.

"Has the cat got your tongues?" Chandra rudely asked: "You heard my queen – do you consent to your role as servants? Rohini cannot wait all day to assign your menial tasks."

Aswini straightened her shoulders. She held her head high and made her way to the door with decisive steps. Her younger sisters followed her lead and trooped behind her.

Rohini shouted at their retreating backs: "Oh, drop your veneer of hauteur! Don't you want to know what chores I have in mind for you?"

Not a break in their strides, Aswini and her sisters crossed the threshold and walked away without a backward glance. Chandra and Rohini scornfully watched their departure.

Chandra looked down fondly at Rohini: "We are well rid of that gaggle! Now we have the palace to ourselves!"

"And what shall we do with all this privacy?" Rohini smiled up at him seductively, moving back to lean her head on his muscular chest. She reached back with her uplifted hands to clasp his neck, garlanding him with her slender arms. Chandra's hands encircled her slim waist.

Daksha's daughters dimmed into a fast receding speck on the horizon.

⁂

"Chandra!" The furious voice was a resounding clap of thunder which shattered the short-lived privacy of the palace.

Chandra and Rohini jumped up at Daksha *prajapati*'s peremptory summons. Rohini blanched with fear. Chandra reassured her with a confident smile and pressed her hands.

"Chandra! Come out at once!" Daksha's command rang through every nook and cranny of the abode.

Chandra, with Rohini clinging to his side, walked to the entrance with studied nonchalance and confronted Daksha *prajapati* and his twenty-six daughters.

"Welcome!" he said, with an elaborate gesture of invitation.

Daksha locked eyes with him. "It is not I who seek an invitation into your palace: it is my daughters who come to claim their rightful place in your life." He glared at his son-in-law. "For the last time, are you willing to accept my daughters as your lawfully-wedded wives?"

"Father-in-law, of course I accept that I married your twenty-six daughters, and Rohini. On your part, I'm sure you will accept that it is the wife's duty to serve her husband." He shrugged indifferently. "I have made it clear to your daughters time and again: I am always willing to accept their services as servants."

"Chandra!" Daksha roared in dire warning.

Chandra calmly ignored his shout and continued: "If they give me their consent to serve and obey Rohini and me, I am ready to invite them in."

"You insolent reprobate! Do you not know that wives are queens, as well as servants, to their husbands?" Daksha drew himself up to his full height. "Hear me, you degenerate ..."

"Oh, we are going to pronounce curses, are we?" Chandra's voice dripped with sarcasm. He glared at Daksha defiantly. "I dare you to do your worst!"

Daksha's measured words rang ominously in the charged silence of the palace: "Hear me, Chandra: your arrogant body will be ravaged by tuberculosis. The horrendous disease will lay waste to your overweening pride and lust. You will decline until you wane into nothingness. This is the curse of Daksha *prajapati!*"

The cocksure Chandra retorted sarcastically: "I am indeed blessed!"

The fuming Daksha turned his angry eyes on Rohini. "As for you, Rohini, your father's malediction will bring you immeasurable grief. You took pleasure in tormenting your sisters. Now, you can derive pleasure from tending your disease-ravaged husband!"

To Chandra's stunned disbelief, Daksha's curse took its terrible course immediately. Chandra's handsome body, in the prime of youth and vigor, weakened by the hour. His health wasted away, along with his arrogance and pride.

Rohini labored in deep sorrow to mitigate her inconsolable husband's pain.

As the debilitating disease went on the rampage in Chandra's physique, its effect impacted the workings of the cosmos. Chandra's rapidly diminishing radiance was faithfully reflected by the decreasing light of the moon. As the moon waned, the trees, creepers and herbs which derived nourishment from its light languished and decayed. Medicinal herbs, particularly dependent on the energizing pull of the moon, wilted – as a consequence, people fell prey to fatal diseases. An imminent dearth of medicine and food threatened the balance of the universe. The earth, lacking the cool benediction of moonlight, heated up with the lingering warmth of the sun. As the moon's radiance diminished, darkness reigned supreme at night.

The agitated *devas* milled about in confusion, seeking the reason for this strange lunar phenomenon.

"Narayana!" The chant announced Narada's arrival in *Devaloka*. Indra hurried to him with anxious questions.

"Let us go to Chandra: he will throw light on this catastrophe," suggested the sage.

A contingent of *devas*, led by Indra, accompanied Narada to Chandra's abode. To their shock, Chandra granted them audience, reclining weakly on a couch! His former radiance was now but a flickering, intermittent glow.

Indra exclaimed in consternation: "Chandra! What is the meaning of this? You, the king of medicinal herbs, reduced to such debilitating weakness?! How did you contract this wasting disease?"

Chandra remained in uncomfortable silence, his eyes averted from his visitors.

"Narayana!" Narada advised him. "Come, Chandra: it is always better to confess one's sin and seek reparation. Hiding the root of a problem can only be counterproductive to finding a remedy."

The shamefaced Chandra recounted the chain of events leading to Daksha *prajapati's* curse.

"In my arrogance, I was confident that I was immune to curses," he confessed in abject misery.

"He dared my father to do his worst ... and this is the sorry result!" Rohini sighed in pained resignation.

Chandra turned beseechingly to Indra: "You must free me from this disease," he said.

Indra observed: "Chandra, your falling ill is akin to the cure itself contracting a disease. There is no medicine to combat this disorder." He continued thoughtfully: "It is the curse which directs your malady. The only solution is to annul the curse."

"Well said, Mahendra!" said Narada. "And that can be done only by Daksha *prajapati*."

"Yes, let us all accompany Chandra to Daksha's palace and plead his cause," suggested Indra.

∞

On hearing Indra's impassioned appeal on Chandra's behalf, Daksha *prajapati* paced the floor of his vast audience chamber, immersed in thought. Finally, he came to stand before the anxious group of *devas*.

"Chandra has undeniably sinned. He repeatedly ignored my counsel and warnings. You must admit that he deserved to be punished." He frowned darkly at his offending son-in-law. Daksha turned to the king of the *devas*. "However, Indra, as your grandfather, I do not have the heart to turn down your request."

He made his decision and declared: "I will rescind my curse – but only on one condition: Chandra must swear to accord my twenty-seven daughters his impartial love and care. There must be no preferential treatment meted out to Rohini, or any other one of them. Unfair discrimination in any form will not be tolerated."

Indra turned to Chandra with his eyebrows raised in interrogation.

Without any hesitation, Chandra prostrated himself at Daksha's feet and took a solemn oath to cherish his twenty-seven wives with impartial affection.

Rohini now came forward with tear-filled eyes. "Father, I see the error of my ways ... I beg your forgiveness!" she sobbed.

Daksha nodded and turned to the expectant *devas*: "Indra, I am ambivalent about rescinding my curse absolutely." He pondered a moment. "When Chandra bathes at the auspicious site of the River Saraswati's confluence with the ocean, his disease will ebb. This invigorating bath will ensure that his radiance grows progressively brighter for fifteen consecutive days. Subsequently, for the next fifteen days, his luminescence will gradually decrease."

He paused and gave his son-in-law a meaningful glance. "From this time, Chandra's bath in the River Saraswati will serve as a surety for his good conduct."

"Grandfather," Indra asked uncertainly. "Does this mean that Chandra will beam with increasing light for the first fifteen days of the month and then lose his radiance over the next fifteen days?"

"That's right, Indra," Daksha nodded. "Every month, Chandra will be the waxing moon for fifteen days and then wane for the following fifteen days. On every new moon day, when his light has reached its nadir, he must renew himself with his bath."

"Narayana!" said Narada in approval. "This is a solution acceptable to all!"

The satisfied *devas*, along with Narada, made their departure.

Chandra turned to Daksha *prajapati* with folded hands. "Father-in-law, please forgive me!"

"You received my forgiveness when I withdrew my curse." Daksha advised Chandra. "Maintain the cycle of waxing and waning by bathing at the confluence of the River Saraswati with the ocean. Above all, love your twenty-seven wives equally."

Chandra then begged Prasooti's pardon and obtained his mother-in-law's blessings. Finally, his eyes filled with tears of repentance, he asked forgiveness from Aswini and her sisters.

Taking his leave of them all, Chandra made his way to the holy point where the River Saraswati met the ocean, and immersed himself in the cool waters. To his blessed relief, the wasting disease was checked and Chandra recovered his old radiance.

After spending a few days at Daksha's abode, a much-subdued and wiser Chandra returned to his palace with his wives. From that day, Chandra became known as 'the husband of many wives' – and one who lavished his care impartially on them all.

Trees, plants and herbs flourished under the renewed light of the life-giving moon. Living creatures thrived, blessed with nourishment and good health. The earth's happiness was but a reflection of the radiant joy which filled Chandra's abode.

"And that is the story of Chandra's life!" Nirvikalpananda smiled at his enraptured disciples.

"Master," said Vimalananda, with a twinkle in his eyes, "It appears that Chandra is an aesthete!" He chuckled. "Just look at him: eloping with the beautiful Taara before his marriage and favoring Rohini after wedlock!" There was a slight tinge of disdain in the student's voice.

"That is just the superficial aspect of Chandra's nature, Vimalanada," Nirvikalpananda cautioned. "We must subject the matter to analysis and ascertain the underlying, deeper truth." He paused for emphasis.

"Remember, Chandra is one of the *Navagrahas*. As he is divine, we cannot apply our contemporary rules and traditions as a yardstick to gauge his virtue."

He addressed them seriously. "Divine entities always contribute to the well-being of the three worlds. As a result of Chandra's love for Taara, the cosmos was blessed with Budha's incarnation as a *Navagraha*. Again, Brhaspati used his wife's adulterous behavior to categorically assert that a woman will be absolved of the sin of adultery through menstruation. Brhaspati not only proclaimed this ideology, but also applied it in his own life."

He continued after a pause. "Coming to Chandra's partiality towards Rohini – this is the root cause for the waxing and waning of the moon. This has benefitted the environment. In short, the worlds enjoy prosperity because Chandra, surrounded by his twenty-seven stars, graces the sky."

"Your logical explanation has erased our doubts, master," declared Shivananda.

Nirvikalpananda smiled. "Very well, then. It is time for you to hear the life story of Kuja, the third of the *Navagrahas*. You recall that Kuja took form from a drop of perspiration from Paramashiva's brow and Bhudevi accepted him as her son. Kuja grew up under her care ..."

The master resumed his discourse.

THE LIFE OF KUJA

"Mother, what does the name, Kuja, mean?"

Bhudevi, goddess of the earth, smiled and directed her fond gaze towards her beloved son. Kuja was now in the prime of youth. He towered over her like a tree which has been nurtured from a sapling with the utmost care and devoted attention. Bhudevi's eyes filled with pride: her handsome Kuja was no ordinary tree – he was a unique *Saiva* tree, imbued with Lord Shiva's own essence!

"Mother!" Kuja waved his long, shapely fingers before her face. "Stop staring at me and answer my question."

"I never tire of looking at you, Mangala," Bhudevi said lovingly.

"Ahah!" Kuja exclaimed. "Another name: now, you have to tell me its meaning too!" He laughed merrily.

"Very well, Angaaraka," his mother smiled.

"Yet another name!" Kuja's eyes twinkled in glee. "Yes, my son: and I shall tell you its meaning too!"

Kuja came to sit close beside her, then stretched out his long limbs on the ground and lay his head in her commodious lap. He looked up into her eyes with his endearing smile.

"Mother, I don't know why it is, but there is nothing which gives me more solace than resting in your lap."

"That is my good fortune, son," Bhudevi smiled serenely. "Innumerable living beings, sorely exhausted by their trials and tribulations, seek balm for their souls in the comfort in my lap. I am the blessed mother who rocks her infants to restful slumber in her soft lap."

"You are the very personification of patience, mother," Kuja's voice was filled with fond pride.

"One of my many names is Kshama – Patience," observed Bhudevi.

"Is it? And mine is Kuja ..." He looked up at her in interrogation.

"Alright, my son: listen." She paused to collect her thoughts. "I have myriad names, including Bhumi, Achala, Ananta, Viswambhara, Sthira, Dhara, Dharani, Dharitri, Dhaatri, Kshoni, Ila, Jagati, Ratnagarbha, Sarvamsaha and Kshama – which I mentioned earlier. Again, Sarvamsaha connotes one who patiently bears every burden. Another of my names is the single-lettered 'Ku.' As you were born to me, Ku, Lord Shiva named you Kuja – one who is born of Ku."

She smiled at him and continued. "Which means that you can derive names for yourself from each one of my own numerous monikers! You are Bhumija ... Bhuputra ... do you understand, son?"

"Oh, yes!" Kuja clapped his hands in glee. "Like mother, like son: there is no dearth of our names!" He paused and asked: "And what about my second name, Mangala?"

"That is derived from the fact that you were born on the day of *Mangala*," explained Bhudevi. She elaborated further, "As for Angaaraka, it means fire. The name denotes your fiery complexion, which glows with the shades of raging flame."

"Well, mother, it's obvious that none of my names are mere empty titles," Kuja laughed.

"No, my son, each one of your names is replete with its own significance – and all of them are uniquely you!" She gave him an impish smile and tugged gently at a lock of thick hair. "Now, out with the truth! Don't tell me you were genuinely unaware of the meanings of your names?!"

Kuja laughed into her eyes. "Can I ever fool you, mother?! Of course, I know all the meanings!"

"Then why this unnecessary inquisition?"

"Because I always use any pretext to hear my mother's sweet voice," he confessed charmingly.

"My mother's sweet voice," Bhudevi repeated softly to herself. She pondered for a moment and then came to a decision. She looked intently into Kuja's upturned face and said, "Kuja, I would like to tell you something which I have kept to myself over all these years."

"Go ahead, mother," Kuja shrugged nonchalantly. "Your loving words are always ambrosia to my ears."

Bhudevi nodded silently. "I want you to know ... I want to tell you ... I ... I am not your mother!" she ended in a rush.

"Mother!" Kuja gave a bewildered cry and struggled to come to his feet. Bhudevi laid a strong, but gentle, restraining hand on his head and held it firmly in her lap.

She bent to lock eyes with him and declared softly: "My precious son, I did not beget you ..." She paused to let him digest this startling disclosure. "You were born from a sacred drop of perspiration adorning the brow of none other than Lord Shiva himself." She explained slowly. "At that time, Lord Shiva was immersed in ferocious *tapas*. As the droplet flowed down his face, my gravitational force pulled it into my lap – where your head now rests!" Her warm hands caressed his thick hair.

She continued: "At the instant the droplet came into contact with me, it vanished and, in its stead, you appeared as a newborn infant. The holy drop of perspiration from Lord Shiva's brow metamorphosed into you. The Lord, awakening from his meditation, addressed me: "Bhudevi," he said, "this infant has sought the shelter of your munificent lap. Raise him as your own child." And that is how you became my very own child," Bhudevi smiled down at her son.

A frown marred Kuja's brow. "Mother, why did Lord Shiva not raise me himself?"

"My son, at that time, Lord Shiva was leading a life of solitude. This was in the aftermath of the tragic events precipitated by Daksha *prajapati's yajna*. Lord Shiva's consort, Satidevi, burnt herself to ashes in a yogic fire."

Bhudevi continued her explanation. "Lord Shiva was well aware that a mother's tender care is essential for an infant's welfare. Let me tell you something, Kuja," she pointed out: "Lord Shiva is none other than my elder brother. When her brother's baby is motherless, it is but natural for a sister to step in to nourish the child with her own milk." Her voice radiated love. "Do you know what divine bliss and happiness I derived from suckling you?!" Her tears of joy fell as a benediction on Kuja's upturned face.

He gazed gravely into her eyes and declared passionately: "Mother, whatever be the nuances of your relationship with Lord Shiva, or mine with you, one thing is engraved in stone for all eternity – you are my mother!"

"That will never change, my son," Bhudevi's voice was equally impassioned. "You are my son forever. Let it be known that Bhudevi will bless anyone who earns your favour with the gift of ownership of land."

She continued on a thoughtful note. "Kuja, I think it is time for you to consider the implication of having a true mother." She calmed his impatient movement with a gesture. "Yes, my son – she is none other than the consort of your father, Lord Shiva. Satidevi has taken the *avatar* of Parvatidevi, the daughter of Himavanta, the Lord of the Himalayas. She is now reunited with Lord Shiva in marriage." She smiled down at Kuja. "Like me, she too has various names, including Durga and Chandika. You have not yet met your real mother, my son -"

Kuja asked innocently, "Mother ... my father's consort ... is she beautiful, like you?"

Bhudevi was effusive in her praise: "Believe me, she is the acme of beauty, my son! She is Soundarya Lahari- waves of beauty incarnate! Her exquisite form is unmatched in the three worlds! She is Shivaani and Trijaganmohini." She said eagerly, "Kuja, you must seek her *darshan* and obtain her blessings – she will be eager to bestow boons on you."

Kuja shrugged indifferently. "When I have you, I own the entire universe – I do not require anyone else's blessings or boons!"

Bhudevi's face was suffused with love for her passionate son. She cajoled him: "Now, Kuja, don't be unreasonable! The grace of Adiparaasakti, Lord Shiva's consort, is a gift beyond compare. You are fortunate indeed to have the Cosmic Mother as your own mother."

She continued on a more practical note: "You have completed your education and have reached the appropriate age for marriage. Receiving Goddess Parvati's benediction will be an auspicious beginning to our search for a bride." She added the clinching argument: "Kuja, this will please me."

Kuja immediately agreed to her proposal and said, "Alright, mother. If it pleases you, I shall pay a visit to Kailash tomorrow itself."

Bhudevi smiled at his alacrity but shook her head thoughtfully. "No, my son. The best path to obtaining the blessings of gods and goddesses is to make them condescend to appear before you – not go in search of them." She advised him: "Do not expend energy in travelling to Kailash. Instead, devote your entire being towards achieving mastery over your mind and body. Exercise iron control over your senses. Focus single-mindedly on your *tapas* and meditate on Adiparaasakti. Invoke her grace and draw her irresistibly to you."

Kuja bowed his head in silent acknowledgement of his mother's words.

A tranquil clearing in the forest was the chosen scene of Kuja's penance in propitiation of Goddess Parvati. Adhering to the guidelines suggested by Bhudevi, Kuja immersed himself in the deepest meditation. He was lost to the physical world. The wheel of time continued its relentless circle, pushing the present into the past and pulling the future into its place. Kuja remained oblivious to the passage of time, and the coming and going of the seasons. The dry leaves of autumn which covered his immobile body gave way to the stark landscape of winter. The tender green leaves and buds of spring became the ripening fruits and blossoms which basked in the warmth of the summer sun. Kuja sat still as a statue under the spreading branches of a tree.

Lord Shiva and Goddess Parvati strolled arm in arm on the banks of the holy *Manas Sarovar*, the Lake of the Mind. A pair of swans trailed behind them in the water. The birds, swimming closely in tandem, seemed but a warm extension of the divine couple's intimacy.

"*Swami ...*" Parvati addressed her Lord.

Lord Shiva's thick, beautiful eyebrows met in an interrogative arch under his awesome Third Eye, as he turned to his consort.

"Your son, Kuja, is engaged in rigorous *tapas* – are you aware of this?"

"Is that so?" Lord Shiva's voice was studiedly innocent. "Whom does he wish to propitiate?"

"Me ..." said Parvati hesitantly.

Lord Shiva smiled impishly. "Then, you are the one who should be aware of his penance, not I!"

"But, he is your son! I did not beget him!" Parvati said in bewilderment. "Why does he choose to meditate upon me?"

"Look into my eyes and categorically tell me that my son is mine alone and does not belong to you too!" Lord Shiva challenged her with a twinkle in his eyes. "Are you ready to disown him?"

At Parvati's musical laugh, the swans in the *sarovar* drew near to share her joy. "You know very well that your son is also my son: how can I refuse to accept him?"

"Then, why all these questions?" Lord Shiva teased her.

"Because he emerged from you before I became your consort. This makes him your son first and foremost. I wanted to know the boon you wish me to bestow on him."

"Now, now, my love: a father presuming to advise a mother as to what is best for their son – that is nothing less than humiliating motherhood! A mother is a better judge than a father as to what best contributes to her son's welfare." He smiled down at her. "After all, a mother is ever-ready to shower her children with every gift of their asking – in addition to a million others which they never thought to ask for!"

Parvati moved close to Lord Shiva and warmly embraced him with her slender arms. "*Swami*, how beautifully you have described a mother's heart!" Her voice was thick with emotion.

Lord Shiva chuckled. "I have no mother: perhaps that makes me better equipped to portray a mother's heart!"

Parvati rewarded him with a sweet smile.

Lord Shiva looked into her sparkling eyes. "Tell me, Parvati: when are you going to condescend to appear before our son?"

Parvati laughed mischievously. "That's a secret – a divine secret!"

Lord Shiva and Parvati made their way companionably towards their abode. The swans left the waters of the *Manas Saravor* and followed close on the heels of the divine couple. Lord Shiva turned back at the sound of their softly padded footfalls – his mischievous gaze then fell on Parvati, walking with infinite grace by his side.

"Parvati, why do you think those swans are following in our footsteps?" He asked innocuously.

Parvati gave an elegant shrug and smiled. "*Swami*, I confess that the heart of a swan is a closed book to me!"

"Well, I know why," said Lord Shiva.

"Shall I tell you?"

"Yes, yes," she said eagerly. "I long to know why!"

"They are intent on the swaying of your shapely hips, my dear – they wish to study the secret of your beautiful gait!"

Bending to scoop some water from the lake in her cupped hands, in a quick, playful gesture, Parvati splattered the ice-cold water over the Lord like a cloudburst. Shiva's delighted laughter ran its merry way through the sparkling ripples on the lake's surface.

Kuja started at the sharp impact of a falling fruit from the branch above him.

A frisson of wonder reached its gentle fingers into his deep trance, awakening his consciousness to renewed awareness of his surroundings. A fragrance-laden zephyr caressed him tenderly. Far in the distance, he heard his name softly enunciated by a voice which was sweet music to his ears. His eyes widened in anticipation and a tremor ran through his body ...

A streak of lightning flashed before his eyes ... no ... it was not lightning ... it was a figure of incredible beauty! It was none other than Goddess Parvati – Shivaani! Trijaganmohini! Durga! Chandika! The sublime beauty of the three worlds!

"Mother!" Kuja gave an involuntary cry of awe.

"That is the very word I came to hear from you!" Parvati smiled sweetly at him. "What is your wish?"

"Mother..." that one magical word was all that Kuja could utter.

"Of course, I am your mother!" Parvati gave a gentle laugh. "What do you want from me, Mangala?"

'Mangala'- the word struck a chord in Kuja's heart. A wish rose spontaneously to his lips. "Divine Mother, I was born on the day of Mangala. And this day – the auspicious day on which I have been blessed with your *darshan* – is again the day of Mangala!" He paused to gaze into the pools of compassion which were her eyes. "Mother, let the name Mangala become a special bond between us. Grant me the honor of linking my name with yours, so that our unique relationship resonates through the corridors of infinity."

"So be it!" She paused. "Kuja, I am deeply moved by your refined intellect and touching devotion. Yes, your name, Mangala, is also the day of your birth, and the day on which you received my grace. In recognition of this, and as an overt manifestation of our intimate connection, from this moment on, I shall also be known as Mangalachandika."

"I am indeed blessed, Mother Mangalachandika." Kuja folded his hands in reverence.

"What more do you want from me, son: ask and it shall be yours."

Kuja bowed his head and said, "Mother, grant me a boon of your own choice."

Goddess Parvati's eyes melted in tenderness. "Kuja, your humility, and absolute faith in me, warms my heart. You are the son who emerged from Lord Parameswara's own perspiration. Just as your name is inextricably linked with mine for all eternity, I now proclaim that wherever you choose to be present, I will also be there with you. This is the boon I bestow on you."

"Mother!" Kuja exclaimed in delight.

"Yes, my son. Wherever I grant *darshan* to my devotees as the fierce goddess, Mangalachandika, you will also be worshipped along with me."

"Mother, I am indeed doubly blessed." Kuja paid obeisance to the goddess with his folded hands touching his bowed forehead.

Parvati smiled magnanimously at him and said, "Mangala, here is another boon for you: whoever worships you will receive my grace in full measure!"

Kuja, immersed in devotion, prostrated himself at the holy feet of his mother, Goddess Parvati. The fragrance which had engulfed his senses slowly faded. He looked up to find himself alone once more.

———

Bhudevi's joy knew no bounds when she heard of the boons lavished on her precious son. "Kuja, I am delighted at the turn of events. The spark of devotion towards the Divine Mother, which has always been inherent in you, has now spontaneously ignited to earn you her priceless grace!" She paused to gain his attention. "The name bestowed on you at birth by Lord Shiva holds my name – Ku. And now, your name is in conjunction with your other mother: Lord Shiva's consort. Kuja, are you aware of the greatness of this honour?"

Kuja shook his head in mute puzzlement.

"Both the mothers whose names are one with yours did not beget you through the normal process of pregnancy. I, Bhumaata, did not give you life – neither did Chandimaata. What is the significance of this?" She answered her rhetorical question. "You have experienced the good fortune of taking birth without undergoing the painful trauma of emerging from the womb. Likewise, both Bhudevi and Chandikaadevi have been blessed with motherhood without enduring pregnancy and the distress of childbirth. This is the momentous significance of your birth, Kuja!"

"Mother, you have made me realize how lucky I am," Kuja smiled, gladly aware of his good fortune.

"Undoubtedly, you are fortunate, my son. And fortune will favour all those who worship you!" Bhudevi continued: "Now, it is time for you to find a suitable bride. Go and seek a wife who will serve you with love and devotion. I wait to solemnize your marriage in the presence of Lord Shiva and Goddess Parvati."

Kuja bowed his head in obedient acknowledgement and said, "Bless me, mother."

"May your search be successful, my son!" Bhudevi placed her hand in loving benediction on his head.

Kuja touched the feet of the earth goddess in respect and set out on his quest.

<hr />

Bhudevi's blessing fructified and Kuja found a beautiful maiden, Sakti, to be his bride. Bhudevi, after obtaining Lord Shiva's consent, celebrated her son's marriage in the divine presence of Lord Vishnu and Lakshmi, Lord Shiva and Parvati, Brahma and Saraswati, and Sage Narada.

<hr />

"Kuja, in accordance with the *Trimurti's* command, Viswakarma has constructed a beautiful abode for your use. Take Sakti, and commence your married life there," Bhudevi advised her son.

"No, mother," Kuja was unequivocal in his refusal. "I will not leave you."

A tender smile suffused the earth goddess' face. "Son, you can no longer dwell with me. Your incarnation, and its purpose, was decreed by Lord Vishnu, the Supreme God. In order for the objective of your birth to be fulfilled, it is essential that you occupy your designated place in the order of things." Her firm tones gave place to softly affectionate assurance. "Kuja, remember that I have no finite boundaries – wherever you are in the vast universe, you will always be able to glimpse me."

"Yes, mother, I will carry you close to my heart wherever I am!"

He bent reverentially to touch her feet. Bhudevi raised him up and embraced him warmly. Sakti looked on this touching scene with tear-dimmed eyes.

———

Nirvikalpananda concluded his account of Kuja's life and serenely examined the engrossed faces of his four *sishyas*.

"Master," Chidananda said in breathless wonder, "the life of each one of the *Navagrahas* is chock-full of significant and wonderful events!"

"Yes, my son," the master smilingly acknowledged. "The life of Budha, which you will hear next, is also replete with wonders and dramatic developments."

"As I recall, Budha was being raised by his grandfather Sage Atri," said Sadananda thoughtfully.

"Yes, Budha reached manhood in Atri and Anasuya's care. The sage decided that the time was ripe for his grandson to live independently and practice his own spiritual discipline of *saadhana*. Atri consulted his wife, Anasuya …"

Nirvikalpananda resumed his enthralling discourse.

THE LIFE OF BUDHA

"**A**nasuya, come sit beside me." Sage Atri beckoned his wife near and continued gravely, "Budha is no longer a child who requires our protection and care. He has imbibed my instruction and become an excellent scholar. He is now a young man – and well equipped to lead an independent life."

"*Swami!*" Anasuya exclaimed in dismay. "Does this mean that you are sending him away from the *ashram*?"

"You know that it is inevitable, my dear," said Atri, with a sympathetic look at Anasuya's grief- stricken face.

"I love Budha more than I ever did my own son." Her eyes filled with hot tears. "Now, to live without him …"

"Don't fret, my dear," Atri comforted his wife. "You have been blessed with the good fortune of bearing the *Trimurti* as your sons. Lord Vishnu and Paramashiva are yet to take form in your womb." Atri smiled as a ray of hope dispelled the despair in Anasuya's eyes at this timely reminder of what remained in store for her.

He continued gently, "Now, dry your eyes and bless our grandson before sending him to Chandra."

Anasuya bowed in resignation.

"Grandfather, are you sending me away?" Budha demanded indignantly. "I heard you tell grandmother so!"

Atri smiled fondly at the young man. "Yes, Budha. It is time you emerged from the cocoon of our protection and took wing on your own. You must learn to be independent. At present, you are in the position of accepting help from others. Next, you must elevate yourself to the state of rendering aid to those in need. It is up to you to earn a good reputation."

He paused. "Go to your father, Chandra, and obtain his permission to establish yourself independently."

"Your wish is my command, grandfather," Budha replied obediently.

"It is not a command, my dear boy," Atri gently corrected his grandson. "It is our fond wish and aspiration for you. We are confident that you will mature into a young man who lives up to the ideals of virtue. You will garner respect and fame for us through your peerless life and achievements." Atri continued his wise counsel. "Take a meritorious woman as your wife and ensure that our lineage flourishes. I lay upon you the responsibility of propagating the line of Chandravamsa: the *gothra* of Aatreya."

There was a rising excitement in Budha's wide eyes. At this, Atri stopped – his face turned somber and his voice was grave, as he inserted his note of stern warning. "Budha, you are now a young man. It is time you were aware of your father's major defect: Chandra reaped much trouble as a result of his weakness for women. Do not let your father be your inspiration in matters of the heart. Accept the woman you love as your wife. Make her happy and find your own happiness in her."

"Yes, grandfather," Budha said.

"Be ready to begin the journey of your new life tomorrow. Go first to Chandra's palace and then set out in search of your destiny with your father's approval."

Atri fondly caressed his grandson's obediently bowed head.

Budha touched his father's feet in respect.

"My son!" Chandra's face was wreathed in an affectionate smile. "How you have grown since I last saw you!" He embraced his son warmly and looked intently at him. It was like seeing his own younger self reflected in a mirror! Chandra's eyes glowed with pride at the sight of the handsome youth. His son had inherited all his beauty!

'If only Brhaspati could see Budha now ..." he thought. 'He would not have the least doubt as to the boy's paternity!'

"Aswini! Bharani! Krthika! Rohini!" He called out excitedly to his wives. "Where are you? My son is here!"

Chandra's wives came running in answer to his enthusiastic summons. "Look at my handsome son!" Chandra proudly exhibited his child.

Aswini and her younger sisters crowded round Budha in affectionate admiration.

Budha prostrated himself before the group and said: "I seek the blessing of my mothers."

"May you always be happy, son!" Aswini's benediction was echoed by her sisters in a joyous chorus.

"We are indeed fortunate to be the mothers of such a handsome son," Aswini added with an affectionate smile.

"Mother, my own good fortune is twenty-seven times yours!" Budha's fond glance encompassed them all.

Chandra's wives laughed in appreciation of the boy's wit and facility with words. The father beamed with pride.

"*Swami*," said Rohini eagerly, "let us make arrangements for Budha's permanent stay with us."

"Of course," Chandra agreed. "My son has come home to stay." He turned questioningly to Budha. "What do you say, son?"

Budha shook his head regretfully. "Father, my grandfather sent me here with the express instruction to obtain your permission to begin an independent life."

"An independent life?" Rohini was bewildered at this.

Chandra explained: "Yes, Rohini – when a boy attains maturity, he is granted personal freedom, along with the responsibility of becoming self-sufficient. He takes on the mantle of independence and strives to achieve success without leaning on his parents for support."

"Does this mean that you are going to send our son away?" Daksha's daughters exclaimed in one voice.

Chandra smiled at their aghast faces. "Budha will stay here for a couple of days, basking in his mothers' loving care." He paused. "After which he must go to the forest, where accommodation awaits him – in accordance with Brahma's decree."

After enjoying the attention lavished on him by Chandra and his wives, Budha prepared to set out for the forest.

Chandra advised him: "Take care, my son. Remain faithful to your grandfather's teaching." He paused to smile fondly at him. "And do not forget to visit us on every full moon day: your mothers and I eagerly anticipate your arrival."

Budha looked intently into father's affectionate eyes. "Father …" he hesitated.

"What is it, my son?" Chandra urged him on.

"I … I … there is one thing I want from you," Budha's eyes pleaded silently with his father. "Will you grant me a boon?"

Chandra's own eyes melted in affection. He said, "Tell me what you want, Budha – it will be yours!"

"Father, grant me your permission to visit my mother once."

Budha's request fell on his listener's ears like a bolt from the blue! Chandra stood motionless as a statue, while Daksha's daughter froze into a tableau of startled surprise. Budha's words echoed in the women's ears … they also reverberated in Chandra's heart.

"Budha …" said the stunned Chandra, slowly recovering from the shock of his son's unexpected request.

"Father, I long to behold my mother with my own eyes … will you grant me this boon?" Budha's eyes shone with rising hope.

A radiant smile banished the clouds of doubt on Chandra's face. He hugged his son close, stroking his strong back with fond hands. "Go, my son," there was an underlying tremor in Chandra's voice. "Go and see your mother – with my whole-hearted blessings!"

Budha gently extricated himself from his father's clasp and gazed with deep gratitude into Chandra's eyes. "Father, truly I am blessed!" he said.

Daksha's daughters bid a tearful farewell to Budha as he wordlessly folded his hands in respect towards them. Their misty eyes followed him with their unspoken benediction.

Brhaspati listened attentively, as his class of disciples recited their lessons in droning unison. A sudden movement in the distance caught his attention and he looked up – it was a young man, silently making his way towards the hermitage on the grass-covered footpath. Instantaneously, a vivid sense of déjà vu possessed the *deva-guru*: time stood still and a startled gasp escaped his lips.

'Chandra!' his mind screamed the name. His heart raced and anxiety clouded his eyes. 'Yes, it is Chandra,' concluded Brhaspati, 'there can be no doubt about it! How dare that fraudster show his face here again? Is he hoping to beguile Taara away once more?'

Brhaspati's indignant thoughts made his blood boil and fury coursed through his veins. His disciples fell into abrupt silence as their master's face darkened like storm clouds. Brhaspati glared in silent condemnation at the intruder. His body shook with suppressed rage as the young man sedately approached him.

The youth touched his feet in a gesture of respect and straightened up to introduce himself: "I salute you, master! I am Budha, grandson of Atri and son of Chandra."

Brhaspati's eyes widened in amazement and the wild beating of his heart slowly subsided.

'Atri's grandson ... Chandra's son ...' the words fell on his ears with blessed relief, pouring oil on the troubled waters of his anger.

"Budha," the word involuntarily rose to his lips.

"Yes, master!" Budha bowed obediently. "Honour me with the position of your disciple and bless me!"

Brihaspati's hand rose in instinctive benediction and he said, "Long may you live!" Somewhere in the depths of his memory, that other blessing he had pronounced on Chandra stirred and rose to the surface: 'May you be happy!' Brhaspati shook his head to clear his roiling thoughts.

"Master," Budha continued humbly, "I am here to make a request." He hesitated. "If you will permit me ... I wish ..." He came to a fumbling halt.

Brhaspati heaved a deep, shuddering sigh of regret. This was the child his wife had carried in her womb – the baby who was born in this very house. This was the son who belonged to his wife, but not to him. With a mighty effort of the will, Brhaspati came back to the present and looked intently at the youth standing in patient supplication before him. His perceptive gaze took in the eyes, wise beyond their years, and the boy's humble stance.

"My dear boy, speak your mind," Brhaspati said kindly.

"I beg your leave to see my mother, Taaradevi."

Brhaspati was reduced to speechless amazement. 'What an incredible request!' he thought. 'Here was a son, humbly seeking his permission to visit his own mother!' A wave of intense emotion convulsed the *deva-guru's* body.

On his part, Budha was astounded at the master's continued silence. This was Brhaspati – acclaimed preceptor of the gods and reputed powerhouse of wisdom. This was Vaachaspati – orator par excellence: in fact, a veritable wizard at debate! And yet, here he was, apparently at a loss for words!

Budha ventured again: "Master, all I ask is a single glance of my mother ... I will leave immediately after that one glimpse." His voice choked with emotion as he pleaded: "I ... I yearn to see my mother."

Budha's impassioned appeal broke down the walls of Brhaspati's defenses and melted his heart. The *deva-guru* looked compassionately at the boy's tear-streaked, hopeful face. A million masterful sentences rose to his lips but he remained silent: the skilled orator was well aware that the moment needed no words. Brhaspati smiled benignly at Budha and inclined his head, gesturing towards the hermitage.

Buhda's face bloomed with joy. Folding his hands in instinctive reverence and gratitude, he hurried in the direction indicated.

Brhaspati turned sternly to his curious disciples, who quickly resumed their recitation of the days' lessons.

Budha stood hesitantly on the threshold of the *ashram*, his anxious eyes eagerly searching its every nook and corner. The room was empty. He took a small step forward, only to come to an abrupt halt – the door set in the opposite wall opened softly and a woman stood outlined by its frame, a basket of flowers in her arm. It was Taara! She froze in wide-eyed wonder at the sight of the unexpected visitor.

'Is it Chandra?' Taara's thoughts were a frantic, chaotic buzz in her head. 'Has Chandra returned after all these years?' She remained motionless. Then, slowly, the mists of the past cleared and she realized: 'No, it is not Chandra! It is Chandra's replica – the living symbol of his love for me! It is the child I carried in my womb. It is my precious baby boy: Budha!'

A thrill of pure delight coursed through Taara's body as Budha instinctively drew near. Some inherent, invisible bond pulled him to her like an irresistible magnet. An impassioned cry of need rose from the unknown depths of his being and fell on her receptive ear.

"Mother!"

Taara thrilled to the sound of that sweet word. She had conceived and carried him in her womb for nine months, endured the pain and fulfillment of delivery – and it was only now, after the passage of all these years, that the cherished word 'Mother,' fell on her rapturous ears for the first time!

The hard block of dark ice, concealed in the depths of Taara's being since her baby was taken from her, melted at the sound of his affectionate call – it dissolved into a rush of warm, renewing love which coursed through her parched body. She trembled in ecstasy at this long dreamed-of reunion. Her eyes filled with tears of happiness and her breasts swelled with the nourishing milk of motherhood.

"Son!" She walked to meet him halfway, her eyes never leaving his face.

Taara and Budha fell into each other's outstretched arms and remained clasped in a close embrace. Time stood still – the intervening years of separation fell away as if they had never been! Budha was bathed in his mother's tears of joy, as she covered his beloved face with countless kisses and fond caresses.

"Mother ..." It seemed as though he would never tire of enunciating the sweet word.

Taara held her son away from her and examined him adoringly from head to toe. She fiercely brushed away the tears which threatened to form a divisive, opaque curtain between them. "Son, I carried you in my womb for nine months ... I cradled you in these arms for ten days." Taara held out her arms in a poignant gesture of loss. "When you were a ten-day old infant, suckling at my breast with your perfectly-formed, tiny lips ... these same arms gave you away." Her broken sentences conveyed the desolation of her aching heart.

"Mother ..." Budha own eyes dimmed with unshed tears.

"Yes, my son. I gave you away in a flood of tears and that flood continued unabated for years." She paused and gazed at him with eyes brimming with love. "Budha, I was sure that I had lost you forever. I was tormented by the thought that there was absolutely no possibility of our ever meeting: I was unaware of your identity, and you were ignorant of my whereabouts." A radiant smile lit up her face. "But ... but, now ... you have come to me!" She reached up to tenderly plant a kiss on his forehead. "I have heard you say the word 'mother' – with that one magical word, you have transformed all my past misfortune into the greatest luck!"

"Mother, all these years I have dreamt of meeting you and basking in your affection and tears of joy. And now that dream has come true." He gazed adoringly into her eyes. "I am here to receive your priceless blessing."

"My blessings are always with you, my son." Taara stroked his cheeks with her palms, as if to reassure herself that this was not a dream.

"I am on my way to establish my own household." Budha explained his plans to her.

"Taara!"

Mother and son turned towards the door at the sudden interruption. It was Brhaspati.

"Swami!" Taara hurriedly wiped her tear-streaked face with the edge of her saree.

Brhaspati's voice was gentle. "Let Budha stay to savor the food prepared by his mother's loving hands."

"Swami!" Taara exclaimed in happy surprise, her eyes conveying their gratitude to her husband.

"After all, you once carried your son in your sated womb: now it is time for you to sate his hungry stomach!" Brhaspati's eyes twinkled as he left them together.

Taara gazed lovingly at her son, her heart too full for words.

Budha picked up the basket which had fallen from his mother's hand and gathered the flowers which lay scattered on the floor.

———∞———

Budha made his way to the forest, as decreed by his father, his mind continuously replaying the joyous scenes of his reunion with his mother at Brhaspati's ashram. His ears thrilled to the endearments she has showered on him. At last, he had experienced a mother's love at first hand.

Yes, his grandparents, his father and his twenty-seven wives had, each in their own way, lavished their care and affection on him: but, there was something in a mother's love which set it apart from every other emotion in the world.

Budha smiled to himself as he pondered on this subtle difference. The unstinting affection bestowed on him by the others was the labored, deliberate breeze sent his way by the vigorous workings of a palm-leaf fan. On the other hand, his mother's love was a spontaneous, fragrance-laden zephyr, which washed over him as naturally as the cool breeze on a balmy spring day.

Budha recognized that Brhaspati, in all the magnanimous warmth of his welcome, had not made any reference to his father. Likewise, Taara had not mentioned Chandra, or enquired about his well-being.

'Well,' thought Budha, 'it looks like mother has put the past firmly behind her.'

Taara had stood speechless at the time of her second parting from her son. But her beautiful eyes had said it all – they had brimmed with unconditional love and devotion. As he bent to touch her feet, her tears fell on his head like an auspicious shower of sacred rice grains. The tender kiss she planted on his brow whispered a million silent blessings into his ear.

On his part, Brhaspati had placed his right palm in benediction on Budha's head and said: "Dear Budha, your dream of meeting your mother has come true." He paused. "Now, go your way in peace and safety. I see in you the seeds of potential greatness. And, one more thing ..." He smiled at the boy. "You do not need my permission to see your mother – you are welcome to visit the *ashram* whenever you wish."

Budha smiled in remembered pleasure at the graciousness of his send-off. The *deva-guru's* kindness lingered with a warm glow in his heart.

A sharp turn in the footpath brought Budha to a small lake. He ceased his reminiscing as he became increasingly aware of the beauty of his surroundings. Every breath of the fresh, unspoiled air was an invigorating tonic to his mind and body. A gentle breeze rippled the crystalline waters of the pond and caressed the beautiful lotuses which floated serenely on the surface.

'Wouldn't it be a treat if the hermitage built for me by Viswakarma was located in the environs of this serene pond?!' Budha thought.

He surrendered to the irresistible temptation of the cool water and waded into the pond to slake his thirst. Standing knee-deep in the water, he bent to scoop it up with his cupped hands. Suddenly, he froze in surprise – the inverted image of a man in yellow silk attire, holding a lute in his hands, shimmered amidst the lotus stems. Budha slowly straightened up and looked round him.

"Narayana! Narayana!" It was Sage Narada, standing on the shore of the lake.

"My *pranam* to you, Sage Narada," said Budha, folding his hands in reverent greeting. He continued politely: "This unexpected encounter with you is a piece of good fortune."

"You are fortunate indeed, son of Taara!" exclaimed Narada. "Lord Brahma himself has entrusted me with the task of escorting you to your hermitage and explaining the duties assigned to you."

"Lord Brahma?!" exclaimed the surprised Budha.

"Narayana! You shouldn't be surprised at Brahma's personal interest in you, son of Chandra!" Narada smiled at him. "Think – who is sage Atri, your grandfather? Brahma's *maanasaputra*! And your father, Chandra? A part of Brahma's essence!" The sage continued: "My father, Brahma, does not distinguish between his own son and his grandson, Chandra, who is his incarnation."

Budha raised his hands in salutation towards the heavens and said, "I am indeed blessed."

"Coming to the point," continued Narada, "the hermitage earmarked for your use is in the vicinity of this lake. And your present duties are light indeed – follow your daily ritual of ablutions, prayers and meditation; sate your hunger with the readily available bounty of edible roots and sweet fruits; spend your leisure absorbing the beauty of your sylvan surroundings."

Narada set out towards the hermitage with Budha at his heels.

———∞∞∞———

Budha settled down to the comfortable routine of his days at the hermitage: the morning ablution, the prescribed prayers, the mind-cleansing meditation and simple, satisfying meals. The *ashram* teemed with life: the warbling of birds thrilled his ears from dawn to dusk; peacocks danced on the dew-drenched grass; rabbits sported fearlessly within reach and the gentle deer trustingly sought his companionship.

But Budha's heart often ached with an unfathomable emptiness. There was a void in his life: an expectant waiting filled his restless soul.

One evening, Budha went on his usual ramble in the forest. Suddenly, the familiar, serene calm of dusk was rudely shattered by the frenzied barking of hounds, the thrashing of animals through the undergrowth, the thunder of horses' hooves and the excited shouts of hunters.

Budha stopped to listen, recalling Sage Narada's words on his first day at the hermitage. "Budha, this forest adjoins Vaivasvatha's kingdom. Do you know who he is?" Narada went on to explain. "Vaivasvatha is the eldest son of Surya and Samjna. His name is derived from Vivasvantha – one of Surya's many names." He paused. "Vaivasvatha married Sraddha and, with Surya's approval, is now reigning over the realm bordering this forest."

Narada twinkled at Budha. "It is always good to know one's neighbours!"

Budha smiled at Narada's remembered words. He had no desire to make his neighbour's acquaintance. All he wanted was for Vaivasvatha's hunters to refrain from killing the trusting animals who lived in his vicinity, and to leave the tranquil ambience of his hermitage undisturbed.

He turned away deliberately from the raucous sounds of the hunting party and made his way back to his hermitage.

A few days later, Budha emerged from his hermitage at dusk. A couple of rabbits rushed to sport with him, while a dappled fawn nuzzled his legs. Budha chuckled and bent to caress the animals. Gently pushing aside the peacocks which were happily entangled with his feet, threatening to trip him up, Budha set out on his customary evening stroll in the forest.

He stopped at his favourite spot on the shore of the crystalline pond, admiring the exquisite beauty of the lotus blossoms which seemed to turn into gold in the reflected light of the setting sun. The drowsy murmur of sleepy birds was a soothing balm to his senses. He turned to make his way back to the *ashram*. He froze as the sound of hunters assaulted his ears: this time, the loud shouts and excited barks came from the direction of his own dwelling!

'I must divert them from the hermitage,' Budha thought. He hurried in the direction of the hunting party.

Even as Budha rushed towards the hunters, an incredible chain of events unfolded.

Prince Sudyumna, son of King Vaivasvatha, accompanied by a large hunting party, gave chase to an elusive antelope. The prince, an avid hunter, was determined to run down the animal which had narrowly escaped his last arrow. The panting animal ran for its life, with Sudyumna's sturdy steed in hot pursuit. The prince, crouched low on his saddle, furiously urged his mount on, leaving most of his soldiers far behind. Only a few hardened riders managed to keep pace with the prince's blistering speed.

The hunted animal streaked through the woods. The hunters' steeds foamed at the mouth at the break-neck pace imposed on them by their riders. Abruptly, the dense trees and thickets gave way to a clearing. Prince Sudyumna drew up short at the beautiful garden which suddenly lay before him. There was no sign of his elusive quarry. Thinking that the antelope had probably sought cover in some thicket in the garden, the prince, followed by his remaining escort, approached the flower-lined pathway.

At the very instant at which the hunting party crossed the garden's boundary, a bizarre transformation took place: in the place of the masculine company which had crossed the border, there now stood a group of women! The men's hunting attire and weapons vanished – in their stead, delicate *sarees* were draped round the feminine figures. Even the steeds were not spared: the majestic hunting stallions were now mares!

Prince Sudyumna and his escort jumped down from their mounts and stared at each other in uncomprehending terror. Their minds could not digest the dreadful evidence of their eyes. As they stood rooted to the spot by the horror of their predicament, the spooked mares whinnied in terror and bolted from the garden. The prince's erstwhile soldiers instinctively ran in pursuit of the fleeing horses and were soon lost to view in the dense forest.

Prince Sudyumna slowly awakened from his frozen disbelief. He ran his fingers over his body and recoiled at its distinctively feminine characteristics. In the distance, he heard the neighing of the mares and the contours shouts of frantic female voices. Gripped by a surge of panic, he called out to his soldiers. The sound of his voice compounded his horror: his masculine tone was now the dulcet treble of a woman!

Completely at a loss as to the cause of this incredible phenomenon, Sudyumna walked in a trance towards a small lake which mirrored the cerulean sky in its clear waters. His former majestic, decisive stride was now the graceful, swaying gait of a maiden. The prince stopped on the shore and gazed into the water. A beautiful young woman looked back at him from the surface: his heart raced at the realization that this portrait of feminine charm was his own reflection.

Sudyumna thoughtfully removed his upper garment and gazed intently at the image in the water: his flat, iron-hard chest had given way to breasts which shimmered like two lotus buds on the rippling surface of the lake. He continued to stare at his reflection, noting every detail of the change – even the masculine ornaments he had carelessly put on that morning were now pieces of exquisite feminine jewelry. His transformation into a woman was complete in every sense of the word!

In instinctive modesty, Sudyumna covered his upper body and gazed unblinkingly at the beautiful image in the water. A name rose unbidden to his lips – 'Ila!'

Ila wandered the narrow forest paths in aimless bewilderment. A fog of confusion clouded her mind. What were the choices before her? If she returned to Vaivasvatha's kingdom, not a soul, including her own father and mother, would recognize her as Prince Sudyumna. More to the point, her sanity would be called into question – who would believe her incredible tale? She would undoubtedly be labelled a mad woman! And what would be her position as a lone woman, bereft of male protection? No, she could not go back to her father's kingdom: that path was irrevocably barred to her.

But, what other choice did she have? She could not remain alone in the forest much longer. She thrilled with fear at every rustle in the undergrowth. She, the intrepid hunter, who had unflinchingly confronted lions as a man, was now startled when a gentle deer broke through the undergrowth before her!

Her desolate thoughts were interrupted by the fast-approaching strains of sweet music. Ila waited with bated breath on the lonely forest track. A man came into view round the bend, tranquilly playing his lute: it was Sage Narada. At the unexpected sight that met his eyes, Narada's music broke off in the middle of a note.

"Narayana!" the sage exclaimed in amazement. "Who are you?" His words conveyed urgent warning. "It is not safe for a beautiful woman like you to wander about unaccompanied in the forest!"

Ila looked up at Narada with shy, anxious eyes, but remained speechless.

"Come, speak up!" the sage urged her gently. "I hope you are not dumb ... can you speak? Who are you?"

"My name ... my name is Ila," she managed to say.

"Ila ... a very apt name for a beautiful woman!" Narada complimented her with a reassuring smile. "Now, tell me who you are and what you are doing here." He repeated his warning: "It is unsafe for you to loiter in these dark woods: unknown dangers lurk everywhere."

Ila was speechless in wonder – this was Sage Narada, who had visited her father's palace several times and interacted with her as Prince Sudyumna. Yet, here he was, patently unable to recognize her in this female form.

'If the divine sage himself is oblivious to my past identity, it is clear that no one will accept me as the former prince,' Ila thought disconsolately. Then, a ray of hope broke through her despair: surely the wise sage would find a solution to her predicament!

"My name is not Ila ..." she began hesitantly.

"Narayana!" exclaimed the puzzled sage. "Were you by any chance in a trance when you pronounced that name a moment ago?" He shook his head wryly. "Very well, we will let that pass: now, tell me your real name." Narada smiled encouragingly at her.

"I ... I ... I am not a woman ..."

"Narayana!" Narada threw up his arms in surrender. "I give up!" He looked her searchingly up and down and continued: "This Narada might be a confirmed bachelor, but I swear he can recognize a woman when he sees one!"

"Sage Narada," Ila asked, "Are you acquainted with Sudyumna, King Vaivasvatha's son?"

"Yes, of course." Narada's eyes were curious. "Why? Did he trifle with you in the name of love?"

"No: remember I told you that I am not a woman. I was transformed into one only a few minutes before your arrival." Ila confided the details of her bizarre, sudden metamorphosis to the astonished sage. "I was Sudyumna before my transformation -"

"Narayana!" the sage interrupted her in wonder. "Is this really you, Sudyumna?"

"Yes," Ila murmured in forlorn tones. "When I found myself in feminine form, I instinctively assumed the name, Ila."

"Narayana! Then, Sudyumna ... Now, Ila ... then, male ... now, female!" He shook his head in disbelief. "A young man has metamorphosed into a young maiden!"

"*Maharshi*, tell me – why has this misfortune befallen me?" Ila eyes filled with tears of sorrow.

"Why? Hmm ..." Narada pondered a moment. "Narayana!" his face lit up in sudden comprehension. "Did you, by any chance, enter the Kumaravanam?" he asked Ila urgently.

"The Kumaravanam?" Ila shook her head in puzzlement. "I don't know where that is ..." She paused. "But, I did enter a garden." Ila elaborated on the chain of events which led to her transformation.

"Narayana!" said Narada resignedly. "I must tell you that you are fated to spend the rest of your life on this earth as Ila. This is not just your fate: it is the ordained fate of all living beings who enter the garden." He proclaimed gravely. "Every being which enters the garden, whether man or animal, must live and die as a female!"

The sage proceeded to explain the provenance of the garden: "Kumaravanam is Lord Parameswara and Goddess Parvati's private garden. The goddess particularly delighted in the delicious seclusion afforded by her exclusive bower. Once, the divine couple was enjoying the garden's beauty, reveling in their moments of intimacy. Oblivious to the goddess's sensibilities, some renowned sages entered the garden seeking their *darshan*. Parvati's embarrassment turned into rage at this boorish invasion of her privacy. She pronounced a curse on the hapless *rishis*: any male being who dared intrude into her beloved Kumaravanam would be instantaneously transformed into a female. Lord Shiva seconded his consort and their implacable curse has endured over the ages." Narada looked gravely at Ila.

"Sage Narada!" Ila was aghast at the fact that she had inadvertently blundered into the Kumaravanam. "Is there no hope of redemption from Aadisakti's curse?" The light of hope faded from her eyes.

"The immutable will of the mighty Chandika is engraved in stone: there can be no turning back! One can only humbly accept Aadisakti's mercy or malediction." Narada continued, "You will remain a woman in the eyes of the world – and you will be treated as one!" He echoed her own thoughts: "Beautiful women cannot live in security without male protection. I advise you to stay away from the capital."

"I have no one to turn to!" Ila's voice reflected her despair. "What awaits me in the future?" She turned her pleading eyes to the sage. "Be my guide."

Narada closed his eyes for a minute. He then predicted: "Travel eastwards through the forest. Fortune will favor you with dependable male company. The mists of uncertainty will clear and your future will take firm shape."

"You want me to follow this path?" Ila gestured uncertainly towards the east.

"Yes, this is your ordained path right now. Begin your journey confidently." Narada's eyes were compassionate. "May fortune smile on you!"

Ila set out in the direction suggested by Narada. The depth of her transformation became increasingly clear to her by the minute: the change was not just a matter of external appearance, but a complete recasting of her entire psyche! Frissons of alarm ran through her body at the least rustle of a bush, or the snap of a branch. Her old passion for the hunt had vanished without a trace: now, the deer and rabbits which crossed her path evoked a deep tenderness in her. She fondled them with gentle fingers.

'What a world of difference there is between the sensibilities of a man and a woman!' she wondered.

The sound of approaching footfalls made her freeze in terror. A young man stood before her – immobilized in his turn by the unexpected sight of a lone woman on the forest track.

Her heart raced with a strange excitement as her eyes took in every detail of the youth. He towered among the bushes like a tree in its prime. He was the embodiment of masculine beauty. His muscular body glowed with the vigor of physical well-being. Like iron filings to a magnet, she was irresistibly drawn to his large eyes. The sensuous lips were parted in the beginnings of a smile. Her admiring eyes took in the broad chest ... his dazzling complexion ... she stopped, suddenly distracted by the insistent flapping of her upper garment in the wind.

She looked down – the wayward garment had fallen away to expose her body. An intense flush of embarrassment spread over her face: Ila quickly shielded her breast with her crossed left hand and groped for the fluttering edge of her *saree* with her right. In acute discomfort, she bowed her head in order to avoid his penetrating gaze.

A vague awareness came to life in her, like a water lily slowly blooming under the silver light of the moon – she had been absorbed in the young stranger to the complete exclusion of all else: she had even failed to notice her own uncovered body. He had cast a spell on her.

She asked herself: Was he that handsome? The answer emerged from the comely image etched on her downcast eyes – but a truer response came from her wildly beating heart, which had gathered him into its warm embrace.

Framed against the sylvan beauty of the woods, the young woman who stood before him was the epitome of loveliness. Her face was a lotus in full bloom. Her body glowed like a lissome, golden creeper against the rich forest green of the thickets. The wide eyes were lamps which shone with a radiance which equalled the light of the setting sun. He found himself unable to avert his eyes from her body, even as she grappled with her upper garment, finally draping it into place with trembling hands. The beauty the *saree* now concealed remained fresh in his mind's eye.

Who was this exquisite beauty? From where had she suddenly descended, to appear on this familiar forest track? The young man vainly attempted to voice his questions, but remained dumbstruck. In a trance, he moved to one edge of the narrow path to give her passage and slowly walked forward. The woman also moved towards him – they crossed each other with downcast eyes and continued a few paces in opposite directions.

Then, as if impelled by some unknown signal, both of them paused and turned back simultaneously. They stood facing each other once more. Their eyes locked in silent yearning. Their lips quivered with unasked questions. The man broke the silence.

"My name … is … Budha," he continued to gaze deep into her eyes. "You are …?"

"My name is … Ila," she replied.

"I am the son of Chandra and Taaradevi." His voice gathered strength. "I live in a hermitage nearby. What about you?"

"I … I … I do not have any family." Instinctively, Ila concealed the history of her strange circumstances. A cautious voice whispered in her ears: Don't risk scaring him away with the incredible truth … he may abandon you …

"The sun will set in a few minutes. The forest is fraught with danger." There was eager invitation in his words. "Why don't you rest tonight at my hermitage?"

"Yes," Ila agreed impulsively.

Budha set out in the direction of his *ashram*. Chased by the beauty of her haunting eyes, all thoughts of the huntsmen vanished from his mind.

At the hermitage, the deer and rabbits accorded Ila their own welcome, with warm nuzzles and rubs against legs, while Budha lavished his hospitality on his unexpected guest.

———

At dawn, the lotus buds on the surface of the water bloomed, as if the pond was opening its beautiful eyes to the morning sun. Ila, damp from her earlier swim, sat on the bank of the pond, weaving miniature garlands with the tiny flowers which carpeted the shore. It seemed that her transformation had bestowed on her all the inherent flair of a natural-born woman. She looked up occasionally to feast her eyes on Budha, who had just entered the pond for his own morning ablution.

Budha soon came to sit beside her. He held out a deep red lotus in offering to her, gazing intently at her face in mute appeal.

Ila smiled and said softly, "There is an unspoken message stirring in the depths of your eyes."

"The eyes are windows to the soul, Ila." His searching eyes never left her face. "It is not only my eyes – my lips also yearn to tell you something."

"So, let them!" Ila broke into teasing laughter.

"Ila, I came here to the hermitage to pursue an independent life. But my initial joy of liberty was short-lived. A deep void soon engulfed my soul. I was possessed by an increasingly urgent sense of expectancy – I seemed to be waiting for the arrival of something, or someone. Each day dawned in eager anticipation, only to end in disillusionment. The emptiness grew, until it threatened to consume my very being. And now ..." Budha paused.

"And now?" Ila gently urged him on.

"That emptiness has miraculously vanished without a trace!" Budha smiled.

"Has it!?" she exclaimed.

"Do you know the exact moment at which the void loosened its grasp on my soul?" His impassioned voice supplied the answer: "At the very moment at which your beauty lit up my eyes!"

Ila looked down bashfully as Budha continued. "From the first instant of our encounter, a strange excitement coursed through my blood. In all these years, no other woman has ever evoked such a reaction from me."

Ila raised her head in happy recognition. "But,that is exactly how I felt when I first set eyes on you!" She blushed and went on: "I have never ... stared at any man like that! No other man has attracted me so powerfully!"

"Really?!" Budha exclaimed in surprised exhilaration.

"I swear on this lotus which you gifted me – it is true," Ila smiled gently at him.

"The elders of my family sent me here to achieve self-sufficiency and independence. My grandfather entrusted me with the duty of protecting others. I want to carry out his charge." Budha paused and gazed intently into her lovely eyes.

"And how would you go about that?" A teasing smile played on her lips.

"By extending my protection to you."

"How?" Her eyes twinkled.

"By seeking protection from you!" Budha retorted.

"How?" The word sparkled with mischief.

"By ... by making you my wife."

"How?" Her question was now a sensuous whisper against his ear. The tantalizing smile of her lips was reflected in her eyes.

Budha sought the answer within himself. "Like this!" he whispered in turn and drew her to him with a gentle pull of his arms which were entwined round the slender column of her neck. Ila closed her eyes as Budha's beautiful face hovered over her.

The lotuses in the pond rippled in the caressing breeze, giving their nod of approval to the tender scene of love unfolding on the shore.

———

As the golden dusk enveloped the *ashram*, and the animals quieted in anticipation of the night, Budha turned to Ila. "My dear, let us live here as husband and wife," he said gently.

Ila looked up at him with an inscrutable expression. Abruptly, she turned away and ran into the hermitage. The bewildered Budha stared at her retreating back in anxious concern and thought: 'Why has she run away from me? Is she afraid of me? Is the idea of marriage abhorrent to her? Have I been too hasty?' Before he could follow her to make amends, Ila was walking back to him. Her radiant face and resolute stride reassured Budha.

Ila came to stand before Budha. The hand she held concealed behind her back slowly emerged, bearing a garland of fragrant blossoms. She paused for a moment, her eyes melting in devotion. Then, she reached up to place the garland round Budha's neck.

"Ila ..." Budha murmured in surprise, his voice choked with emotion.

There was a barely perceptible tremor in his hands as he removed the garland from his own neck and placed it around Ila's. Her eyes brimmed with tears and a deep sigh escaped her lips. The string of flowers rose and fell with the passionate heaving of her breast. She bent to gather the end of the garland and looped it over Budha's head in a sensual gesture of union. Budha looked down in delight at the single garland which was now a steadfast chain of affection binding their two bodies together forever. His eyes were bottomless pools of love as he drew her into his embrace. They were now husband and wife – one heart and one soul.

The sweet chorus of the *ashram* birds echoed the auspicious strains of nuptial music; the animals sported in an eruption of joy and the peacocks danced in gay abandon, even in the absence of rain clouds.

Budha and Ila, lost to the world in each other's arms, remained oblivious to the celebration unfolding around them.

"Narayana!" Sage Narada stood before Lord Brahma, elaborating on the strange chain of events which saw Prince Sudyumna transformed into Ila, and her subsequent marriage to Budha.

"Well, my son," Brahma smiled knowingly. "You do seem to have played a pivotal role in these developments!"

Narada's eyes twinkled as he bowed to his father in wry acknowledgement. He asked: "Father, what are the implications of this transformation? Does Sudyumna have to remain in his feminine form for the rest of his life?"

"Who knows what fate has in store for anyone?" Brahma replied with a tranquil smile.

Saraswati, seated beside Brahma, broke into the exchange between father and son: "Now, *Swami*, don't tell me you don't know what has been ordained!" She gave her consort a teasing smile. "Was it you who set things in motion to transform a man into a woman and make her Budha's wife?"

"No, Saraswati," Brahma shook his head. "I had no part in this. It was Parameswara and Parvati who were responsible for the bizarre transformation of the hapless Sudyumna into Ila."

He turned to his son in approval. "Narada did well to direct the maiden towards Budha's hermitage."

"Narayana! As for the marriage, this bachelor had nothing to do with that!" Narada laughed. "Budha and Ila took matters into their own hands there!"

A frown marred Saraswati's brow. "What if Ila returns to her original form?" she asked.

"Narayana!" Narada was aghast at the thought. "I leave that conundrum to my father!"

"Let's take things as they come," advised Brahma. "And what is coming next, is the continued growth and prosperity of the Chandravamsa, with the children born to Budha and Ila."

Lord Brahma smiled in contentment.

Budha and Ila led an idyllic life in the seclusion of the hermitage, devoted to each other. In due course, Ila became pregnant. On an auspicious day, she gave birth to a boy. Budha named his son Purooravas.

It seemed to his fond parents that, in a matter of days, their son had left the shelter of their laps to crawl all over the hermitage in curious exploration. He soon graduated to playing games of hide- and-seek, leading his parents on merry chases. To their delight, Purooravas grew up strong and healthy, demonstrating his virtuous character.

Purooravas was now five years old. The birds and animals of the hermitage were his constant companions and playmates. Ila's unbridled joy in the company of her doting husband and adorable son erased all thoughts of her past male life. She relished her new life like a juicy, tangy *amla* fruit. Ironically, it was her cherished motherhood which was instrumental in making her forget her own abandoned parents.

Vaivasvatha and his wife, Sraddha, continued to grieve for the loss of their only son, Sudyumna. The king persisted in his efforts to trace the prince, dispatching soldiers to all corners of the land and commanding his numerous spies to focus exclusively on gathering information on his son's whereabouts. Finally, Vaivasvatha, accompanied by Sraddha, sought the aid of Sage Vasishta, the revered preceptor of his clan.

"Master," the king bowed in respect to the sage. "You are all-knowing! Five years ago, Sudyumna and his company of soldiers disappeared without a trace while on a hunt. All my efforts to find him have been futile." He sighed deeply. "All I ask is for you to tell us whether our son is alive or dead. Let the knowledge grant us at least the fortitude of resignation."

The esteemed sage looked at the grief-stricken parents with compassionate eyes. "Vaivasvatha, the parameters of your fruitless search have been confined to the gross limits of your physical skills. Let me now harness the incomparable power of the spirit in our endeavour."

The sage immersed himself in intense transcendental meditation, concentrating his formidable spiritual strength on envisioning Sudyumna's fate. His labor was soon rewarded: in his mind's eye, Vasishta clearly perceived the prince's past and present circumstances.

Awakening from his trance, the sage turned to the anxiously waiting royal couple. "Vaivasvatha, your son is alive."

"Master!" the king erupted in joy. "Your tidings gladden my heart!"

"Oh, King," Vasishta's gesture urged restraint. "Hear me out first." He continued somberly. "Your son is no longer the Sudyumna of old. He has metamorphosed into a woman called Ila and is now living in a hermitage as a young man's wife." He paused to let the parents digest this incredible information. "There is more: he is the mother of a little boy."

"Master! Can this be true?!" exclaimed the king.

His wife remained in stunned silence for a moment. Then, her face grew thoughtful. "*Swami*," she gently reminded her husband. "Do you recall that our son was originally born a girl?"

The king brushed aside his reservations and turned resolutely to Vasistha. "Master," he bowed in supplication. "Bring our son back to us."

The *rishi* rose to make his departure. "I will set out for the hermitage at dawn tomorrow."

The bewildered Vaivasvastha murmured to his queen: "Born a girl ... transformed into a boy ... now a girl once more!" The king shrugged his dejected shoulders.

❄

"My dear, I am Vasishta."

With this innocuous introduction to Ila, the sage stood at the threshold of Budha's hermitage.

At the sight of this familiar figure, Ila attempted to control her wildly racing heart. She summoned an inviting smile to her lips and managed to say, "*Pranam*, Sage. Welcome to our hermitage. My husband is foraging in the forest ..."

She was distracted by her son, who came rushing up in curiosity at the arrival of a stranger at their door.

"Hmmm ..." The sage looked intently at the boy. "Your son's visage reflects the inherent qualities of a great emperor."

Vasishta seated himself on the grass mat laid out by Ila. He smiled up at her and asked in apparent innocence, "So, I am a stranger to you, am I?" The frisson of alarm which ran through her body did not escape his perceptive eyes.

With lowered head, Ila murmured, "Yes, *Maharshi*."

"Let me give your memory a gentle nudge," the sage smiled. "Perhaps you made my acquaintance earlier as Prince Sudyumna?"

"*Maharshi!*" exclaimed the aghast Ila.

"I am aware of your dual identity. I discovered your present whereabouts through the power of meditation." He smiled reassuringly at her. "Now, tell me the details of your transformation."

After her initial alarm subsided, Ila heaved a deep sigh of relief. Sage Vasishta was privy to the secret which she had concealed for years. There was nothing to be gained by remaining silent. At long last, she could unburden her soul to someone. Ila gave the sage her account of the chain of events which had culminated in the present circumstances of her life as a wife and mother. She explained that the major factor which motivated her actions was her conviction that no one would give credence to her bizarre tale.

Vasishta remained in grave contemplation for a while. Then, coming to a decision, he said: "It is your duty to resume your former identity and return to the capital. You must shoulder the responsibilities of the kingdom and relieve your father, King Vaivasvatha."

Ila shook her head in quick rejection of his proposal. "Master, I am perfectly content with my present identity and life." Her voice was resolute. "I will not return to the kingdom."

"This is the voice of selfishness. You are concerned only with your personal happiness and comfort." Vasishta's piercing eyes bored into her own. "It behooves you to render service to your parents as their only son.

Your father is old: it is your duty to take over the reins of the kingdom from him." His words rang out with finality in the small chamber. "You cannot evade that which has been ordained by fate."

Ila remained silent. She was only too aware of the truth of the sage's words.

"Your parents are bowed down with grief. You owe it to them to end this separation and make their last years happy."

"Master ..."

"You will not have to endure the return to the kingdom as a woman." He reassured her. "I will use the power of my penance to intercede with Paramashiva on your behalf. It is my responsibility to ensure that you regain your former male identity as Prince Sudyumna." He paused in sympathy. "Of course, you realize that Sudyumna cannot continue to be Budha's wife."

Ila began to speak, only to fall silent at Budha's arrival.

Vasishta introduced himself to Budha, who prostrated himself before the sage and touched his feet in reverence. "My hermitage is blessed by your presence, *Maharshi*," Budha said. "May I know the reason for this unexpected honour?"

"My dear Budha, I bring you sad tidings." Vasishta's gaze was compassionate. "However, it is essential to acquaint you with the facts. Let me explain ..." Vasishta narrated the circumstances of Ila's life to the astounded Budha.

Wide-eyed and open-mouthed in disbelief, Budha turned questioningly to his beloved Ila.

"*Swami*, from the first moment of our meeting, I fell deeply in love with you." Ila's voice was broken with grief. "I decided right then that I wanted to spend the rest of my life with you. Fearing that you would reject me, I concealed the truth from you." She bowed her head in penitence. "Please forgive me."

Budha moved to stand close beside Ila and placed his arm protectively around her shoulders. He locked eyes with Vasishta and said, "*Maharshi*, I do not care about my wife's previous identity." His voice blazed defiance. "All I want is my Ila – I refuse to let her go!"

Ila's eyes brimmed with tears at her husband's categorical declaration of love.

Vasishta heaved a sympathetic sigh, but shook his head in mild disapproval. "My dear Budha, calm yourself and introspect for a moment." He continued, "Consider this imaginary scenario: I take your little son,

Puroravas, from you and raise him as my own. The decades pass and your son becomes a young man. You and your wife are now old. You approach me and ask for your son's return. If your request was turned down, how would you feel?" He paused to make his point. "Can you now empathize with Vaivasvatha and his wife?"

"*Maharshi!*" Budha exclaimed in consternation.

Vasishta was implacable. "Vaivasvatha and Sraddha are now old. Sudyumna is his father's sole heir: there is no other legitimate ruler for the kingdom." He paused for emphasis. "Let me make it clear to you both – if not today, at some point in the near future, Ila will revert to her previous identity. Her transformation into Sudyumna is inevitable – it is only a matter of time!" He turned to Budha. "Once that happens, you will be unable to retain Ila as your wife."

"Master!" Ila's tremulous whisper was laced with pain.

"Yes, dear." The *rishi's* voice was gentle. "Remember, your father is no ordinary man: he is Surya's son. He will not tamely accept the loss of his heir." Vasishta addressed Budha directly. "Budha, my words are not meant to intimidate you in any way. However unpalatable it may be, I have but laid the bare truth before you."

"*Maharshi,*" Budha's call was a cry of agony from the soul. "Will you take Ila away from me?"

"Budha, my objective is to restore Sudyumna to his parents: not to separate you and Ila." He turned to Ila. "My dear, tell me something – who gave you the name Ila?"

"It was my own instinctive response to my feminine form, master," Ila replied.

"There is a reason for this," Vasishta said. "You were born a girl. Ila was the name bestowed on you by your parents."

Budha and Ila gasped and exchanged startled glances.

"Ila was born as Ila ... and then transformed into Sudyumna?" Budha wondered aloud.

"Yes, Budha." Vasishta smiled enigmatically. "It was I who transformed the baby girl into a male infant. Come, I will tell you the story of Ila's birth."

Budha and Ila seated themselves before the sage, looking up at him in awe-struck wonder. Vasishta smiled at the child on Ila's lap and beckoned him close. "Purooravas, my son, come here."

The boy rose obediently and came to sit on the sage's lap. Vasishta stroked the child's hair with surprisingly gentle fingers and planted a tender kiss on his plump cheek. He looked above the little head at his listening parents and commenced his strange tale.

"Vaivasvatha is Surya and Samjna's eldest son. He married Sraddhadevi and assumed the reins of his kingdom with his father's blessing. The couple remained childless for many long years. As the preceptor of his clan, I advised Vaivasvatha to perform a *yajna* for progeny. Vaivasvatha bowed to my counsel and set out to conduct a *yajna* for a male heir.

"However, unknown to her husband, Sraddha instructed the presiding priest to recite the prescribed *mantras* to beget a girl child. The *yajna* was completed and soon bore fruit: Sraddha became pregnant and, in due course, delivered a baby girl. The bewildered Vaivasvatha summoned me and asked how a *yajna* seeking a boy could culminate in the birth of a girl. Through my great powers of meditation, I supplied the answer: the *yajna* had indeed been conducted with the objective of obtaining a daughter.

"The king sank into despair. His hope of being granted son who would be his heir, and the guardian of his lineage, was dashed forever.

"Vaivasvatha's consuming grief moved me to pity. Acknowledging the fact that his vast kingdom was desperately in need of an heir, I appealed to Sri Mahavishnu. Using the power of my *tapas*, I changed the baby girl into a boy. The delighted king named his son Sudyumna."

Budha and Ila listened in speechless amazement to Vasishta's fascinating tale.

The sage now addressed them with great sympathy. "Do not let emotion cloud your intellect. As Vaivasvatha's heir, it is inevitable that Sudyumna will soon ascend his father's throne." He paused and smiled tenderly at the child in his lap. "In his turn, our little Pooruravas will become king. It is your duty as parents to ensure that the child comes into his rightful inheritance." He continued gravely. "The transformation of Sudyumna to Ila is the consequence of Shiva and Parvati's curse. I will undertake *tapas* to propitiate Lord Shiva and restore Ila to her previous identity."

"*Maharshi*, I understand your position." Budha admitted sorrowfully. "But it does not change the fact that you are depriving me of the wife who is the light of my life."

"My dear Budha," comforted Vasishta: "You are Chandra's son. Your birth was divinely ordained for a reason. I am confident that Lord Shiva, who made his wife, Parvati, one-half of his own self would never countenance the separation of a husband and wife."

The sage smiled at them. "Let's leave the future in Lord Shiva's eminently capable and compassionate hands."

Sage Vasishta left for the capital and acquainted Vaivasvatha and Sraddha with the prevailing state of affairs.

He assured the king: "It was I who changed your baby girl into a male heir. Now, I take upon myself the responsibility of again transforming Ila into Prince Sudyumna."

Vaivasvatha folded his hands in deep gratitude and respect. "Master, I beseech you to restore my son to me and ensure the smooth succession of my dynasty. Our bloodline will remain eternally indebted to you."

"It is my bounden duty as your preceptor, Vaivasvatha. I will immediately commence my *tapas*: the rest is up to Parameswara's divine magnanimity."

Vasishta set out on his mission with a resolute stride.

Sage Vasishta, the formidable spiritualist, and Brahma's *maanasaputra*, soon achieved his objective of obtaining Paramashiva's *darshan*.

The Lord smiled at him in benediction and asked, "Vasishta, what do you require from me?"

"*Bhagavan*, is there anything you are unaware of?! Your curse has transformed Sudyumna, the only son of Vaivasvatha, into a female."

"Who, as the beautiful Ila, accepted Budha as her husband and gave birth to a son!" There was a twinkle in Parameswara's dark eyes.

Vasishta continued: "Vaivasvatha and Sraddhadevi are grief-stricken at the loss of their only child, born after long years of barrenness. Vaivasvatha's kingdom languishes without an heir." The sage folded his hands in humble supplication. "Lord, in your mercy, withdraw your curse and bless Vaivasvatha by restoring his son to his original male form."

"The curse is a combined one: as my part of it is only half, I can revoke only half of it!" laughed Lord Shiva mischievously.

"Half?!" exclaimed the bewildered sage.

"Yes, Vasishta. I insist that the revocation of the curse be fair to both Vaivasvatha and Budha – both of whom have equal claims on the victim of the curse. On one hand, a son and heir is essential, while on the other, a beloved wife is needed." The Lord paused and then declared: "This is my word: the bearer of the curse will assume the identity of Sudyumna for one month and the form of Ila for the following month. This immutable cycle will prevail for the rest of his life."

"Parameswara!" Sage Vasishta bowed his head in acceptance.

"Sudyumna will rule his kingdom for one month; Ila will serve Budha as his loving wife for the next month." Paramashiva extended his arm in benediction. "May good fortune prevail!"

The Lord vanished.

⁘

The rising sun painted the water in sparkling hues of gold and red. The surface of the pond was carpeted with lotuses in full bloom. Budha, carrying the dripping Purooravas in his arms, finished his bath and made for the shore. He set his son on the grassy bank and wiped him down with a dry towel. Purooravas submitted unthinkingly to his father ministrations: his eyes were fixed on his mother, who continued to swim in the lake.

Purooravas returned Ila's radiant smile and tugged at Budha's hand. The child pointed to his mother saying, "Father, look – there is a new lotus blooming between those two lotuses: don't you think it is the most beautiful flower in the whole pond?"

Budha turned in the direction of his son's pointing hand: his heart melted at the sight of his wife's exquisitely lovely face, which easily outdid the sparkling lotuses in beauty.

Ila waved to her two admirers on the shore before diving into the water. Budha and Purooravas stood with their eyes glued to the spot where they expected her face to resurface among the blossoms.

There! A smiling face appeared between two lotuses. But … wait … that was not Ila's face … it was the face of a man!

"Father!" Purooravas' alarmed eyes sought Budha's. "Where is mother?"

The nonplussed Budha could not summon up the words to answer his son. His chaotic thoughts raced through his mind: 'Who is this man? Where is Ila?'

The stranger waved merrily at the father and son standing transfixed on the shore, and made his way to them with firm strokes. Standing in the shallows before them, the stranger smiled at Budha and Purooravas with easy familiarity.

Budha glared angrily at the stranger. "Who are you? What have you done to my wife?" His voice was harsh in accusation.

The man's eyes widened in bewilderment. "*Swami* ..." The man stopped abruptly, obviously shocked at the harsh sound of his own voice. Slowly, he bent to survey his body – he froze for a moment in abject terror and then looked up at Budha with agonized eyes.

Budha's heart turned over: Was this Ila, the love of his life? Had Sage Vasishta accomplished what he had set out to do? Had his wife been transformed into this stranger? Budha's heart ached at the sight of his son's desolate face – was Purooravas now a motherless child?

"*Swami!*" the stranger turned to Budha beseechingly. "It is I – your Ila. What you see now is my former male identity."

"Ila ..." the word was wrenched from Budha's wounded soul.

"*Swami*, Sage Vasishta has succeeded in restoring Prince Sudyumna's identity," there was a world of painful resignation in those sorrowful words. Budha sank to the ground in despair.

"Father, where is mother?" His son's plaintive cry lacerated his aching heart.

Budha gathered Purooravas into a tight embrace and heaved a racking sigh. "My son, your mother has left us."

———⁂———

A pall of gloom hung over the hermitage. Budha and Sudyumna sat in stunned silence on the dais. Budha could not help stealing quick glances at Sudyumna: the strong, muscular physique, the handsome face sporting a luxuriant moustache with its connotation of courage and manly pride ...

Purooravas, tired and fretting, had finally given up his constant refrain, 'I want mother.' The child rested on his father's lap – an occasional sob convulsed his little body. Even the birds and animals of the *ashram* had ceased their happy cries, as if aware of the impending tragedy of separation.

"My dear Sudyumna!" Vasishta's exclamation of happy surprise startled the silent company. The sage descended from his chariot and walked towards them, a spring in his step.

"Master!" Sudyumna rose and made his obeisance to the sage.

Vasishta looked intently at the young man with the chiseled features of royalty and beamed in triumph. "May happiness be yours! We meet after the passage of long years, Prince Sudyumna – thanks to Paramashiva's magnanimity! Imagine your parents' delight at your reunion with them!"

"Yes, *Maharshi*," Sudyumna said despondently. "The joy of reunion on one side ... and the sorrow of separation on the other." He gestured to Budha. "Take a look at that father and son."

Vasishta turned his smiling gaze to Budha and Purooravas. Budha prostrated himself at the sage's feet, with Purooravas promptly following his father's example. Sorrow was etched in deep lines on Budha's face.

"Long may you live!" Vasishta laid his hand on the child's head in a gentle caress. "Purooravas is a credit to his respectable parents!"

"*Maharshi* ..." Budha managed a tremulous greeting. His eyes brimmed with unshed tears.

"My dear Budha," the sage's voice resonated with warm sympathy. "Dry your tears and rejoice: your anticipated separation from Ila will be neither permanent nor continuous."

"*Maharshi!*" A gleam of hope flickered in Budha's anxious eyes.

"Yes, Budha," smiled the sage. "Did I not assure you that Paramewara would not countenance the separation of a husband and wife? Of his own volition, he has kept your welfare in mind and revoked the curse in a manner benefiting all the concerned parties."

Vasishta paused and looked at the two men in turn. "This is Lord Shiva's eminently fair decree: Sudyumna will be Prince Sudyumna for one month – and then take on the identity of Ila for the next month."

"*Maharshi*, can this be true?!" Budha exclaimed in delight.

"Yes, Budha. Vaivasvatha's child will rule his kingdom for a month as his father's son, Sudyumna; the following month he will serve you as your wife, Ila." Vasishta smiled in satisfaction.

"Master, my parents and I are indebted to you for all eternity!" Sudyumna exclaimed in impassioned gratitude.

"Sudyumna, you are indeed twice-blessed!" Vasishta smiled at the prince. "You are now the grandson of Surya, and the daughter-in-law of Chandra!"

The sage turned to Budha. "Budha, you too are fortunate: united with your wife one month and separated from her the next! This cycle of union and separation will continuously renew your conjugal relationship, keeping it ever-fresh and tender."

Vasishta paused to look at the little boy clasped in his father's arms. "I have another suggestion to make, Budha. As befitting Purooravas' position as a future king, it would do him good to live in the palace instead of at the hermitage. It is essential that he receive the education appropriate to his royal status."

Budha blanched and his visage clouded with sorrow. "How can I live without my son?" he cried out in despair.

"Budha, look at it from this perspective: I'm sure you agree that it is best for the child to remain in his mother's care. By accepting my counsel, you will ensure that Purooravas constantly enjoys his mother's affection – whether as Ila in the hermitage, or as Sudyumna at the palace."

"The *Maharshi* is right," Sudyumna assured Budha. "I will take Purooravas with me – I will also arrange for him to visit the hermitage frequently, with an escort of soldiers."

Budha wordlessly lifted Purooravas into his arms and gazed intently into his face. "Son, listen carefully to my words." He gestured to Sudyumna. "This is your mother … she has changed into a prince named Sudyumna for a month. At the end of the month, the prince will change back into your mother." He smiled tenderly at his son. "So, tell me now: who is inside Sudyumna?"

The little boy exclaimed in delight: "Mother! Mother is inside the prince!" He continued excitedly, "And, after a month, the prince will be inside mother!"

Budha patted his son approvingly on his shoulder. "So, since Sudyumna and Mother are one and the same, you should go to the capital with the prince." The little boy frowned doubtfully. Budha quickly reassured him. "You can always come to see me here."

"When can I come back home, father?" There was a forlorn note to Purooravas' query.

"Whenever you wish – all you have to do is let me know and I will arrange an escort of soldiers to take you to the hermitage." Sudyumna assured the child, stroking his hair comfortingly.

At that, excitement banished the clouds of doubt from the boy's brow and he raised his trusting arms to Sudyumna. "Take me to the capital in your chariot!" He turned to Budha. "Father, I will come back home soon to see you!"

Budha embraced his son and kissed him tenderly. Sudyumna touched Budha's feet in respect and then lifted the child into his arms.

"Purooravas, there are two people in the palace who are looking forward eagerly to playing with you," said Vasishta, a twinkle in his eye.

"Who are they, master?" asked the child eagerly.

"Your grandparents, who love you very much."

The sage turned to the prince. "Come, Sudyumna. The king and queen await your arrival – their yearning eyes strain to glimpse the dust raised by our chariot wheels. Let us be on our way!"

"And that, my dear boys," said Nirvikalpananda to his disciples, "is the story of Budha's life. What do you think of it?"

"Master, the life story – and your expert narration, are both riveting!" Vimalanada exclaimed.

"I have a doubt, master ..." It was Sadananda.

"What is it, Sadananda?" asked Nirvikalpananda with a benign smile.

"We know that Budha married Iladevi." Sadananda paused. "However, some accounts of the *Navagrahas* hold that Jnaani is Budha's wife. Does this imply that Budha married twice?"

"Good question, Sadananda ... but one which evades a definite answer. Nowhere in the *Puranas* is it said that Budha married again: nor is there any disclaimer regarding Ila's position as Budha's wife." He paused emphatically: "The epics categorically state that Sudyumna, son of Vaivasvatha, was transformed into a woman, Ila, and this Ila became Budha's wife. Their marriage laid the foundation for the Chandravamsa bloodline. Purooravas, their son, is an eminent descendent of Chandra's lineage."

"But, master, who then is Jnaani?" Sadananda persisted in his query.

"I think we can safely assume that Jnaani is another name for Iladevi." The *guru* continued in a thoughtful vein. "Ila created history by being born a female, changed into a male, again being transformed into a woman and back once more into a man! In recognition of this, Ila and Jnaani may be considered to be one and the same individual. Perhaps Ila was bestowed the name, Jnaani, at the time of Budha's elevation to the pantheon of the *Navagrahas*."

The four disciples nodded in agreement. "That is well reasoned, master. And it also recognizes Ila's unswerving loyalty to Budha," said Vimalananda in satisfaction.

"Very well ... and now we come to the story of the fifth *graha* – Brhaspati." Nirvikalpananda took a deep breath. "Let us refresh our memories: Taara returned to her husband after her elopement with Chandra and resumed her role as a dutiful wife to Brhaspati. All was now well with their marriage ..."

THE LIFE OF GURU

Brhaspati, eager to commence his ritual morning worship, looked up at his wife's approach. "Taara, I have been waiting for quite awhile – Punjikasthala is yet to return with the flowers for the morning *puja*." He frowned. "Is the maid loitering somewhere? Or have you dispatched her on another errand?"

Taara shook her head and reassured him. "Her only chore was to gather the flowers, *Swami* – she will be here soon." She continued: "As for me, I am on my way to the river for my bath. I will return with the water for the *ashram*."

Brhaspati watched his wife depart. He gave a tetchy sniff and rose to pace up and down, impatiently awaiting the arrival of the tardy maidservant.

Punjikasthala strolled leisurely through the garden, picking flowers and dropping them into the woven-grass basket in her hand. She reached up to bend a flower-laden branch – only to freeze in sudden alarm: as shrill laugh shattered the serene morning calm of the deserted garden. The maid pricked up her ears in surprise and remained motionless: again, peals of merriment reached her on a gust of wind. She noted the distinct male and female timbres in the happy chorus.

Who were these intruders? Why were they in the hermitage garden? And what was the reason behind their undiluted mirth? Stirred by strong curiosity, Punjikasthala moved stealthily in the direction of the laughter ...

The sounds of glee became increasingly distinct. The woman's laughter was punctuated by small silences: it trilled out again and again in little bursts of sensuous delight, as though spasms of pleasure coursed intermittently through her aroused body. Punjikasthala crouched behind a thicket and furtively drew aside a branch. As she peered into the bower which lay before her, a soft gasp of surprise escaped her lips and the basket fell from her nerveless fingers. Her heart raced in excitement as she stared in fascination at the amorous scene unfolding under her gaze.

A *gandharva* couple lay coiled in tight embrace on the soft grass of the concealed arbor. Their gossamer-fine vestments did nothing to hide the sheen of their flaming figures, streaked with the juice of betel leaves and areca nuts. Punjikasthala could not tear her eyes away from the inflamed bodies, writhing in the erotic throes of uninhibited carnal pleasure. Her errand long forgotten, the maid surrendered to her prurient interest in the *gandharvas'* lascivious coupling. Her own sexual deprivation made her doubly receptive to the eroticism on display before her. Time stood still for Punjikasthala: goosebumps prickled on her arms; the perspiration poured from her burning skin.

In a sudden flash of thrashing limbs, the *gandharva* couple vanished from the bower. But the maid remained rooted to the spot: the sexual exploits of the lovers played itself in a continuous loop in her febrile imagination. Her sweat-drenched body shuddered in delicious remembrance.

Coming to her senses, Punjikasthala mechanically picked up the discarded basket and resumed picking flowers. Her fingers trembled ... the erotic scene continued to haunt her: she could not banish the vivid images from her heightened senses. She ached with the urgent need for sexual release and yearned for the sight and touch of a male. Suddenly, the handsome Brhaspati flashed through her churning mind, and things fell into place: yes, her master – he whom she served with such devotion – he was the only man who could give her fulfillment she craved.

Brhaspati would be alone in the *ashram* – the maid was well aware that this was the time of Taara's usual, extended visit to the river. Punjikasthala quickly filled her basket and hurried to the hermitage, her arousal a swarm of bees buzzing in her head.

Brhaspati stopped his impatient pacing and frowned darkly at the maid. "Punjika, where have you been?" His voice was harsh in reprimand. "Do you realize that the time of worship is almost over?"

Punjikasthala, undaunted by his dark frown, came to stand close beside him.

Brhaspati eyed her sweat-drenched body with distaste and raised his eyebrows in interrogation. "What is the meaning of this?" He continued in sudden realization. "Oh, so you have been larking in the river fully dressed? You silly, irresponsible girl!"

Punjikasthala did not deign to reply. Her eyes, gleaming unnaturally, held Brhaspati's own indignant gaze. In an abrupt gesture, she emptied the basket of flowers into the folds of her upper garment. Her hands moved again – the fragrant blossoms rained gently on the astounded *deva- guru*. Along with the flowers, her upper garment also dropped to the ground.

"These flowers have not been gathered for devotion, but for passion." Punjikasthala gave a husky laugh. "I offer them, not to the god of the universe, but to the god of love!" She pointedly ignored her exposed breasts.

"Punjika!" Brhaspati's shout was a cross between horror and fury. "What insolence! Have you by any chance lost your mind, girl?"

Punjikasthala burst into throaty amusement. "I am not insolent ... I am amorous! My body craves sexual fulfillment in your arms. Make me yours."

Before the aghast Brhaspati could gather his wits, Punjikasthala pulled him into a close embrace and lifted her face expectantly to his. He felt the heat of her physical arousal and struggled in vain to free himself from her tight hold. Her clinging arms were creepers implacably twined round a tree. "Master, I am yours: take me," she murmured in ecstasy. "Our union will surpass that of the *gandharvas* in exhilarating pleasure."

"Punjika!" Brhaspati howled in frustration as he fought to break free from her iron clasp.

"Master, like the *gandharvas*, let us pledge ourselves to each other in the seclusion of the bower."

Brhaspati stared with disbelief into her face as she mumbled meaningless endearments. In a flash of comprehension, he realized that the girl had witnessed the coupling of a *gandharva* couple.

"Master," the demented girl raved on. "My body burns with lust. Only your passionate embrace can douse the consuming flames. Come," she urged him on. "Come with me to the sweet, flower-carpeted bower."

Brhaspti's body shook with uncontrollable rage. His fury gave him the strength to wrench himself out of Punjikasthala's clinging arms. He flung her roughly to the ground and stood towering over her, his eyes blazing in anger. The maid picked herself up and, oblivious to his wrath, stared into his eyes in seductive invitation.

"Punjika!" Brhaspati's voice was a terrifying clap of thunder.

"Let us go to the bower, master," she was blissfully immune to his tempestuous reaction. "A soft bed of flowers is waiting to receive us …"

"You shameless hussy! How dare you ask me to commit the sin of adultery?!" Brhaspati roared.

Punjikasthala cackled in unbridled mirth. "Master, how naive you are! Tell me: how is it a sin for you to bask in the same carnal pleasure which your wife, Taaradevi, enjoyed with another man?" Her voice took on a pleading note. "Sacrificing my own personal needs and aspirations, I have dedicated my life to your comfort. Just as I offered you my services, I now offer you my body – it is ripe for the plucking. Please … make me yours!"

Some vestige of pride reared its head in the besotted girl as she continued: "And, let me remind you, master, I am no mere mortal: I am a divine nymph – one endowed with extraordinary beauty."

The astounded Brhaspati stared into her eyes, which burned with unquenched lust. Her red lips were parted in erotic invitation. The *guru's* gaze travelled over her body. Her exposed breasts rose and fell in rhythm with her panting desire. Misinterpreting his keen glance, Punjikasthala eagerly moved closer to him.

"Stop right there!" Brhaspati's angry command reverberated like the roar of a goaded lion in its den, halting Punjikasthala in her tracks. "You harlot! You are aflame with abnormal lust: your illicit sexual appetite is sinful and depraved!" His impassioned voice held deep contempt. "Your lust mimics the insatiable concupiscence of the simian race." His piercing eyes held hers in implacable fury. "This is the curse of Brhaspati: you will become a female monkey!"

Brhaspati's malediction rang in Punjikasthala's ears; a cold apprehension took root in the depths of her being. 'You will become a female monkey!' Her body shivered in mind-numbing terror. It was now drenched, not in the heat of desire, but in the cold sweat of abject dread. The insane delirium which had possessed her vanished without a trace, leaving in its wake cold sobriety. She – a heavenly nymph of incredible loveliness – to become a monkey!

She hurriedly draped her upper garment over her shoulder. Bursting into tears, Punjikasthala fell prostrate at Brhaspati's feet in wracking remorse. "Master ... be merciful to your poor servant! I was bewitched ... the sight of the *gandharvas* in flagrant sexual intercourse cast an evil spell on me." Her body convulsed in sobs. "Deliver me from your curse, master. Forgive me!"

Brhaspati's heart melted at Punjikasthala's pitiable remorse. He looked down in sympathy at the prostrate figure. "Punjika, stand up, girl," he said kindly.

She stood and looked at him with pleading, tear-filled eyes.

"Punjika," Brhaspti continued gently, "my curse cannot be revoked..."

"Master!" it was a cry of despair.

"But, let me tell you this: my malediction is actually a boon in another form." The girl's eyes mirrored her bewilderment.

"Yes, Punjika: my curse is your boon." He explained: "As a monkey, you are destined to marry a male monkey of heroic character. The carnal pleasure you craved will be an integral part of your conjugal life." Brhaspati's voice assumed new gravity. "You will beget a son who will shine as a warrior par excellence. He will achieve total mastery over his senses and attain immortality." He paused. "There is more: your son will serve Lord Vishnu's incarnation in the *Tretayuga* and will come to be worshipped by all. Your own name will achieve renown and live on through him."

At Brhaspati's inspiring prophesy, Punjikasthala dried her tears and stood tall. "Truly, I am blessed, master," she smiled bravely.

"Yes, indeed, Punjika," her master smiled encouragingly at her. "Now, be on your way."

The maid bent to touch Brhaspati's feet in respect. "Where should I go, master?" she asked.

"Follow your heart, Punjika: it will show you the path ordained for you. Be true to the dictates of your inner self. May fortune smile on you!"

Without a backward glance, Punjikasthala resolutely walked out of the hermitage. Brhaspati stood watching her retreating figure with a poignant smile on his face.

Taara, back from her trip to the river, looked askance at the scattered flowers and the signs of her husband's incomplete morning worship.

"*Swami!*" she exclaimed, "Whose handiwork is this?"

"Those flowers are not offerings of devotion, but the outpouring of undiluted lust, Taara," Brhaspati explained. "Your maid, Punjikasthala, showered those flowers on me!"

Taara looked at him in surprised consternation. Her face shone with pity as Brhaspati narrated the events of the morning to her.

"Oh, poor Punjika!" She turned accusatory eyes on her husband. "You could have forgiven the misguided girl – surely, she does not merit such harsh treatment?"

"Taara, an impulsive curse, pronounced in the heat of anger, may be undeservedly harsh on the transgressor." He paused. "However, in this case, my curse was invoked only after deep thought and prescience." Brhaspati smiled benignly at his troubled wife.

"Prescience?" she frowned in incomprehension.

"Yes, it was foresight on my part to turn Punjika into a she-monkey. Think, Taara: in all these years, Punjika has never looked on me with anything but respectful devotion. Yet, her erotic voyeurism robbed her of her sanity and goaded her to seduce me."

He paused thoughtfully. "Sexual desire is a natural passion which springs from the depths of the heart and body – it is the sublime expression of true love. What Punjika experienced was far removed from this: it was an unnaturally incited passion which craved prohibited pleasure. It was the same desire for uninhibited carnal delight which is inherent in the simian race." He turned to Taara with a gentle smile. "Now, tell me – was I right in making Punjika a monkey? In her new form, she can enjoy the bodily pleasure she desperately craved."

"You know best the tenets of righteousness." Taara smiled back at her husband. "After all, you are the preceptor of the gods!"

The cool night breeze wafted into the open window of the bed chamber, laden with the fragrance of flowers. Taara waited for Brhaspati's return from Indra's court. He was rather late today. Well, she would soon hear the wheels of Maatali's chariot. Engrossed in her thoughts, Taara trimmed the sputtering lamp and closed the window shutters. The increased glow illuminated every corner of the room.

"Taara!"

She turned towards the door – it was Brhaspati. He brought in his wake a divine fragrance which spread across the chamber to captivate her senses.

Brhaspati remained motionless at the door, gazing at his wife standing beside the lamp. The flickering flame cast an enticing pattern of light and shadow on her dappled beauty. Her exquisite loveliness was mirrored in her flawless face. Beneath the shapely arch of her eyebrows, her eyes outdid the lamp in its radiance. Her crimson lips were parted in a wordless invitation which reached out to him in the silence.

Brhaspati's transfixed eyes hungrily drank in Taara's beauty as he walked slowly towards her. The tantalizing perfume hung about him like a thick cloud. He stopped before her and held out his hand: an exotic flower gleamed on his palm like an ornament studded with the precious *navarathnas*.

"Indra's queen, Sachidevi, sends this flower as a gift to Brhaspati's queen, Taaradevi."

Taara did not take the proffered bloom from his hand. Instead, she stooped over his palm with infinite grace and softly inhaled the exquisite fragrance of the divine flower. An enigmatic smiled played on her parted lips as she raised her head to lock eyes with Brhaspati. She deliberately turned her back on him and stood still.

As if in a trance, Brhaspati moved forward and instinctively pinned the flower to her braided hair. The blossom radiated light on her lustrous, black locks like a jeweled ornament. Now, in his turn, Brhaspati bent over the flower and sniffed its fragrant petals. He placed his hands on Taara's slender shoulders and gently turned her round to face him. Her eyes met his in glowing intensity.

"Why is the window closed, Taara?" Brhaspati asked softly.

Taara avoided his gaze.

"Why, Taara?" he insisted on an answer.

"I ... I can see him at the window ... he is peeping into our room..."

"Who? Who is he?" Brhaspati frowned in bewilderment.

"He..." After a moment's hesitation, she murmured softly, "Budha's father ..." Her words trailed away into the silence.

"Taara!" Brhaspati exclaimed.

"I cannot bear the sight ... it repels me!"

"Taara!" Brhaspati was deeply moved by his wife's open repudiation of her former lover. He drew her into the warmth of his embrace and looked down searchingly into her lovely face. "My beloved, my heart rejoices in your devotion. Any boon you desire will be yours."

Taara's eyes lighted up in surprised delight.

"Tell me, Taara: what is your heart's desire?" Brhaspati's arms tightened their hold on her.

Taara placed her soft palms on his chest and looked up into his adoring eyes. "*Swami*, bless me with a handsome, intelligent son," she whispered huskily.

"And do you think that is a boon for you alone?!" Brhaspati gave a soft chuckle. "That is a blessing to be shared by both of us!"

"*Swami* ..." The lamplight concealed her blushes.

"A son of exemplary intelligence and good looks will be born to you, Taara." Brhaspati's blessing was accompanied by a shuddering sigh of delight. Taara nestled her head in the hollow beneath his throat.

A sudden gust of wind extinguished the lamp ...

⌘

Brhaspati's boon fructified and Taara was soon pregnant.

Taara sat on the raised, earthen platform under the spreading branches of a tree in the hermitage garden, smiling contentedly. At her side was a bamboo basket, filled with fruits, edible roots and tender shoots. An expectant crowd of birds and animals, all in various stages of pregnancy, hovered before her, waiting eagerly for the tempting bounty.

Brhaspati stopped near the jostling crowd and laughed in pure enjoyment of the scene. "This is indeed a sight for sore eyes: an assembly of pregnant ladies!" His eyes twinkled in merriment. "And what is the reason for this solemn gathering, may I know?!"

"*Swami*, I just cannot comprehend how these creatures got wind of my pregnancy!" Taara shrugged her shoulders in wry bemusement. "Every morning and evening, they faithfully arrive at the hermitage to pay me a visit! So, I have decided to receive them here daily with their favourite delicacies!"

"Isn't it wonderful?!" Brhaspati exclaimed. "It does seem that they empathize with your condition and are here to wish you luck."

Taara smiled and offered a ripe berry to a parrot which hovered over her.

"This gathering warms my heart," Brhaspati said.

"It would be even better if the offspring of all the soon-to-be mothers were gathered here!" Taara laughed at him.

In due course, the hermitage teemed with fledglings, fawns and litters of rabbits. And, as if to assume the role of playmate to these tiny creatures, a son was born to Taara. With his fair complexion, wide eyes and shapely nose, the boy was the epitome of masculine beauty.

"*Swami*, see how beautiful my son is!" Taara glowed with pride.

"He takes after his beautiful mother," Brhaspati said, "and will grow up to be a handsome young man."

The *deva-guru* gently fondled his son's tiny feet, velvety-soft like pink lotus petals.

The entire company of *devas* graced the naming ceremony of their preceptor's son.

Brhaspati turned to Indra: "Mahendra, I have decided to name my son Kacha."

"So be it, master," Indra inclined his head in agreement. "Needless to say, your every decision is sure to be founded on firm reason."

Indra and his consort, Sachidevi, showered the infant with rich gifts. "Master, Kacha will surpass the *devas'* sons in handsomeness. He will thrive under your tutelage. It is my wish that you raise him to become a well-wisher of the gods and a worthy heir to their esteemed preceptor."

"So be it, Indra." Brhaspati held his arm in benediction over the king of the *devas*.

Kacha, nursed on his mother's milk, glowed with health and vigor. The hermitage echoed with the happy music of his childish laughter. The birds and animals were his constant companions and playmates.

In due course, Brhaspati, teacher par excellence, commenced his son's education ...

———

The years rolled by and Taara was once again pregnant.

"Another handsome son will soon be ours," she remarked complacently to Brhaspati.

Her husband smiled. "It is Brahma, the Creator, who ordains the particulars of every birth. We parents are but the instruments of his will."

A tiny seed of doubt took root in Taara's being at her husband's enigmatic words. Her qualms were justified at the end of nine months. She gave birth to a son at an auspicious time and day.

However, Taara shuddered at the sight of the infant: the tiny body was entirely covered with fine hair, while the wrinkled face glowed a fiery red. She covered her eyes in horror at the sight of the little tail wagging at its rear end. Taara was engulfed in sorrow. This monkey-child was a punishment imposed on her by destiny, she thought.

Brhaspati attempted to console his grieving wife. "Taara, this child is but an expression of the Supreme Lord's will. His simian form is no cause for lamentation. I assure you, he is extremely good-looking by the standards of his race." He smiled gently at her. "You are a beauty among women, dearest, while your son is a beauty among monkeys. It is patently unfair to impose one race's ideals of beauty on another race."

"Swami ..." Taara faltered.

"I see a great future ahead of your son, Taara. He is no ordinary monkey. I repeat – he is the result of God's divine will." He continued thoughtfully: "He will not remain under our care for long, but will grow up independently in the forests. He will be tall and enjoy a very long life."

"Swami, why all these elaborate details now?" Taara interrupted her husband's prophecy.

"Listen well, my dear," said Brhaspati. "I bestow on him the name, Taara: this will make your own name eternally renowned. It is ordained that your son will dedicate his considerable strength and valour to the service of Lord Vishnu at the time of the Supreme God's incarnation on earth. He will achieve undying fame." Brhaspati paused solemnly. "Taara, your son, and the son who is to be born to Punjikasthala in her monkey-form, are ordained to jointly serve Lord Vishnu in his future incarnation."

"My son is to have the honour of serving the Supreme Lord?!" A smile replaced the lines of sorrow on Taara's face.

"Yes, my dear." Brhaspati proclaimed: "I shall bestow on our son formidable strength and stature, combined with sterling mental faculties …" He paused as his elder son came rushing into the room.

Kacha peered curiously at the newborn infant and looked questioningly at his mother.

"This is your little brother, Kacha," Taara said. "His name is Taara: just like mine!"

"Oh, is this my brother?!" Kacha exclaimed in delight. "He is beautiful! Just look at his cute little face!" He turned eagerly to Taara. "Mother, when can I play with him?"

Brhaspati smiled at Taara, with an 'I-told-you-so' look in his eyes. "Kacha instantaneously appreciated the infant's beauty, which escaped even your motherly eyes. Indeed, beauty does lie in the eye of the beholder!

⁂

The little Taara grew in leaps and bounds, his prodigious physical stature and strength impressing one and all. Soon, the hermitage trees could not match the demands of his boisterous romps and exercises. The perceptive Brhaspati noted the increasing signs of restlessness and ennui evident in his younger son.

The *deva-guru* spoke to his wife: "Taara, our son finds himself cruelly stifled within the restricted confines of the hermitage. We must give him the vast spaces and open horizons required for the development of his extraordinary body and mind." His eyes rested tenderly on the monkey-child swinging on the branches of the tree above them. "It is time to let him enjoy the freedom of the dense forest."

Taara nodded in silent concord. Brhaspati summoned the young Taara and gave him the option of leaving for the forest. The monkey-child eagerly accepted the offer and prepared to set out at once.

Brhaspati, Taara and Kacha bade him a fond farewell and looked after him with misty eyes as he excitedly swung from tree to tree and set out on his own path. He soon disappeared from their view.

"Mother, when will I grow to be as tall and strong as my brother?" It was Kacha.

Taara, eyes moist at this sudden separation from her younger son, wordlessly ruffled Kacha's hair. She heaved a sigh of sorrow and turned towards the hermitage. The loss of her son, although he was a monkey, weighed heavily on her heart ...

◦◦◦◦◦◦

There was a moment's silence as Nirvikalpananda came to the end of his narrative.

"Master, is that the end of Brhaspati's story?" A vein of disappointment ran through Vimalananda's voice. "It seems rather brief!"

Nirvikalpananda smiled at his disciple's chagrined expression. "At this juncture, I have restricted my narrative to the extent required for your straightforward comprehension. It must be noted that the lives of Brhaspati, preceptor of the gods, and Usana, preceptor of the *asuras*, are intertwined to a great extent. Therefore, I will give you further information on Brihaspati when we come to Usana's story."

There was a mild reprimand in his next words. "Always bear in mind that each one of the *Navagrahas* has his own unique history. It is not the length of the narrative which matters, but the significance and glory of each."

"Your fascinating discourse compels interest, master!" exclaimed Chidananda.

"That is good to know: a worthy narrative should seamlessly combine information and appreciative interest." Nirvikalpananda smiled.

"Now, let us examine the life of Sukra, the sixth *graha*. We are aware that Usana, the son of Puloma and Bhrgu, was anointed preceptor of the *asuras*. Installed at the court of the *asura*-king, Vrshaparva, Usana was highly respected – both as the king's mentor and as the the young *rakshasas'* teacher." He paused to gather the threads of his narrative. "And now we come to the events of the day which laid the foundation for Usana's transformation into Sukra ..."

THE LIFE OF SUKRA

As he entered the *durbar* hall, Usana's keen eyes took in the dejected posture of the *asura* king on his ornate throne.

"Vrshaparva, why the dark frown upon your brow?" Usana asked. He continued proudly: "As long as I am your preceptor, there is no need for anxiety on any score. Surely you know that I, the son of Puloma, can make the impossible possible, and snatch victory from the jaws of defeat!"

"*Gurudev*, I would not dream of doubting your exemplary skills!" The *asura* king heaved a deep sigh of regret. "However, I confess that I have grave reservations regarding my own strength!"

Leaning back on his seat of honour, Usana raised his eyebrows interrogatively at Vrshaparva.

The king bent forward: "I am deeply distressed by the disparity in wealth between us and our arch rivals, the *devas*. Just think, master – Kubera, the lord of wealth himself, is Indra's treasurer!"

"So, it is the *deva's* wealth which you covet," Usana remarked thoughtfully. "That is something which can be easily set right!"

"*Gurudev*, I am surprised at your confidence: as far as I can see, the only way to redress this inequity is to declare war on the gods and impound their wealth – and that is easier said than done!" Vrshaparva gave another sigh of despair.

"Vrshaparva," Usana said. "Tell me one thing: who is richer – Indra or Kubera?"

"Kubera, of course! He is the acknowledged master of all the wealth in the universe!" the *asura* king declared emphatically.

"Now, let us consider this scenario: what if all Kubera's wealth found its way into your own treasury?" Usana's eyes gleamed. "Who then would be richer – Indra or you?"

"Master?!" Vrshaparva gasped in open-mouthed surprise.

"You would obviously be the richer of the two, Vrshaparva." Usana said matter-of-factly.

A stir of excitement ran through the assembly of *asuras*. Agog with curiosity, the *rakshasas* clustered round their enigmatically smiling preceptor.

Vrshaparva himself rose to his feet to ask: "*Gurudev*, do you suggest that we go to war against Kubera? Surely you can see that it would quickly exacerbate into a full-scale war against the combined might of the *devas*?" His voice was clouded by doubt.

"Vrshaparva, war is not the solution to every predicament!" Usana gently chided the king. "A keen intellect can render the sharpest of swords redundant."

"You are speaking in riddles today, master," Vrshaparva complained disconsolately.

Usana sat up with a proud gleam in his eyes. "Vrshaparva: my formidable yogic powers will bestow Kubera's wealth on you!" Usana smiled complacently at the excited *rakshasas*, who broke into a chorus of startled gasps and cries of bewilderment.

"Yes, Vrshaparva: Usana's incomparable mystic powers will be instrumental in depriving Kubera of his wealth." He elaborated on his nefarious scheme. "I will harness my extraordinary yogic powers to exert complete control over Kubera's mind." He chuckled mirthlessly. "Do you know what the consequence of my 'hostile takeover' will be? Kubera's body will remain his, but his mind ... his mind will be mine!"

Vrshaparva broke into delighted applause. "*Gurudev*, your scheme is a surefire winner! As always, I bow to your superior intellect!"

∞

Usana arrived at Alakaapuri, Kubera's capital, to a warm welcome from the god of wealth. Usana returned the *deva's* greeting with companionable warmth. "Kubera, although I am the preceptor of the *rakshasas*, I am always keenly aware that we are all the descendants of Lord Brahma." He smiled ingratiatingly at the *deva*. "Your own grandfather, Pulasthya, is Brahma's *maanasaputra*: as is my father, Sage Bhrgu."

Kubera was quick to acknowledge their bonds of kinship. "Yes, yes, *Acharya*," he agreed eagerly, "we are all descended from one bloodline." He paused and bowed to Usana. "Alakaapuri is blessed by your esteemed presence. Please tell me how I can be of service to you."

"An irresistible desire has brought me here, Kubera: I am possessed by the urge to irrefutably demonstrate that you and I are indeed kindred souls. I aspire to prove that Usana is Kubera ... and Kubera is Usana."

Kubera frowned in incomprehension. "I am totally at sea as to your meaning ..."

Usana was quick to reassure the bewildered *deva*: "It is very simple, Kubera – listen to me." Usana's eyes were half-lidded as he sank into a yogic trance. His voice assumed a hypnotic cadence. "Usana is Kubera ... Kubera is Usana ... Usana is Kubera ..."

Kubera's breathing stilled as he gazed into the mysterious depths of Usana's unblinking eyes. The god of wealth was mesmerized and enslaved by the awesome power of Usana's yogic skills. A strange glow slowly spread across Kubera's visage and a vacuous smile appeared on his face.

He fawned over Usana and gushed: "Oh, it is indeed true, *Acharya*! There is a strong empathy between us: I can feel the unity of our psyches! We are one and the same!"

"Yes, Kubera ... I am not Usana ... I am Kubera himself." Usana's magnetic voice continued to weave its insidious spell on the god of wealth.

"*Acharya*," Kubera's own dazed eyes were heavy-lidded. "I have a small wish to make ..."

"Tell me, Kubera." Usana's voice was exultant. He was only too aware that the hapless Kubera was completely in the thrall of his devious hypnotism. Kubera was himself only on the exterior plane: he was Usana in his innermost self!

"It is but a small wish, *Acharya*," the bewitched Kubera said plaintively. "I humbly beg you to accept my wealth: the gold, the precious *navarathnas*, the priceless *sankha* bestowed on me by Lord Brahma, the complete treasure of Padma – in short, my wealth in all its entirety!"

"How can I deny you your 'small' wish, Kubera?" Usana crooned triumphantly. "So be it!"

Usana extended his right hand, palm upwards, towards Kubera. With his left hand he offered the *deva* the sacred *kamandalam*. Kubera mechanically performed the ritualistic pouring of water, prescribed in the scriptures, which enshrined the legitimacy of a donation.

Mission accomplished, Usana rose to make his departure. "Kubera, you are indeed fortunate," he commended the god of wealth. "Your wish has come true! I will take leave of you, now."

Kubera, a pathetic smile plastered on his face, urged him: "*Acharya*, don't forget to take all my wealth with you."

"Kubera, don't worry: the moment you poured water from your palm into mine, your wealth reached the safety of my treasury."

He favoured the god of wealth with a sardonic smile and walked to the exit.

As the day drew to a close in Alaakapuri, Usana's hypnotic spell weakened and melted away into the night. The shocked Kubera realized that he had fallen prey to the *asura-guru's* formidable yogic powers. Usana's devious plan had robbed him of all his wealth. Kubera, the richest individual in the universe, was reduced to being a pauper: his fabled treasury was bare!

"*Swami!*" exhorted the furious Bhadra, Kubera's wife. "You must immediately declare war on Vrshaparva and his scheming mentor, Usana." Her voice rose in indignant righteousness. "Usana must be exposed as a blatant cheat and given the punishment he rightly deserves." She urged her husband: "You must recover the wealth!"

The chagrined Kubera shook his head. "Bhadra, that is easier said than done. Usana may be a fraud, but his formidable yogic powers cannot be bested using either intellectual or physical prowess." He continued thoughtfully. "His mystic power can only be subdued by a superior spiritual force."

"*Swami*," said Bhadra hesitantly. "If you yourself possessed such power, Usana would not have succeeded in defrauding you."

"Bhadra, in my being resides an extraordinary force which surpasses the combined yogic powers of the universe in its might!" Kubera's impassioned voice rang through his abode as he declared: "Paramashiva's grace dwells in my heart: He is my strength and refuge. I will seek his intercession."

The *asuras* erupted into boisterous celebration as Kubera's incredible wealth poured into their treasury.

Vrshaparva, exhilarated by the turn of events, heaped honours on Usana. "*Gurudev*, as the god who brought us wealth untold, it is only right that you assume command of our treasury. You are both our preceptor and treasurer!"

The *rakshasas* cheered themselves hoarse in emphatic agreement.

Usana smiled triumphantly. "Vrshaparva, my mother gave birth to me for the sole purpose of ensuring that the *asura* clan categorically surpasses the *devas* in every aspect. Now, you are richer than Indra – this brings us one step closer to achieving our objective." Usana's voice brimmed with confidence. "I will chalk out a strategy by which the war will end with our *asura* soldiers inflicting a death blow on the *devas*."

Lord Shiva's body convulsed in a paroxysm of rage as Kubera, his devoted companion, recounted the tale of Usana's perfidy. Shiva's eyes widened in fury: sparks of anger flew from the awesome Third Eye which flashed on his darkened brow.

He tossed back his fiery copper tresses and cried: "Kubera!" His shout echoed through the peaks and ravines of majestic Mount Kailash. "Usana has committed an unpardonable crime: he has abused the divine mystique of yogic power. He cannot evade punishment!"

He raised his *trishul* in a terrifying gesture of challenge and lifted his head to the skies. "Usana!"

The earth trembled at Lord Shiva's thunderous roar and the waters of the oceans frothed in agitation. Kubera cowered in awe and raised his arms in devout worship.

"Where is Usana?" The call reached out to every corner of the cosmos.

———∞∞———

Usana entered Vrshaparva's hall at the head of an adulating crowd of *asuras*, who showered him with fragrant flowers and sang his praise. He complacently reached out to accept the golden vessel of wine offered to him by the *rakshasa* king – only to freeze in sudden concentration.

The *asura-guru* raised his hand in an urgent gesture for quiet. In instant obedience, the raucous *asuras* fell silent. Usana frowned and strained to catch a distant echo. His face blanched and abject terror replaced the initial curiosity in his eyes.

"Usana! Where is Usana?"

The terrible cry, with its threat of impending doom, resounded in his being with the ominous drum-beat of Lord Shiva's *damaruka*.

Usana's voice quavered as he addressed the *asura* king. "Vrshaparva, I am the object of Lord Shiva's wrath!"

"*Gurudev!*" Vrshaparva gasped in wide-eyed alarm.

"Kubera is, apparently, a devoted companion of Lord Shiva: the god of wealth has sought Shiva's aid."

"What do we do now, *gurudev*?" Vrshaparva, gripped by terror, shuddered. "Once aroused, Rudra's wrath becomes an unstoppable tide of retribution!"

Usana abruptly came to a decision. "I must propitiate Lord Shiva in person!"

"*Gurudev*, think well before ..." Vrshaparva began cautiously.

"That is the only way to appease his anger, Vrshaparva," said Usana and disappeared.

———∞∞———

"Where is Usana?"

Usana concealed himself behind the branches of a dense thicket and peered out cautiously.

Even while standing a safe distance away from the furious Lord, the *asura-guru* shuddered at the columns of heat which blasted him.

"Where is Usana?" The thunderous query shook the heavens yet again.

Resigning himself to the impossibility of evading *Trinethra's* omniscient gaze, Usana finally mustered the courage to step forward. He stood trembling before the Lord – in an instant, the frenzied Rudra plucked him from the ground and swallowed him in one, incensed gulp.

Usana found himself whirling dizzily within the infinite dimensions of Maheswara's being. The Maharudra deliberately blocked all the nine orifices of his body, depriving Usana of any means of escape. Unable to bear the unspeakable agony of the intense heat which licked at him with tongues of fire, Usana summoned all the spiritual prowess at his command and launched himself into a passionate paean of praise to Lord Shiva.

The *asura-guru's* heart-felt plea for mercy moved Lord Shiva and, in instinctive response to Usana's devout repentance, Lord Shiva ejected him through the opening of his phallus. The shaken Usana stood cowering before Lord Shiva, who glared at him in withering contempt and unabated fury.

Fortunately for Usana, Goddess Parvati came to stand beside her spouse and said: *"Swami*, let your anger be appeased." Her dulcet tone was balm to Shiva's smoldering rage. "Usana has emerged from your genitals: this makes him my son. And so, you will agree that he is now your son too!" She placated her Lord gently. "Be merciful to him and let him live."

Lord Shiva gradually calmed down. He smiled tenderly at Parvati. "My dearest, I will fulfill your desire. As you have accepted him as your son, I will grant him manifold power."

He paused and turned to Usana. "Your passage to renewed life was through the track of my *sukram* – henceforth you will be known as Sukra."

Parvati smiled in benign satisfaction.

Usana prostrated himself before Shiva: "Lord, I am indeed blessed!"

"Sukra," the Lord reprimanded him. "You erred grievously in your lust for wealth. Kubera is ordained to be the master of wealth: it was patently wrong of you to plunder his treasury. Your ill-gotten booty will be returned to Kubera." He paused and his voice lost its harshness. "However, you did not rob Kubera for your personal gain – your selflessness on that score pleases me."

The Lord raised his hand in benediction over the bowed head of the *asura-guru*. "Sukra, I grant you a boon: those who seek wealth through your intercession will be granted their wish. You will be given the necessary wealth required for the distribution of largesse to your votaries."

Sukra gazed at Lord Shiva in adoration. *"Bhagavan,* well do I know that your anger is always tempered with compassion. That is why I did not hesitate to throw myself on your mercy." He turned to Goddess Parvati. "I am indeed blessed to have the Divine Mother of the universe as my own beloved mother!"

"Long may you live, Sukra!" Parvati smiled at him in serene benediction.

⌁⌁⌁

"Son, you are fortunate indeed!" Sage Bhrgu exclaimed in astonished delight. "You were blessed to dwell in Lord Shiva's abdomen and to emerge as his son – yet, you have retained the body we gave you at birth!" He continued solemnly. "It is your bounden duty to ensure that the name Sukra, bestowed on you by Lord Shiva, resounds with glory eternally."

"Goddess Parvati herself gave you your new life!" Puloma's heart was full as she looked at her beloved son. "May you always enjoy the grace and mercy of Lord Shiva and Parvati!"

"Mother," said the excited Vrshaparva, who had accompanied Sukra to Bhrgu's hermitage. "We share your happiness at our preceptor's good fortune." But the shadow of grief dimmed the smile on the *asura* king's face. "Unfortunately, we have lost the vast wealth our *gurudev* obtained for us from Kubera!"

"Vrshaparva," Sage Bhrgu chided, "the wealth of wisdom, which my son embodies, far surpasses the material wealth which you so fleetingly possessed. As long as Sukra is with you, you own riches beyond comparison."

"Maharshi, your words give me comfort and courage," Vrshaparva said dutifully.

⌁⌁⌁

However, the *asuras* king's cruel disappointment at the loss of Kubera's wealth was far from assuaged. He lamented to Sukra: *"Gurudev,* the wealth which was so tantalizingly ours, has disappeared!" He sighed in regret. "Our spies report that the *devas* are celebrating our loss: they revel

in their perceived sense of material and spiritual superiority." His brow
darkened in anger. "Their arrogance is hard to stomach!"

"Vrshaparva," Sukra said thoughtfully. "When the enemy is basking
in smug self-confidence – that is the right time to strike a decisive blow
against them!"

"Master, are you suggesting that we declare war on the *devas*?"

"Yes," Sukra asserted. "Complacency leads to carelessness: Indra
and his cohort are wallowing in their arrogant conviction that they are
superior to the *asuras* in physical and yogic strength. We will exploit
this pride as the fatal chink in their armour. Prepare our army – I will
determine an auspicious time to launch our offensive."

The *asura-guru* rose to his full majestic height. His stentorian
voice galvanized the attentive king. "Vrshaparva – have faith in the
incomparable power of my wisdom. Gather your forces and prepare to
march on *Swarga*!"

Bowing to Sukra's counsel, Vrshaprava went on the offensive and attacked
Swarga. To his horror, his army was decimated and scores of *rakshasas*
lost their lives. The *asura* army retreated from the battlefield to lick its
wounds. The chagrined Sukra was aware that Vrshaparva held him to
blame for the fiasco: particularly as the so-called 'auspicious' time fixed
by Sukra had in no way worked to their advantage!

"If our soldiers continue to drop like flies, it will be next to impossible
to defeat the *devas* and take over their kingdom," lamented the *asura* king.

A sudden flash of inspiration made Sukra consider Vrshaparva
thoughtfully. His brow wrinkled in deep cogitation. "What if our soldiers
did not die in this war?" Sukra's question hung in the air.

Vrshaparva stared at his preceptor in patent bewilderment.

"Think, oh king of the *asuras*!" Sukra goaded him on. "What if our
soldiers could evade death on the battlefield?"

"That is beyond the realm of possibility, *gurudev*!" Vrshaparva
humored his *guru*.

"I have told you, Vrshaparva: Sukra can make the impossible possible!"

"*Gurudev*!" the *asura* king gasped in astonishment at Sukra's blatant
conviction.

"Just think, Vrshaparva: what if *every* *asura* soldier killed by the *devas*
came back to life time and again?!"

"The dead coming back to life?!" The wide-eyed Vrshaparva was astounded. "How could such a miracle happen?" He shook his head. "Who can bestow life on the dead?"

"Mrtasanjeevani can restore the dead to life," declared Sukra triumphantly. "And I will master the science of the Mrtasanjeevani!" He was resolute. "I will propitiate Lord Shiva with my *tapas* and ask him to grant me the boon of the Mrtasanjeevani."

"*Gurudev!*" there was the faint stirring of hope in Vrshaparva's cry.

"I will obtain my parents' permission to commence my penance tomorrow itself," Sukra announced his decision.

"*Gurudev!* We *asuras* are blessed to live under the protection of your iron resolve and mental strength." Vrshaparva wondered aloud: "Mrtasanjeevani ... dead *rakshasa* soldiers brought back to life ..." He burst into an excited rhapsody of joy: "If you pull this off, *gurudev*, the goddess of victory will be permanently enshrined in our homes!"

"Vrshaparva: a word of warning," Sukra said gravely. "On no account must you resume your war against the *devas* until I return with the Mrtasanjeevani." He paused for emphasis. "Once I am master of the Mrtasanjeevani, the war the *asuras'* wage against the *devas* will be the war to end all wars!"

"Your wish is my command, *gurudev*. I assure you that we will go to war against the *devas* – that too at an auspicious time of your own choosing – only after you return armed with the mighty Mrtasanjeevani!"

Vrshaparva warmly clasped Sukra's hands in his own.

With his parents' blessings, Sukra set out for the forest to commence his *tapas*. On their part, the *asuras*, under Vrshaparva, performed the prescribed the rites to ensure the success of their preceptor's phenomenal mission.

At this juncture, Sage Narada happened to visit the *rakshasa* court. The sage commiserated with Vrshaparva on his recent defeat at the hands of the *devas*. To Narada's surprise, the *asura* king was cheerfully indifferent to past setbacks. In the course of the ensuing conversation, the sage cleverly ferreted out the news of Sukra's determination to master the Mrtasanjeevani.

Highly alarmed by the implications of Sukra's quest, Narada rushed to *Swarga* with his tidings of impending danger.

Indra blanched at the urgent warning carried by Sage Narada and turned beseechingly towards Brhaspati.

The *deva-guru's* eyes mirrored his own anxiety. "Mahendra, Sukra poses a grave threat to the *devas*," he said somberly.

"Master, if he commands the Mrtasanjeevani, it will spell doom for us: the *devas* will face certain defeat and death!" Indra was aghast at the unfortunate turn of events.

"There is no time to be lost! Do what is necessary to disrupt Sukra's penance," urged Brhaspati.

"I will dispatch the divine nymphs to shatter his concentration," said Indra eagerly. "Entrapped in the coils of romance, he will throw his quest for the Mrtasanjeevani to the winds!"

"Indra, it is you who must guard against throwing caution to the winds!" Brhaspati gently reprimanded the king of the *devas*. "Think well before you choose a plan of action."

"*Gurudev* ..." faltered Indra.

"An impetuous solution will prove counter-productive. Anyone can come forward with hasty schemes without considering their full implications." Brhaspati smiled sardonically at the bewildered Indra: "The idea of sending nymphs to seduce Sukra from the path of penance is worthy of the soldier standing guard at your door – surely Brhaspati and Mahendra can do better than that!"

"I am always ready to bow to your superior wisdom, *gurudev*!" Indra inclined his head in respect.

"What happens if we send the divine nymphs?" Brhaspati asked. "Let us assume that their irresistible charm and captivating beauty exerts its spell over Sukra and his penance is disrupted ..."

"But, master, isn't that exactly what we aim to do?!" Indra frowned in puzzlement.

"Yes, Indra: but this tactic would only gain us temporary respite – it would not prevent Sukra from resuming his *tapas*!" He paused meaningfully. "What we need is a permanent solution."

"What do you suggest, master?"

"Let us send your daughter, Jayanthi, to Sukra."

"*Gurudev*!" Indra was aghast at this proposal.

"Listen to me, Indra – this would solve many of our problems at one go." Brhaspati elaborated on his argument. "Jayanthi is an exquisitely beautiful girl. If Sukra succumbs to her charms and accepts her as his wife, what will happen?"

"What will happen?" Indra was at a loss. "Enlighten me, master," he said.

"Sukra will be your son-in-law – and, of course, a son-in-law will obviously be obliged to support his father-in-law!"

"What a deliciously devious plan, *gurudev*! Our foe will become our natural ally!" Indra was rapturous. But, there was a niggling doubt in his mind. "Master, what if Sukra does not agree to marry Jayanthi?"

"Then we lose nothing: Jayanthi will merely have accomplished the task you intended to assign to the nymphs!" Brihaspati smiled confidently. "Mahendra, I assure you that Sukra will marry Jayanthi. And, once they are abandoned by Sukra, the *asuras* will be orphans, to all intents and purposes!"

"I will send Jayanthi to Sukra at once!" There was a palpable excitement in Indra's words.

"On no account must Sukra, the *rakshasas'* evil genius, complete his penance!"

Her father's urgent words echoed in Jayanthi's ears. "Your mission to disrupt his *tapas* is crucial to the very survival of the *deva* clan: you must succeed at any cost!"

Jayanthi stood at a distance, transfixed by the beauty of the youth seated in meditation under the spreading branches of a tree. Her lips parted in an involuntary smile of admiration.

'It is obvious that my father has never set eyes on Sukra,' she thought, 'he would never think to use the adjective 'evil' to describe such a handsome man!'

She drank in his beauty: A comely face, enhanced by a glowing complexion ... broad chest ... rounded shoulders ... long hands. She was irresistibly drawn to the magnetism of the wide eyes, half-hidden by the heavy eyelids, and emphatically framed by the arch of thick eyebrows above.

'Even the heavens cannot boast of such handsomeness!' she thought. Then, she shook her head to clear her mind and recalled Indra's grave exhortation: "My dear, keep this in mind – if that wicked man succeeds in obtaining the Mrtasanjeevani, we will all be in dire peril." Her father had continued emphatically: "Exploit your beauty and charm to seduce him. I give you complete freedom to exercise your ingenuity: either make him your husband or ensure that he becomes a depraved voluptuary. Use your discretion – just do whatever is necessary to disrupt his *tapas* – Sukra must not obtain the Mrtasanjeevani!"

'Seduce him ... make him your husband ... ensure that he becomes a depraved voluptuary ... Sukra must not obtain the Mrtasanjeevani ...'

Indra's injunctions grated harshly on her ears and Jayanthi impatiently banished them from her mind. Her feet instinctively made their way towards Sukra. Her eyes hungrily roved over him like caressing hands. He radiated youthful vigor. His single-minded concentration mirrored his iron resolve. Drops of perspiration, like tiny dew-drenched blossoms, covered his body.

Jayanthi heaved a shuddering sigh and surrendered to the spell of Sukra's magnetism. 'Well,' she thought, with a defiant shrug of her shoulder, 'my father has given me 'complete freedom' in this situation.'

Jayanthi made her choice: she decided to accept Sukra as her husband. However, she would not be instrumental in disrupting his penance. On the contrary, she would do everything in her power to ensure that he mastered the Mrtasanjeevani. What a coup that would be for her would-be spouse!

Having resolved on her course of action, Indra's daughter dismissed all thoughts of her father, and his commands, from her mind. She bent tenderly over Sukra, holding up the edge of her *saree* to gently fan his perspiring body. But Jayanthi abruptly realized her error: the fluttering of her garment was definitely a seductive distraction! It was service that Sukra required from her – not sensuous temptation!

She quickly dropped her *saree* and looked searchingly about the place: the swaying fronds of a banana tree caught her attention. She eagerly ran to pick two long leaves and hurried back to her station. She held one wide frond over Sukra's head, as a shield from the heat of the glaring sun, while the other leaf became an improvised fan with which she sent a cool breeze his way.

Sukra remained serenely immersed in his *tapas*, oblivious to the devoted ministrations which eased his path.

Every morning, Jayanthi swept clean the ground round the meditating youth; she then sprinkled the bare earth with water from a nearby mountain stream and made it her canvas for the auspicious designs which she drew using pollen gathered painstakingly from multi-hued flowers. Collecting pure water in a cup fashioned from a lotus leaf, Jayanthi dipped the edge of ·her *saree in* it and sponged Sukra's body. She faithfully gathered a pile of fresh fruits and edible roots, in the slim hope that he would remember to take some nourishment for his body. At nightfall, she slept on the bare ground before him, pillowing her head in her hands.

The days passed: Sukra remained immersed in his penance, while Jayanthi continued to lavish her devoted service on him. They were united in their single-mindedness of purpose: Sukra's sole objective was his *tapas*; Jayanthi's only goal was unswerving devotion to Sukra.

"*Swami!*" Sachidevi's call to her husband reflected her anxiety. "Do you realize that it is quite a long while since Jayanthi left on her mission?"

"*Devi*," Indra replied with a wry smile, "I can give you the exact duration of our daughter's absence – right down to the last minute!"

"I am worried about Jayanthi ..."

Indra gently interrupted his wife. "Jayanthi will be back, my dear." He paused and frowned. "I was confident when I sent her to disrupt Sukra's penance in the place of the *apsaras*. However, I must confess that this inordinate delay worries me too." Indra consoled Sachidevi. "I have summoned *Acharya* Brhaspati. He will discern the reason for the delay with his yogic power."

"Mahendra!" Brhaspati entered Indra's private chamber.

"*Pranam, gurudev!*" Indra respectfully rose to his feet and welcomed his preceptor.

Without preamble, the worried king of the *devas* rushed into the reason for his summons. "Master, time flies by, but Jayanthi is yet to return. Sachi is anxious about her. I would like to know whether our daughter has accomplished her mission or ..." his voice faltered, "has she met with some unknown danger?"

Brhaspati seated himself and smiled comfortingly at the parents. "Rest assured that Jayanthi will return – whether victorious or vanquished! Defeat is the only danger she faces." He continued reasonably. "As we all know, Sukra is no ordinary ascetic: he is possessed of such power that he emerged alive from Lord Shiva's stomach! Breaking such a renowned mystic's concentration is no easy task: it requires time and patience."

Sachidevi fretfully shrugged aside this explanation. "All this is irrelevant to me, *gurudev* ... I am extremely anxious about my little daughter." She gave her husband a rather accusatory glance. "This task should have been assigned to the nymphs – not to Jayanthi!"

"Indrani," Brhaspati placated the distraught mother, "have courage. Let us not underestimate Jayanthi's ingenuity and pluck."

He turned to the king of the *devas*. "Mahendra, let us put aside the matter of Sukra and Jayanthi for a while and direct our attention to the *asuras* – without Sukra to bolster their confidence with his guidance, they are as vulnerable as they will ever be! This is the right time to mount an attack on the *rakshasas*."

Indra nodded thoughtfully in agreement.

"The *asura* army is demoralized and weak at present: I will determine the auspicious day and time to declare war!" Brhaspati was categorical in his stand.

A worried Vrshaparva mulled over Sukra's continued absence, with his ministers adding their voices of concern to his anxiety.

Their somber deliberation was interrupted by the abrupt arrival of a breathless *asura* spy who saluted the king hastily before bursting out with his momentous report: "Oh king, the gods are making preparations to declare war on us. They only await Brhaspati's decision as to the auspicious time in which to launch their attack!"

Vrshaparva's court erupted into a chaos of excited voices and loud arguments.

One of the agitated ministers shouted: "Yet another example of those ruthless *devas'* guile! The accursed Indra is deliberately taking advantage of our *gurudev's* absence!"

Another minister inserted a note of caution: "Let us not forget that our *gurudev* emphatically warned us not to wage war against the gods in his absence ..."

The spy broke in with his warning: "My lord, we need not wage war on them – they will attack us in any case!"

Vrshaparva called for order. An expectant hush enveloped the hall as the *asuras* turned to their king for his decision. "Our master advised us not to wage war on the gods." He paused meaningfully. "However, he did not give us any standing instructions regarding self-defence – he did not counsel us to refrain from retaliation in the face of an unprovoked attack."

His voice rose in exhortation to his cohorts. "Self-defence is a must for survival! Let us show these gods what we are made of! Make preparations for war!"

⚬⚬⚬

The *asura* forces met the attacking *deva* army head-on and halted their advance. A colossal battle ensued. True to Sukra's dire prediction, the *devas* set on the hapless *rakshasas* and subjected them to wholesale slaughter. The *asura*'s woeful lack of combat strategy, in the absence of their preceptor, was pitifully evident. Vrshaparva was caught on the horns of a painful dilemma: to stand firm was to court certain defeat … to retreat was to invite pursuit and complete rout. In either case, destruction and death stared him in the face!

In a last resort to save his army from complete annihilation, the *rakshasa* king rushed to Sage Bhrgu's hermitage. Vrshaparva explained the dire predicament of the *asura* forces in their son, Sukra's, absence. Lamenting that his soldiers were dying like flies, the king beseeched Bhrgu and Puloma to come to their aid. Arriving on the battlefield with Bhrgu's permission, Puloma used the awesome power of her chastity to immobilize the *deva* army. The exultant *rakshasas* then fell upon the helpless gods and slaughtered them with impunity.

Indra was enraged by the massacre of the *devas* in their frozen trances. On Brhaspati's advice, the king of the gods rushed to Lord Vishnu and pleaded for his intercession. Sri Mahavishnu appeared instantaneously on the field of battle. Vishnu immediately perceived that the *devas* would remain locked in their trance-like state until Puloma was neutralized – and the only way to nullify her formidable power was to kill her. Left with no other alternative, Lord Vishnu let fly his discus, *Sudarsana*, and severed Puloma's head. At the instant of her death, the gods regained their mobility and resumed their battle with the *asuras*.

Vrshaparva rushed to Bhrgu's hermitage with the tragic news of Puloma's death at Lord Vishnu's hands. The enraged sage stormed to the war field. He tenderly joined his wife's severed head to her trunk. Drawing upon the powers accumulated through years of rigorous penance, Bhrgu restored Puloma to life. Puloma touched her husband's feet reverentially and stood before him, whole.

Sage Bhrgu now turned to the astounded Vishnu and burst out in fury: "You beheaded my wife without paying her the respect due to her sex: you have committed the unpardonable sin of killing a woman!" The sage's voice crescendoed: "I will not let you evade justice! This is my curse: you will be born on earth as a mortal and will endure the agony of pain, separation and grief!"

Bhrgu's curse banished the *devas'* euphoria regarding their upper hand in the ongoing battle with the *asuras*. Indra quickly realized the impossibility of their winning the war and wisely sounded the retreat.

Vrshaparva prostrated himself at the feet of Puloma and Bhrgu and expressed his deep gratitude to them for the *asuras'* deliverance.

"Indra will not dare to attack the *asuras* in the near future!" Puloma counselled the *rakshasa* king. "Use this intervening time to strengthen your army and await our son's return with the Mrtasanjeevani."

Jayanthi awoke with a start: had someone disturbed her sleep? She turned on her side and looked at Sukra – he remained immersed in his penance, oblivious to hunger and thirst as usual. She wondered how long his *tapas* would continue: however long it was, she was determined to persevere in her devoted service.

As the first flush of dawn streaked the sky, heralding the sunrise, Jayanthi rose. Again, her gaze was drawn irresistibly towards Sukra. In her adoring eyes, the radiance emanating from his penance surpassed the sun's brilliance.

Jayanthi made her way to the gurgling mountain stream. She smiled in pleasure at the thought of the familiar, daily routine which stretched before her: sprinkling water on the ground round Sukra, drawing the auspicious patterns with flower pollen, shading him from the glaring sun, fanning with banana fronds …. Jayanthi contentedly entered the cool water for her bath.

Suddenly, a distinctive sound broke the silence of the tranquil forest – it was the drum-beat of Lord Shiva's *damaruka*. Sukra's inert body instinctively throbbed in rhythm with its mesmerizing cadence and his long-unmoving eyelids fluttered.

The insistent beat of the *damaruka* faded into divine silence ...

"Sukra!" The resonant call penetrated his psyche like a drum-roll of thunder. Sukra emerged from the depths of his penance and opened his eyes.

"Sukra, my son!" The voice brimmed with affection.

Lord Shiva stood before Sukra's delighted eyes. The *asura-guru* prostrated himself before the Lord whose face was wreathed in a radiant smile.

"Sukra, I am here in response to your penance," Lord Shiva declared. "Tell me what you desire."

Sukra stood before the Lord with hands folded in reverence. "*Bhagavan!*" Eyes overflowing with tears of joy, he gazed adoringly at his favourite god. "Grant me the gift of the Mrtasanjeevani."

"So be it, Sukra!" Shiva smiled magnanimously and beckoned him close. "Come: I will impart to you the Mrtasanjeevani *mantra*."

Sukra obediently approached Shiva – hands folded in respect, he closed his eyes in devotion and inclined his right ear towards the Lord. A tidal wave of immense mystic power poured into Sukra's being, as an awesome silence enveloped his heart and soul with a fullness of extraordinary significance.

"My son," Shiva said, "the divine Mrtasanjeevani is now yours to command. I charge you – ensure that its secret remains undisclosed to womankind." The Lord raised his hand in magnanimous benediction and said, "May you prosper!" before he disappeared.

Sukra stood frozen in awe, overwhelmed with gratitude towards Lord Shiva for his unstinting munificence.

⤜⤛

Emerging from his trance, Sukra looked about him in amazement. He took in the well-tended ground, decorated with glowing designs executed with the pollen of multi-hued blossoms. He frowned in puzzlement. Whose handiwork was this? The smoothened earth was obviously the result of long months of labor. Had someone been serving him during his *tapas*? His curiosity was aroused – who was this mysterious person and what could be the reason for this evident devotion?

As if in answer to his question, the dulcet tinkling of anklets reached his ears. Sukra turned in the direction of the sound. A narrow footpath lay

before him – someone had beaten a rough track through the wild brush
with their constant passage to-and-fro in that direction. The sweet music
of the anklets grew louder and then came to an abrupt halt!

Sukra gazed in startled surprise at the figure which stood before him
– it was a beautiful maiden! Her dripping clothes indicated that she was
returning from a bath in the nearby stream. Her damp body glowed like
flame behind a curtain of snow. The green creeper twisted about the
tree beside her lost its sheen, and looked desiccated, beside the glowing
freshness of her exquisitely lovely, lissome body. Dark hair rippled down
to her knees in lustrous waves, from whose ends sparkling dewdrops of
water dripped to the ground. Her elongated eyes seemed to reach to her
ears in soft caress, their dark irises darting to and fro like startled fish.
Those wide, fearless eyes held Sukra's own in an outpouring of desire and
devotion. She held a lotus-leaf cup in her hands.

Sukra was mesmerized by this lovely apparition and irresistibly drawn
to her. Her incomparable beauty bound him with invisible, unbreakable
chains. 'This is no ordinary beauty,' he thought, 'there is a divinity in her
charm! Who can she be?'

The jingle of her anklets was the only answer to his unspoken question
as she walked towards him with the graceful glide of a swan, her voluptuous
hips swaying to the even rhythm of her gait. The anklets grew silent and
she stood before Sukra. A sudden flush spread over her damask cheeks
and she lowered her gaze in self-conscious embarrassment. Abruptly, she
stooped and gently poured the water from her lotus-leaf cup over his feet:
in a poignant gesture of reverence, she dipped the slender fingers of her
right hand into the water which had bathed his feet and sprinkled it over
her own head. She slowly rose to her feet and met his eyes.

"Who are you?" the astounded Sukra asked.

Her full lips, glistening with the deep-red of ripe ivy gourds, parted
to reveal sparkling-white teeth shaped like fleshy pomegranate seeds.
"Jayanthi ..." her voice was a whisper.

Sukra raised his eyebrows in interrogation.

"Indra is my father," she revealed, "and Sachidevi is my mother."

Sukra's mouth fell open at her words. "Indra's daughter!" he gasped.

"Yes," she asserted. "My father sent me to disrupt your penance ....
but, from the very moment of our first encounter, my heart and body
melted and merged into one entity of immeasurable love for you. I have
dedicated myself, heart and soul, to your service for all eternity." She
gazed adoringly at him.

"With or without my conscious volition, I have been the recipient of your devoted care – this makes me indebted to you. What boon do you want from me, Jayanthi?" There was an underlying note of triumph in Sukra's words. After all, the daughter of Indra himself was offering her services to him! It was a coup indeed for the *rakshasas*!

"I have openly declared my love for you," replied Jayanthi. She gazed into his eyes. "Accept me as your devoted wife."

Sukra looked at her in silence. His thoughts were in a whirl as he worked out the possibilities and choices before him. He was Puloma's son – he was the preceptor of the *asuras*! He lived by his own rules and principles. It was impossible for him to accept Jayanthi as his wife: nor was it possible for him to deny her the boon he had promised.

'No!' he thought to himself, 'I will not go back on my word!'

Sukra, past-master at stratagem, and determined contender against all odds, had fashioned certain guiding principles to help him through trying, unavoidable circumstances – his 'Sukra Neethi,' or Sukra's moral code of conduct. He now cleverly resorted to this unique code to resolve his present dilemma: he would accept Jayanthi as his companion – not as his wife!

Sukra smiled at Jayanthi and said, "I cannot accept you as my wife ... however, I am willing to make you my companion. I assure you that this position is, for all practical purposes, in no way inferior to that of a lawfully wedded wife."

"*Swami* ..." Jayanthi said hesitantly.

"If you accept my proposal," Sukra continued persuasively, "we will live together happily as husband and wife for ten years. During this decade, we will live a private life which will be completely invisible to both *devas* and *rakshasas*." Sukra locked eyes with Jayanthi. "Are you willing to be my companion?" he asked.

Jayanthi's own eyes melted in adoration. "It was my deep love for you which made me serve you and pray for the fulfillment of your penance." She sighed and continued. "I was confident that you would accept me as your wife. But, now ...." She remained silent for a moment. Then, Jayanthi lifted her chin and straightened her shoulders in resolve. "As I am completely enamored with you, I cannot turn down your offer." She blushed and held out her hands to him. "Please ... take me!"

Sukra smiled triumphantly. He nodded to Jayanthi and opened his arms wide in invitation. Like a vigorous river running to meet the ocean for the first time, Jayanthi rushed into Sukra's arms and encircled his neck with her clinging hands. Her wet clothes fanned the flames of passion in Sukra's hot body. He drew her even closer into his tight embrace.

In the next instant, Sukra and Jayanthi merged into one single entity and were lost to the view of all eyes.

"Mahendra!" Brhaspati emerged from his mystic trance to address the king of the *devas*. "Your daughter, Jayanthi, has apparently succeeded in her mission! I saw her merge into Sukra's embrace before they both disappeared. For ten long years, as they pursue their conjugal life, they will remain invisible to everyone. Using my mind's eye, this is the only glimpse I could catch of her."

"*Gurudev*, does this mean that Sukra's penance was disrupted?" Indra asked eagerly.

"I think we can safely assume that, Mahendra," Brhaspati nodded thoughtfully. "If Jayanthi had not succeeded in her mission to seduce him, obviously Sukra would not have accepted her." He smiled complacently. "I think we can afford to relax now."

"*Gurudev*, what does this portend for my daughter's future?" Sachidevi asked anxiously.

"It is certain that Sukra has accepted your daughter: I saw them disappear together with my own eyes." He reassured the mother. "Sukra is an ethical intellectual: he will undoubtedly ensure your daughter's happiness as his consort."

Brihaspati paused to reflect. "Sukra is well aware that the *asuras* would on no account be able to digest the news of their preceptor's marriage to the daughter of their arch enemy, Indra. As far as I can surmise, this is the reason for Sukra's decade-long voluntary disappearance. He hopes to delude the *asuras* into believing that he continues to perform his penance to obtain the Mrtasanjeevani."

Brhaspati's logical explanation placated Indra. The king of the *devas* turned to his wife with a confident smile. "Sachi, my dear, don't worry: your clever daughter will bring Sukra to you as your son-in-law!"

Sachi, her fears dispelled, smiled back at her husband and made her departure. Indra turned to address Brhaspati, but held his tongue on seeing the *deva-guru* deep in a reverie.

After a few moments of profound thought, Brhaspati said: "Mahendra, Sukra and Jayanthi will remain invisible for a period of ten years. Think of the implications!" His excitement was palpable. "For one, long decade, the *rakshasas* will languish without their preceptor's guidance. They will be particularly vulnerable during this period. We must exploit this situation to our advantage." Brhaspati gave Indra a meaningful look.

"Shall we declare war on them again, *gurudev*?" Indra asked eagerly.

Brhaspati smiled wryly. "Mahendra, it has already been categorically proved that we cannot defeat the *asuras*, even in Sukra's absence. Sri Mahavishnu will be unable to help us as long as Sage Bhrgu and Puloma are ready to extend their aid to the *rakshasas*."

"You are right ... I forgot the existing circumstances in the heat of excitement."

"It is not a battle of weapons which we will wage against the mentor-less *asuras* ..." Brhaspati's voice exuded confidence. "It will be a battle of wits!

"What does that mean, *gurudev*?" the bewildered Indra frowned.

"We are aware that Sukra has been indoctrinating the *asuras* with his creed of hatred towards the *devas*. The time is now ripe to counteract his teachings," Brhaspati said complacently.

"And how do you suggest we go about that, *gurudev*?" Indra asked.

"During Sukra's absence, we shall ensure that the *asuras* receive a new course of instruction!" Brhaspati chuckled softly. "We shall inculcate in them the belief that the *devas* excel the *asuras* in all aspects: morally, intellectually and physically. We will make them accept that it is only right to acknowledge the inherent superiority of the gods and resign themselves to respecting and serving them. We will convince them that it is unconscionable to even consider waging war on the gods." Brhaspati's eyes gleamed in anticipation. "We will indoctrinate them systematically ... they will be conditioned to accept their subservience. We will instill in them mandatory loyalty towards us!"

"Your idea is incredible, *gurudev*." Indra paused doubtfully. "But will they submit to our persuasion?"

"Mahendra, it will not be Brhaspati or Indra who educates them – their instructor will be none other than Sukra himself."

"Sukra?!" Indra gasped in open-mouthed surprise.

"Yes, Indra, Sukra himself." Brhaspati's eyes twinkled. "Brhaspati, as Sukra himself – I will be his double!"

"You will be Sukra?!" Indra remained clueless.

"It is pure sorcery, Indra: look!" To Indra's astonishment, Brhaspati vanished from the room. In his place Sukra reclined on the couch.

The startled king of the gods jumped up and stared at his companion in awe.

"This is my plan, Mahendra," Brhaspati explained. "I intend to join Vrshaparva's court by impersonating Sukra. In the coming decade of Sukra's absence, I will indoctrinate the *asuras* and convert them into willing servants of the gods." Brhaspati's tones echoed confidently in the chamber.

"*Gurudev*, your plan is magnificent!" Indra exclaimed. "But, what if Vrshaparva, trusting in your mastery of the Mrtasanjeevani, compels you to devise an offensive against the *devas*?" Indra frowned as he voiced his doubt.

Brhaspati, in Sukra's guise, laughed out loud. "Simple, Mahendra – I will assure the *asura* king that I have received the *mantra* from Lord Shiva. I will also tell him that, in order to achieve complete mastery over the *mantra,* and make it truly effective, I need many years of practice in its deployment." He smiled. "Of course, I will impress upon the *rakshasas* that this is Lord Shiva's immutable will!"

He turned briskly to Indra. "Mahendra, leave everything to me. Rest assured that, in the near future, the *asuras* will be your loyal servants and their preceptor will be your obedient son-in- law!"

"I salute your unparalleled intellect, *gurudev!*" Indra paused in sudden consternation and exclaimed: "But, what about your voice?!"

"I will first visit my parents and bring them up to date on the developments regarding the Mrtasanjeevani. After receiving their blessings, I will proceed to Vrshaparva's court." Brhaspati's voice was now a perfect imitation of Sukra's authoritarian tone.

Indra guffawed in admiration.

The unsuspecting Vrshaparva welcomed the imposter with open arms. The entire company of *asuras* rose and bowed to the false Sukra.

"Sukra!" "Sukra!" "Sukra!" The exultant cry echoed through the halls and corridors of the *rakshasa* court.

The *asura* king gave the imposter the highest seat of honour in the *durbar* and reverentially washed his feet. Each of the *asuras* present came forward in turn to dip their hands into the bowl containing the used water and sprinkled it over their own heads.

"*Gurudev!*" exclaimed the joyous Vrshaparva. "You have returned

triumphantly from your penance. We are indeed fortunate: death has lost
its hold over the *asura* clan!"

The court erupted in raucous celebration.

The imposter rose to his feet and signaled for silence. "Yes, Lord
Paramashiva has lavished his blessings on your *guru*." He smiled
triumphantly. "He has bestowed on me the Mrtasanjeevani *mantra*!"

Wild cheers and applause greeted his words.

He waited for silence to be restored and continued: "However,
Paramashiva has also given me clear strictures on its use." He paused to
look gravely at his attentive audience. "Unless the *mantra* is first practiced
the prescribed number of times, it will lose its efficacy: I will be unable
to restore the dead to life."

A murmur of alarm ran through the assembly.

The false Sukra continued: "Lord Shiva himself has ordained that the
mantra must be practiced uninterruptedly for ten years before it is put to
use: only then will it be purified and prove effective."

Gasps of surprise, mingled with cries of disappointment, greeted his
words.

"Ten years!" Vrshaparva was aghast. "*Gurudev*, this means we cannot
fight the gods for a decade!"

"Do not be disappointed, Vrshaparva," the imposter placated the *asura*
king. "Patience has its own reward. When we do fight the *devas*, I will be
able to keep death away from our people."

"But .... Ten years! ... *Gurudev* ... to wait for ten years!"

"Vrshaparva, ten years is not too long: it will pass in the blink of an
eye!" The false Sukra smiled enigmatically. "And, I assure you, we will put
that decade to good use: I have a special course of instruction planned
for our clan."

As the imposter assured Vrshaparva, the ten years did pass: not in a flash,
but at their own plodding pace.

Meanwhile, the real Sukra had enjoyed the pleasure of Jayanthi's
companionship to the full and was ready to return to his old life. Jayanthi,
torn apart by the anguish of her separation from her beloved Sukra, wept
like a child. Sukra comforted her as best he could and gently sent her on
her way to Amaravati, Indra's capital.

Sukra then made his own way to Vrshaparva's court.

⚬≈≈⚬

The *durbar* hall was filled to capacity with *rakshasas*. The false Sukra was ensconced in his customary place of honour on the dais.

"Gurudev," Vrshaparva respectfully drew his preceptor's attention to the passage of the years. "Our decade of waiting is over at last. Are you now ready to deploy the power of the Mrtasanjeevani in our defense?"

Before the imposter could respond, a sudden commotion at the entrance caught the court's attention – Sukra strode into the hall, *kamandalam* in hand. The assembly of *asuras* froze in amazement at the unbelievable apparition. There was pin-drop silence in the court.

Sukra stood before Vrshaparva, glaring at the imposter.

The *asura* king, in his turn, turned to address the false Sukra seated beside him. "Gurudev, who is this interloper?"

"Vrshaparva!" thundered the real Sukra. "Do you not recognize me, your own preceptor?"

"He appears to be an imposter, Vrshaparva," the false Sukra gravely replied.

"Imposter?! Me?!" exclaimed Sukra. "Whoever you are, be assured that I see through your disguise. I will soon deduce the nefarious motive behind your impersonation!"

The furious Vrshaparva intervened and shouted: "You – shut your insolent mouth! How dare you cast doubts on our revered *gurudev*! Do you know that he has obtained the priceless boon of the Mrtasanjeevani from Lord Shiva himself? Stop your nonsensical blathering at once: your tricks will not work here!"

"What?!" gasped Sukra. "This imposter claims to have mastered the Mrtasanjeevani?! Do not fall for his lies, Vrshaparva! Whoever he is, he is misleading the *asura* clan for his own sinister purpose. Hear me: I am Sukra, the son of Sage Bhrgu and Puloma."

Vrshaparva had had enough of this. "Soldiers!" the irate *asura* king commanded. "Throw this imposter out of the court and exile him from our kingdom." He turned to Sukra. "As you are in the guise of our *gurudev*, I will spare your lowly life – this is but a mark of the great respect in which we hold our master."

The imposter seated beside him nodded in head in benign appreciation of Vrshaparva's orders.

Four *rakshasa* soldiers approached Sukra threateningly.

"Stop right there!" roared Sukra. "It was I who mentored you – it was for your benefit that I underwent the rigour of *tapas* and obtained the Mrtasanjeevani. And now, you dare to insult me and question my credentials." His voice rose ominously. "This is my curse on the *asura* clan: you will lose wars for all eternity!"

Sukra's furious voice reverberated through the hall as he stomped out of the court.

⌘

"The decade has passed," Brhaspati was back in Amaravati to meet Indra. "Sukra has returned!"

"Jayanthi has also returned, *gurudev!*" Indra interrupted him excitedly. "However, Sukra has obtained the Mrtasanjeevani!" His face was crestfallen. "My daughter fell under the spell of his personality: she made him her lover but failed to disrupt his penance."

"Mahendra, Sukra made his appearance at Vrshaparva's court. Fortunately, the *asuras* continued to believe that I was their true preceptor. Vrshaparva accused Sukra of being an imposter and banished him from the kingdom." He continued thoughtfully. "However, once Vrshaparva calls upon me to implement the Mrtasanjeevani, I will be exposed as the real imposter."

"You will be in grave danger, master! What do we do now?" asked the alarmed Indra.

"Mahendra, I have already done what needs to be done." Brhaspati smiled complacently. Indra looked questioningly at his preceptor.

"I have discarded the guise of Sukra for good," laughed Brhaspati. "I will not enter the *asura* kingdom again!"

⌘

As the glaring absence of their supposed preceptor extended into days, Vrshaparva suspected that something was wrong. Gradually it dawned on the *asura* king that he had been the victim of a hoax: the imposter had mentored them to look up to the *devas!* The *rakshasas* were deeply ashamed of their gullibility: they had been fooled by the imposter for ten long years and had readily swallowed the pro-*deva* propaganda he had dispensed in the name of education! They broke into cries of self-recrimination for their foolish rejection of their real *guru*.

Vrshaparva cringed at the recollection of his harsh treatment of Sukra. He called an urgent council and decided to lead a delegation to beg Sukra's forgiveness and plead for his return.

On their arrival at Sage Bhrgu's hermitage, the incensed Sukra harshly reprimanded Vrshaparva and his entourage of eminent *asuras*. However, Bhrgu and Puloma interceded and pacified their son.

Puloma reminded Sukra: "Son, these are tricks played by the gods. It is the *devas* at whom you should direct your anger. Remember, they instigated Sri Mahavishnu himself to behead me."

"*Gurudev*, we beg your forgiveness for our sins of ignorance," Vrshaparva pleaded in abject repentance. "We are sorely in need of your guidance, as we plan our vengeance on the gods who were the cause of your mother's beheading." The *asura* king humbly bowed before Sukra. "Master, please accept your position as our preceptor once more and revoke your curse."

The placated Sukra nodded in assent.

⁕

Nirvikalpananda paused and smiled at his entranced disciples. "And that is the story of Sukra. How was it? Did you enjoy listening to it?"

"Oh yes, master!" exclaimed Shivananda. "It was non-stop excitement from start to finish!"

"Master!" Sadananda chimed in agreement. "What fascinating twists and turns – it was absolutely enthralling!"

"There is more to come," Nirvikalpananda assured them. "Sukra's life is filled with extraordinary developments and thrilling events: undoubtedly, you will continue to be fascinated by the coming segments!"

"Master, Sukra sends Jayanthi away at the end of their ten years of companionship – whom does he marry?" asked the curious Chidananda.

"Sukra married a young woman, Urjaswathi, the daughter of Priyavratha and Suroopa. By her, Sukra had two daughters, Devayaani and Araja, and four sons. Once his sons attained the appropriate ages, Sukra appointed them the officiating priests of the *rakshasa* clan."

He paused to survey his attentive disciples. "Sukra's daughter, Araja, demonstrated a philosophical bent of mind right from childhood. Once she attained womanhood, in accordance with her inclination, her parents granted her permission to engage in penance in the nearby forest. This forest belonged to the realm of King Danda, son of Ikshwaaku.

"One day, King Danda, while on a hunting expedition, happened to come across Araja, engaged in solitary meditation. Unable to resist the allure of her beauty, the wicked king fell on the young girl and molested her. The outraged Araja cried out to her father. Hearing his daughter's distressed call for help, Sukra rushed to the spot and heard the account of her tragic defilement.

"Incensed by Danda's crime, Sukra pronounced a horrible curse: within five days, a rain of fire would completely destroy Danda's kingdom, which would later be transformed into a dense forest. Sukra's curse came to pass: an incessant shower of flame rained down on Danda's realm – the conflagration reduced the kingdom to ashes. In the course of time, a dense forest rose from the ruins and was given the name Dhandakaaranya – derived from 'Danda.'"

"So, it was Sukra who was instrumental in the rise of the Dhandaka forest!" exclaimed Sadananda.

"Yes," said the master, "Sukra was a formidable personality who could bestow boons, and pronounce curses, to great effect. I will now tell you how he put the Mrtasanjeevani *mantra* to use."

Nirvikalpananda picked up the threads of his narrative once more.

"Sukra burnt with the desire to avenge his mother's beheading by Lord Vishnu, at the goading of the *devas*. Confident in the power of the Mrtasanjeevani, he constantly incited the *asuras* to wage war on the gods. Sukra immediately restored to life the *asuras* who perished in battle. The *asura* army was now, for all intents and purposes, invincible. The gleeful *rakshasas,* immune to death, attacked the gods without provocation: war had become a sport to them.

"The *devas* were alarmed at the state of affairs. Indra and Brhaspati contemplated their next move...."

⌘

"*Gurudev,*" Indra's voice was grave. "At this rate, we cannot hold out much longer against the demons – we are helpless in the face of their triumph over death."

"The Mrtasanjeevani is the cause of our sorry plight," Brhaspati sighed. "Our numbers are steadily declining."

Indra echoed his preceptor's sigh. "You are right, *gurudev*. Please show us a way out of this predicament. How can we counteract the Mrtasanjeevani?"

"Mahendra, it is impossible to counteract the effects of the Mrtasanjeevani," Brhaspati emphasized. "It is a blessing from Lord Shiva himself: there is no antidote for it!"

"Then we have no choice but to surrender the kingdom of *Swarga* to the *rakshasas* and go into voluntary exile in the dense forests!" Indra lamented in despair.

"Every disease has its remedy: likewise, every problem has a solution." Brhaspati reprimanded him gently. "It is up to us to use the power of our intellects to find one."

"I implore you, find a way out of this peril!"

Brhaspati said thoughtfully. "There is only one way out: we must acquire the Mrtasanjeevani *mantra* for ourselves."

"Acquire the Mrtasanjeevani?!" Indra was wide-eyed in wonder. "That would make any future war a sword for a sword and a mace for a mace!"

"Exactly: a stalemate! Wonderful thought!" Brhaspati smiled in agreement.

"Sukra obtained the Mrtasanjeevani from Lord Shiva through rigorous penance." Indra said excitedly. "Now, you will emulate Sukra and achieve mastery over the *mantra*! Am I right, *gurudev*?" Indra asked hopefully.

"Not so fast, Indra! One can undertake penance – but no one can predict Lord Shiva's reaction to it." Brhaspati sighed. "From Lord Shiva's point of view, Brhaspati is certainly not Sukra!" He paused to explain: "Mahendra, we must remember that the divine couple on Mount Kailash consider Sukra to be their own son."

"*Gurudev*, it is up to you to ensure that our 'wonderful thought' materializes into a wonderful solution." There was a note of challenge in Indra's words.

"At present, there are only two masters of the Mrtasanjeevani: Lord Shiva himself – and Sukra." Brhaspati locked eyes with Indra. "In my estimation, it would be easier to obtain the secret of the *mantra* from Sukra." The *deva-guru* silenced Indra's incipient question with an abrupt gesture and continued: "You are going to ask me how I expect Sukra to pass on the secret of the Mrtasanjeevani to us, the *asuras'* sworn enemies. Remember, Mahendra, a true *guru* is constrained to pass on all his knowledge to an intelligent disciple who serves him with unswerving devotion." Brhaspati paused meaningfully. "Whatever else Sukra may be, he is an exemplary *guru* in the truest sense of the word ..."

"Then, someone should approach Sukra as his disciple ..." Indra felt a rising sense of hope.

"Not just 'someone,' Mahendra." Brhaspati cautioned. "This task requires a young man of sterling virtue: someone who is obedient, devout, smart, dedicated and exceptionally intelligent."

"I know just the person who meets your criteria, *gurudev!*" Indra smiled in pleasure.

"Really?!" exclaimed Brhaspati. "And who is this young *deva?*"

Indra shook his head. "Not one of us, master: he is none other than your own son, Kacha!"

"Kacha?"

"Yes, *gurudev,*" Indra asserted categorically. "Kacha is the only one qualified to obtain the Mrtasanjeevani by serving Sukra."

"I would be only too glad if my son could be of assistance in these circumstances. He would be stepping in to discharge a duty which is his father's by right." Brhaspati continued thoughtfully: "Kacha is a devoted disciple, irrespective of the *guru* he serves."

The *deva-guru* came to a decision and smiled at Indra. "If my son succeeds in this mission, I shall share his credit! I will indeed be a proud father. I will send Kacha to Sukra tomorrow itself."

"I am blessed, *gurudev.* I will come with you to meet Kacha and personally request his intercession on behalf of the gods." Indra folded his hands in reverence.

———

The sonorous chant of *mantras* by the young *rakshasas* reverberated from Sukra's hermitage, situated in a sylvan glade in the forest adjoining Vrshaparva, the *asura* capital. Sukra listened attentively to his disciples, seated in orderly rows under the spreading branches of a tree.

Sukra's daughter, Devayaani, approached him with a vessel of drinking water. Her attention was drawn to a young man entering the hermitage. The youth was a complete stranger to the *ashram,* and to Vrshaparva's court. Devayaani's curious eyes could not drag themselves away from the newcomer's face. His obvious beauty and magnetism held her captive.

The young man came to stand before Sukra with his hands folded in respect. "*Gurudev,*" his mellow voice was infinitely pleasing to the ear. "I, Kacha, the son of Taara and Brhaspati – preceptor of the gods, salute you." He bowed in reverence to Sukra. "I come here to dedicate myself to your service. Please accept me as your disciple and bless me with your teaching."

Sukra's keen eyes appraised Kacha from head to foot. "Did you say son of Brhaspati?" he asked, surprise writ large upon his face.

"Yes, *gurudev*," Kacha admitted. "I come in search of your eminent tutelage. It is my father who has sent me here to further my education. Please accept me as your disciple."

"My dear Kacha," Sukra gave a wry smile. "Do you really believe that there is any knowledge which *Acharya* Brhaspati himself does not possess?"

"My father insisted that studying under your eminent guidance would benefit me a thousand fold more than his own instruction." Kacha remarked with a smile.

'How charming his smile is!' thought Devayaani. Completely bewitched by Kacha, she stared at him, forgetting to offer her father the water she carried in her hands.

Kacha was the son of *devaguru* Brhaspati: that made him the son of her father's arch-rival. Would her father send the young man on his way with a few choice insults? Or, would he condescend to accept him as his disciple? How pleasant it would be if the handsome Kacha lived in the hermitage as her father's disciple! Devyaani waited anxiously to hear her father's decision.

In direct contrast to the love-struck Devayaani, the young *asuras* glared at Kacha in open antagonism. Dark thoughts filled their minds: son of the *devaguru*! He was undoubtedly here, in the guise of a disciple, to steal the *rakshasas'* secrets. Would Sukra fall for his honeyed compliments and accept him?

"Father," prompted Devayaani softly, "if a *guru* is approached by a seeker of knowledge, whoever the supplicant may be, he …"

"Must be accepted as a disciple by the *guru*," Sukra completed his daughter's sentence, his eyes still intent on Kacha.

"*Gurudev*!" one of the *asura* disciples exclaimed in horror. "Do you plan to accept the *deva- guru*'s son as your disciple?"

"Yes, my boy," Sukra replied complacently. "This only demonstrates our magnanimity and enhances our honour." He continued as a teacher. "You must never overlook the noble code of conduct which ordains that a seeker of knowledge should never be turned away."

"Father, have a drink of water." Devayaani belatedly proffered the vessel to her father.

Sukra passed the container to Kacha saying, "Kacha, have some water." He smiled kindly at his new student. "Accepting you as my disciple translates into my accepting and honoring your father, Brhaspati."

Devayaani gave Kacha one more quick glance before running back to the hermitage. There was a new spring in her step.

⎯⎯ ⎯⎯

Sukra assigned Kacha the duty of tending the hermitage cows. Kacha's days were soon filled with the routine of taking the herd to graze in the forest and collecting flowers, fruits, sacrificial twigs and grass for the ritual worship. These chores were in addition to his prescribed lessons. Kacha carried out his errands promptly, with uncomplaining good humour. He was always willing to lend a hand at the hermitage. Kacha's patience and dedication, conspicuously absent in the coarse *asura* youth, appealed greatly to Sukra. By dint of his diligence and obedience, Kacha soon earned his master's approbation and a special place in his heart.

Kacha was often in Devayaani's company, as he helped her with her daily chores in the house and with the care of the cows. His witty conversation and gentle consideration secured her affection. To her delight, he grew accustomed to bringing her delicious fruits and rare flowers from his foraging expeditions to the forest.

Devayaani's initial attraction towards Kacha soon blossomed into full-blown love. While Sukra gave Kacha a special place in his heart, his daughter gave her heart itself to the handsome young man. Deluded by her own love for him, Devayaani mistook Kacha's innate courtesy and charm as signs that her feelings were reciprocated.

As Sukra's affection for Kacha, and Devayaani's love, grew stronger like the rays of the rising sun, the hatred of the *asura* disciples also grew alongside, like lengthening shadows. The young *rakshasas* deeply resented Kacha's rise in their master's estimation and his hold on Sukra's affection.

"Kacha is the son of our enemy's preceptor: this obviously makes him our enemy. Our master is mistakenly lavishing his affection and praise on him – to our detriment." the senior most of the *asura* disciples spoke out in protest. "We must not tolerate this injustice any longer."

"But, what can we do?" asked the others.

"I have an idea," their leader said. "Today, when Kacha leads the cows to the forest, as usual, we will follow him stealthily and kill him."

"Hear, hear!" the *asuras* eagerly applauded the scheme. "This is the only permanent solution to this vexing problem!"

Executing their sinister plan, the *asuras* followed Kacha to the forest. They pounced on the unsuspecting young man as he grazed the cows, tied him to a tree and murdered him in cold blood. Dusk fell over the hermitage and the grazing cows found their way home from the forest without their keeper. Time passed, but there was no sign of the young man.

Devayaani anxiously paced the front yard, peering intently into the gathering darkness of night for some sign of Kacha's return. Her heart raced with fearful thoughts: had he met with some dire peril in the thick of the forest? Had some wild animal attacked him? Had he been bitten by a venomous snake?

Filled with apprehension, Devayaani rushed to Sukra. "Father, the cows have returned to the barn without Kacha. Night has fallen, but there is no sign of him yet. I fear he has met with some untoward accident in the forest. I am worried, father!"

To Sukra's astonishment, the distressed Devayaani burst into tears. "Devayaani, why are you weeping?"

"Father, Kacha is my very life!" she confessed. "Please help him."

Sukra closed his eyes in single-minded meditation, summoning his awesome mystic powers. After a while, he slowly emerged from his trance and looked at his daughter. "Devayaani, Kacha is dead .... he has been bound to a tree in the forest and murdered."

"Father!" gasped Devayaani. Her body was convulsed by racking sobs.

"My dear, wipe your tears: Kacha will return to life. Remember that I possess the power of the Mrtasanjeevani." Sukra consoled his beloved daughter. "Go now, wash your face and compose yourself."

The reassured Devayaani smiled at him in gratitude and left to do as he had ordered.

Sukra chanted the *mantra* which invoked the goddess of the Mrtasanjeevani. Instantaneously, the benign goddess appeared before him, ready to do his bidding.

"Sanjeevani," Sukra said authoritatively. "Kacha is my favourite disciple and very dear to me. He now lies dead in the forest. I command you to bring him back to life!"

The goddess of the Mrtasanjeevani whirled to the forest with the speed of wind. She restored Kacha to life and led him back to the *ashram*. Presenting the young man respectfully to the waiting *asura-guru*, the goddess disappeared.

Devayaani rushed excitedly to meet Kacha. Her face wet with tears of joy, she gazed at the young man. Her eyes brimmed with love. She then turned to Sukra, who looked on, beaming with pride. "Father!" Devayaani fell into his arms.

Sukra held his daughter close and stroked her back in tender caress. He looked at Kacha over her head. "Kacha," Sukra said, "it was Devayaani who noted your absence and grew apprehensive. She would not be consoled until I promised to restore you to life. You are obviously everything to my daughter."

"I am fortunate indeed, *gurudev!*" Kacha bowed in deep gratitude.

"Come, Kacha!" Devayaani said happily. "Mother is waiting for us."

Kacha sat in his hut, under the light of an oil lamp, revising the morning lessons taught by Sukra. Suddenly, a gust of wind rushed in and the flame flickered. Kacha frowned and looked searchingly towards the door which he had earlier shut against the elements: Devayaani stood on the threshold.

She closed the door softly behind her and walked to him. Her white *saree* floated about her like the translucent wings of an angel; her jet-black hair was a rippling cascade down her back; her face glowed like the luminescent full moon; her dark eyes were two mysterious pools of gleaming water ...

"Kacha," her voice was husky. "tell me – what happened in the forest?"

"I have no idea," replied the bemused Kacha.

"Who ... who killed you?" she asked urgently.

"I did not see or hear anyone. Suddenly, I felt excruciating pain: it was as though a flaming bolt of steel pierced my heart ..." Kacha shuddered in remembered horror. "That is all I know ..."

"Do not venture too deep into the forest in future. You must make sure that you are back at the hermitage before sunset." She declared impassionedly: "Kacha, do you realize that I could not endure life if anything happened to you?!"

"Yes, Devayaani, I know – your affection is my shield against the vicissitudes of life," Kacha expressed his heartfelt gratitude to her.

"Do you know why that is so?" she smiled meaningfully at him. "You are my very life!"

"Yes, *gurudev* himself said the same thing to me earlier," Kacha asserted.

Devayaani stood to leave. "From tomorrow, you will stop at the forest edge," she said.

"That depends of the cows, Devayaani," Kacha chuckled softly. "The *ashram* cows seem to have a mind of their own!" He continued more seriously. "You know that the cows, particularly the *homadhenus* used in the rituals, must be given free rein to wander as they will."

"I do not know about such things and I do not care!" She was defiant. "All I care about is your safety and all I know is that you are everything to me!"

Devayaani shut the door behind her and walked into the night.

The next morning, the *asura* disciples were chagrined to see Kacha seated before their *guru*, serenely reciting the *Vedic mantras*. They quickly deduced that Sukra had restored Kacha to life with the Mrtasanjeevani. They held a hurried confabulation as to their next course of action.

Their leader suggested that they kill Kacha once again: only, this time, they would ensure that his body did not remain behind to be reanimated by Sukra. They finalized the details of their nefarious plot and bided their time. An opportunity soon arrived for the conspirators to execute their plan.

A few days later, as Kacha set out for the forest with the herd of cows, Devayaani asked him to bring her some particularly fragrant flowers. The jubilant *asuras*, aware that these rare blooms could be found only in the dense interior of the forest, decided that the time was ripe to do away with their nemesis.

As Kacha ventured deep into the thick forest in search of the exotic flowers, the group of would-be assassins clandestinely followed in his wake. Two *asuras* ambushed the unwary Kacha and stabbed him with sharp daggers. Slinging his corpse over their shoulders, the killers made their way to a small, secluded clearing, where their co-conspirators had arranged a pyre. The triumphant *asuras* flung Kacha's body on the pyre and burnt it. The leader collected the ashes in a bag which he secreted inside his attire. The wicked band stealthily returned to the hermitage, where they had earlier hidden some wine in the thickets.

The ingenious *asuras* now mixed Kacha's ashes into the wine and made their way to Sukra, who was seated at leisure on the dais. In an apparent outpouring of devoted service to their *guru*, the disciples pressed his legs, fanned him concernedly and urged him to drink the wine they offered. In feigned innocence, they emphasized that they had prepared it especially for him. Sukra, pleased with their evident devotion, consumed all the wine.

The *asuras* were jubilant at the success of their plan. "Our master's favourite disciple has now entered our master's stomach through his favourite drink!" Their leader crowed sarcastically. "*Gurudev* now cannot restore the digested Kacha to life!"

Dusk fell and the grazing cows once again headed home without their herder. Devayaani, waiting for Kacha to return with her flowers, was immediately flooded by alarm. She rushed to her father, who was in a pleasantly intoxicated state. Devayaani burst into tears and reported Kacha's alarming absence. In vain, Sukra attempted to console his weeping daughter.

The impassioned Devayaani declared: "Father, I will not let a morsel of food, or a drop of water, touch my mouth until Kacha stands before me!"

His beloved daughter's evident agony cleared the fumes of intoxication from Sukra's mind. He sat up in renewed alertness. "I will use my yogic skills to deduce Kacha's fate. I assure you that I will soon restore him to you." He patted Devayaani on her shoulders. "Now, wipe your tears and go inside."

Devayaani, confident in her father's mystic power, obediently went in search of her mother.

Sukra ritualistically washed his hands and feet and adopted the posture of meditation. He concentrated the mystic vibration of his thoughts into probing tendrils which sought out Kacha's presence. To Sukra's vast surprise, he could find no trace of Kacha in the entire universe, circumscribed by the awesome Lokaaloka Mountain. Undeterred, the *asura-guru* single-mindedly focused on locating Kacha and persisted in his endeavor. Finally, to his chagrin, Sukra divined that Kacha was in his own stomach, in the form of ashes mixed with wine.

Sukra was immediately flooded with deep self-recrimination: it was his

fondness for wine which had led to this sorry state of affairs. He despised
the intoxicating drink which had camouflaged and carried the ashes of
his favourite disciple into his body. Sukra realized that the accumulated
wisdom of several births could vanish in a moment of inebriation.

The incensed *asura-guru* pronounced his malediction on the insidious
intoxicant: "This is the curse of Sukra – the consumption of wine will
hereafter be considered a sin. Wine-drinkers will be pushed into depravity
and find themselves in an excruciating hell."

Consumed by guilt for ingesting Kacha and excoriating himself
for his weakness for wine, the *asura-guru* immediately invoked the
Mrtasanjeevani to restore Kacha to life in a miniature form within the
confines of his stomach. Sukra reached out to Kacha with his mind.

"*Gurudev!*" exclaimed Kacha. "By your mercy, I am alive in the
precincts of your sacred stomach. Please extend your compassion to me
and show me a way out! Save me, master!"

Sukra sank into deep cogitation. The only way for Kacha to emerge
from his stomach was to burst out of its confines. But this would
undoubtedly lead to Sukra's own death. Sukra could be restored to life by
the power of the formidable Mrtasanjeevani. But, again, who could wield
the *mantra* on his behalf? He was forbidden by Lord Shiva to pass on the
secret of the life-giving incantation to a woman: this effectively ruled out
both his wife and daughter. Who was left? Kacha alone. Sukra reached the
inevitable conclusion: the only way out of this predicament was to pass
on the secret of the Mrtasanjeevani to Kacha.

"My dear Kacha," Sukra addressed his favoured disciple: "In order
to return to the outside world, you must burst through the walls of my
stomach. Of course, this will result in my own death."

He continued thoughtfully. "The only way out of this deadlock is for
me to teach you the Mrtasanjeevani before you emerge from my body –
using this *mantra*, you can then restore me to life."

"So be it, *gurudev*," Kacha agreed from the depths of Sukra's stomach.

"Remember, once you regain your original form, I will be inert.
It is up to you to bring me back to life using your mastery over the
Mrtasanjeevani."

"It shall be as you command, master," Kacha assured him.

"Listen carefully, my son: I now impart to you the priceless
Mrtasanjeevani *mantra* ..." Sukra conscientiously taught Kacha the secret
of the life-restoring chant.

"Emerge from my stomach, Kacha!" Sukra's voice rose in grave command. "Make your master whole again through the power of the Mrtasanjeevani!"

In answer to his master's call, Kacha burst out of Sukra's stomach. Instantaneously, he regained his original stature. For a moment, Kacha stared in horror at the mangled remains of his master, who had died to give him life. Kacha quickly gathered his thoughts and, in his turn, recited the

Mrtasanjeevani *mantra*. To his amazed relief, Sukra regained life and sat up, whole. Kacha prostrated himself at his master's feet: Sukra blessed him, his eyes mirroring his own gratitude.

∞

The next morning, the *asura* disciples gaped in open-mouthed astonishment at the sight of Kacha calmly going about his routine chores: obviously, very much alive! In some unfathomable way, their plan had been foiled yet again by their master. They gave up in despair.

Sukra roundly upbraided them: "You have stooped to the despicable level of killing a fellow-disciple, reducing his remains to ashes, mixing those ashes in your own master's wine and ensuring that your master consumed this wine!" He glared at them in withering contempt. "As Kacha has survived your dastardly machinations, I am overlooking your crime this time." His voice rose. "However, be warned: I will not be so merciful in the future!"

The young *asuras* bowed their heads in abject shame. Tremors of fear ran through the group.

Kacha intervened and stepped forward to stand before Sukra. "*Gurudev*," he said. "With your permission, I will make my departure from here." He smiled wryly. "My continued presence will necessitate your daily deployment of the Mrtasanjeevani on my behalf!"

"Yes, my dear Kacha," Sukra nodded in approval. "It is certainly advisable for you to leave a hostile environment which poses a constant threat to your life. Your father sent you to the shelter of my protection. Now, it is time I returned you safely to his custody." He smiled. "On another note, your education here is almost complete. Yes, the time is ripe for you to make your departure from the *ashram*."

∞

Devayaani's adoring gaze lingered on Kacha. "Do you realize that you are even handsomer after being resurrected from death for the second time?" she asked him with a fond smile.

"And the credit for it all goes to you!" Kacha exclaimed. "Master told me that you refused to eat or drink until my return." His voice was thick with emotion. "Devayaani, I am indebted to you – how can I ever repay you?"

"There is a way!" Her hands unthinkingly removed her upper garment in suggestive invitation and then draped it back over her breasts. "Shall I tell you how you can repay me?"

"Tell me." Kacha nodded eagerly, adding: "Whatever I do, I know that it will always be inadequate. My debt of gratitude can never be paid. Even if you consider a life for a life, I cannot repay you with my life." He smiled tenderly at her. "I can only die once – but you gave me the gift of life twice!"

"I do not want your life." Devayaani locked eyes with Kacha. "I want your love."

"Devayaani, surely you know that I have abundant love and affection for you!" Kacha protested.

"I know that: which is why I ask you to repay your debt of gratitude in this way …" Her eyes pierced his own. "Marry me."

"Devayaani!!" Kacha gasped in outright astonishment. "You … have you lost your mind?"

"Yes," she smiled serenely. "I lost my mind the moment I first set eyes on you! From that very instant, my heart was no longer my own – it has been circling you, weaving its songs of love." She asked, "Kacha, my dearest: why this surprise in your eyes? On the day of your arrival in Vrshaparva, Manmatha, the god of love, united us in marriage: the tying of the sacred thread remains a mere formality."

"Devayaani …" the flabbergasted Kacha was at a loss for words.

"I saw you," she whispered dreamily. "and you crept into my heart.I offered myself to you, body and soul, on that very day."

"Devayaani," Kacha said with gentle regret, "you are living in a dream world of your own creation."

"Kacha!" Her cry was anguished.

"Do you know the prescribed relationship between a disciple and his master's daughter?"

Devayaani's voice remained deceptively calm. "I do not know."

"Do you know the relationship between a disciple and his master … between an individual and the person who gave him life?" Kacha persisted.

"I do not know," she replied implacably.

"Yes, you do know!" Kacha burst out. "You know it well – don't deny it! You certainly know that the *guru*'s daughter is like a sister to his disciple. You know that the *guru* and the giver of life are both akin to a person's father!"

Devayaani's unswerving gaze held Kacha's.

"Devayaani, you are my *guru*'s daughter: that makes you my sister. Your father is both my *guru* and my life-giver: that makes me his son." His voice was persuasive. "Please accept this reality and forget your unreasonable demands."

Devayaani's melting eyes hardened and flashed fire. "I understand now, Kacha: you pretended to love me so that you could obtain the Mrtasanjeevani! Your avowals of love and affection were nothing more than cheap lies to help you achieve your objective!" She threw her accusation at him in burning contempt.

"I will say it even now – I have the utmost love and affection for you!" Kacha protested indignantly. "I only expressed the true feelings in my heart. It is you who misconstrued my love into lust." He was now the accuser. "You are the one at fault – not I!" Kacha bowed courteously to her. "My heartfelt gratitude to you for your affection, sister. My *guru* has granted me permission to depart from here." He turned to leave.

"Stop!" Devayaani's shout made him halt in his tracks. Kacha turned back to her.

Devayaani's eyes were balls of fire in her red face. She panted, her chest heaving with the ebb and flow of the angry tide of her emotions. Her entire body trembled in fury. "The scales have fallen from my eyes, Kacha." Her lips curled in contempt. "I see through your charade: you came here for the Mrtasanjeevani! Those stupid *asura* disciples played into your hand with their attacks on you. My father's desire to restore your life was another unexpected stroke of luck."

She paused and locked eyes with him. Her voice crescendoed to a shriek. "Hear me, Kacha: the Mrtasanjeevani ... the *mantra* which gave you life twice ... the *mantra* which my father so trustingly taught you ... this same *mantra* will not work when invoked by you. This is the curse of Devayaani, daughter of Sukra!"

Kacha remained unmoved by Devayaani's fury. "I did no wrong," he insisted. "The only way to obtain the Mrtasanjeevani is to be taught its secret by the *guru* – which is what my master did! And now, your curse has made it impossible for me to use it myself!"

"You shameless cheat!" she screamed. "Do not show me your face again: get out!"

"I will go," retorted the angry Kacha. "But, before I do so, I will repay you in kind for your curse." He locked eyes with her. "As you were consumed by inappropriate lust, you will not marry within your own clan: this is the curse of Kacha, son of Brhaspati!"

Kacha stalked out of the hut and went straight to Sukra. The *asura-guru* remarked the thunderous expression on his favourite disciple's face and looked interrogatively at Kacha.

"*Gurudev*," Kacha asked, "what is the relationship between a disciple and his master's daughter?"

"Of course, my son – they are like brother and sister," Sukra asserted categorically.

"From the very beginning, I have treated Devayaani as my own sister." Kacha paused. "In line with my brotherly affection for her, I have turned down her proposal of marriage."

"You have but followed the code of *dharma*, Kacha. You may leave!" Sukra raised his hand in benediction over Kacha.

"These are the highlights of Sukra's life." Nirvikalpananda smiled at his disciples.

"Master," Sadananda quickly spoke up. "You did not narrate the episode in which Sukra cursed Yayaathi."

"I think the master has forgotten it," said Chidananda.

"No, Chidananda: I did not forget!" The master paused to explain: "That episode is not particularly relevant to our discourse – it belongs to Yayaathi's story." Nirvikalpananda smiled indulgently. "However, since you are interested, I will touch upon it here."

He continued. "One day, Sarmishta, Vrshaparva's daughter, in the heat of a quarrel, pushed Devayaani into an unused well in the forest and abandoned her there. Subsequently, King Yayaathi, who happened to be passing by, saved Devayaani. The vengeful Devayaani instigated her father, Sukra, into making Sarmishta her servant maid. Devayaani married Yayaathi, but he fell in love with Sarmishta and secretly married her too. The enraged Sukra cursed Yayaathi with premature old age."

"Master," it was Shivananda's turn. "What about the story in which Sukra becomes one-eyed?"

"Now, now: you must let me come to each story in my own order – that incident belongs under the segment which delineates the glories of the *Navagrahas*." Nirvikalpananda gently reprimanded his enthusiastic disciples. "Let me first tell you the life story of the seventh *graha*: Sanaischara."

There was an immediate stir of excitement among the four pupils.

"Master, I am certain that Sanaischara's life will ten times more interesting than that of the other *grahas*!" exclaimed the eager Sadananda.

"The *Puranas* give us a very limited account of Sanaischara's life. The enlightened hold that Sanaischara worshipped Brahma and that Lord Shiva was his favourite deity. We are also told that Sani simultaneously impressed the Holy Trinity, the *Trimurti*."

Nirvikalpananda paused to look at his attentive listeners. "A large part of our knowledge of Sanaischara comes from word of mouth passed on from generation to generation. When such information does not impinge negatively on the character, attitude, principles and power of Sanaischara, it is quite appropriate to accept these accounts."

"But, master – they may be just figments of the imagination ..." Vimalananda was hesitant. "Can we accept them?"

Nirvikalpananda smiled serenely. "If we look at it logically, there can be no fiction without fact. Imagination stems from what has been actually heard, seen or read – in other words, from what has been experienced by the senses. Truth is the foundation of imagination and fact is the mother of fiction. There will be an element of imagination in these versions .... but truth will certainly lurk behind such inventiveness."

"Master, your rationale is commendable!" exclaimed Chidananda. "Please continue with the story of Sani's life."

"Very well, Chidananda – listen. As I told you, Sani, Saavarni and Tapati, Chaaya's children, are growing up in Samjna's care. Yama, Samjna's son, returned from his penance in the forest. There was a new radiance in his face ..."

Nirvikalpananda resumed his narrative.

THE LIFE OF SANAISCHARA

Yama, returning from his extended penance in the forest, touched his parents' feet in respect. He straightened up and warmly embraced Sani, Saavarni, Yami and Tapati.

Surya regarded his son fondly. "Yama, I hope you have successfully completed your penance."

"Lord Brahma has blessed me with an incredible position, father – one of the utmost importance." Yama's eyes gleamed. "The Creator has appointed me the Regent of the South!"

"Is that so?!" Samjna glowed with pride, as she looked at Surya. "My son has become a *dikpaalaka*: one of the eight guardians of the directions!"

"Brahma enumerated my manifold duties. I will bind the dead souls with my lasso – the *paasa*. Subsequently, I will weigh their virtues against their sins, prior to deciding whether to banish them to one of the twenty-seven hells under my jurisdiction, or reward them with entry into heaven."

Yama paused and continued gravely. "The Creator instructed me to propitiate Lord Shiva to obtain the required knowledge which would equip me to judge the merits and demerits of the dead."

"Did you follow his advice, son?" Samjna asked.

"Yes, mother," Yama replied. "In accordance with Brahma's counsel, I went to the mighty Himalayan Mountains to win Shiva's favour. In due course, the Lord, pleased with my rigorous *tapas*, appeared before me ... and what happened next was a truly incredible experience!"

Surya and Samjna were all ears as Yama continued: "Lord Shiva initiated me into the mysteries of the renowned *Sikshaasmrthi* – the treatise on punishment, authored by the Lord himself."

Yama paused to get their undivided attention. "Lord Shiva passed on his knowledge to me through the language of transcendental silence. During his entire course of instruction, the Lord's lips did not move – but his awesome voice resounded with crystal clarity in the innermost reaches of my being!"

"Yama," exclaimed Surya, "you are fortunate indeed!"

"*Swami*," asked the curious Samjna, "did Lord Shiva himself formulate the *Sikshaasmrthi*?"

"Yes, Samjna," Surya explained. "Lord Shiva, as the destroyer of the worlds at the time of the *Maha Pralaya*, or Total Annihilation, is the one who gives peaceful repose to the souls who are sorely tired by the cycle of birth and death. Aware of the necessity of computing the virtues and sins accumulated by mortals in the course of each birth, the Lord framed the treatise as the ultimate instrument of fair judgement."

Yama addressed his parents: "Viswakarma, the divine architect, has completed the construction of a city for me on the southern face of the Maha Meru Mountain. The city is called Samyamani. It holds a court of vast dimension – an incredible hundred *yojanas* in length and width! I have been tasked with performing my duties in this court." Yama bowed reverentially to his parents and continued, "I will proceed to Samyamani with your blessings. Once I begin to discharge my duties, I am to be known as 'Yamadharmaraja.'"

"Yamadharmaraja!" Surya exclaimed with a wry smile of approbation. "An eminently suitable name for a person who constantly recites the word *dharma*!"

"My heart brims with happiness." Samjna smiled contentedly. "My eldest son, Vaivasvata has become a king, with the title of 'Manu.' Now, my second son is to be the regent of a direction." She paused to advise

Yama. "Son, before proceeding to Samyamani, visit Vaivasvata and Sraddha and seek their blessings."

"Yes, mother," Yama said obediently, "I will stop to meet my brother and sister-in-law."

Surya's family had listened to the account of Yama's achievements with the greatest pride and pleasure. However, there was one exception to this happy group: as Yama proceeded with his narrative, Sani's dark face was slowly engulfed by hot waves of disappointment and jealousy.

Samjna turned to the children and said, "Saavarni, your brother, Yama, has pleased both Brahma and Lord Shiva with his dedication and devoted penance. Consequently, he has been anointed one of the *dikpaalakas*, blessed with a phenomenal court in a beautiful city and ..."

Surya intervened: "You should all consider Yama as your role model and attempt to emulate his achievements."

"I will achieve greater fame than Yama!" Sani's declaration was an impassioned shout of protest.

The entire family turned to him in surprise. Sani's eyes burned an angry red.

"Sanaischara," Surya said, "What is the meaning of this aggressive fury?"

Sani locked eyes with his father. "Yama could only please two gods: Brahma and Shiva." He drew himself up to his full height. "I, Sanaischara, will propitiate all three of the Holy Trinity: Brahma, Vishnu and Shiva!"

Yama, shocked at Sani's sudden outburst, laid a conciliatory hand on his shoulder. "Brother ..."

Sani roughly brushed aside Yama's hand. "So, you think you are better than everyone else, do you?" Sani leered sarcastically at him. "Well, let me tell you something, 'Brother:' I will surpass you in achievement! I will ensure that your fame is diminished by my success!"

"Sani!" Samjna was aghast. "You are being insolent!"

"It is not insolence: it is self-confidence and self-esteem," Sani retorted. "You will be forced to appreciate me in the way you just gushed over Yama!"

"Sanaischara!" Surya thundered. "That is quite enough!"

"I am leaving," Sani said loudly. "I will not return without obtaining boons from the *Trimurti*."

"Brother ..." Saavarni reached out to him.

"I shall come back in triumph, Saavarni." Sani cut him short and stalked out of the room. There was a moment's stunned silence ...

"*Swami*," Samjna's voice was a sad whisper. "Why is Sani so jealous?"

Surya smiled reassuringly at his wife. "As a goad for the necessary development of his own personality, my dear!"

❦

Sani walked slowly along the narrow forest track. Sage Narada, making his way across the sky, saw the solitary youth and landed some way ahead of him.

The sage walked back to Sani and accosted him with his trademark chant: "Narayana!"

Sani stopped in mid-stride and gave Narada a desultory glance. "*Pranam*, Sage Narada," he said mechanically, folding his hands in salutation.

"I offer your greetings to Lord Narayana," said Narada with a benign smile. "Where are you headed, son of Surya?"

"Narada, you should have added my mother's name and addressed me as the 'son of Surya and Chaaya.'" Sani frowned in reprimand.

"Narayana!" exclaimed the sage. "Of course, you are Chaaya's son: even if I fail to proclaim it, nothing can change that undeniable fact!" He changed the subject. "You are walking very fast – where are you headed to in such a hurry?"

"Are you ridiculing me, Narada?" Sani flushed in anger. "I have been picking my way as if on a thorn-strewn path!" His voice was bitterly accusatory. "You know very well that I am naturally endowed with a slow gait. Hampered in this way, is it possible for me to walk fast? Do not mock me!"

"Narayana!" Narada protested. "I only meant to suggest that your purposeful stride speaks of a definite objective." He lowered his voice. "Are you on a secret mission?"

"Is penance considered a secret mission?"

"Penance?" asked Narada curiously. "And which god do you intend to propitiate with your *tapas* – Brahma, Vishnu or Shiva?"

"I, Sanaischara, consider all the three to be equal, Narada." Sani declared haughtily. "My penance will be directed simultaneously to the *Trimurti*."

"Narayana!" Narada gasped in astonishment. "Why propitiate three gods? After all, any one of them is perfectly capable of showering you with boons in his own right!"

"I have decided to propitiate the Trinity as one entity, Narada." Sani reiterated firmly. "Nothing can make me change my mind." He continued: "Do you know that Yama obtained the favour of two of them: Brahma and Shiva? Now, I shall earn the goodwill of all three!"

"Narayana! Narayana!" Narada smiled knowingly. "I now understand! Of course, your intention is good ... but, are you aware that this objective can be achieved only after a very, very long time?"

Sani locked eyes with Narada. "I assure you that I am very much aware that, if you continue to stand in my way, blathering about inconsequential things, it will definitely take me a very, very long time to reach my goal!"

"Narayana!" the sage gave an appeasing smile. "After all, you are Surya's son: I am here merely to enquire about your welfare – that's all!" He paused. "Of course, it is also for your welfare that I give you my humble opinion: in order to propitiate the three godheads of the Trinity, one is required to choose three different times and three different ...'"

"Narada!" Sani interrupted rudely. "And who told you these conditions? Why do you presume to be knowledgeable about things beyond your experience?" He made an impassioned declaration. "Listen well, Narada: I shall perform *tapas* to propitiate Brahma, Vishnu and Shiva all at once ... understand? Simultaneously – is that clear to you?" Sani's lips curled in contempt, "So, go your way – and let me go mine!"

"Narayana!" Narada's chant reflected his astonishment. "Propitiating three gods all at once! Doing penance to the *Trimurti* simultaneously! It is unprecedented! Such *tapas* has never been attempted in the past: nor will it be replicated in the future!"

"Well, it is going to be executed in the present!" Sani shot back at Narada. "Go, Narada: spread these sensational tidings throughout the three worlds. Go!"

Dismissing Narada with these curt words, Sani resumed his resolute walk. Narada, mouth agape, stepped aside and stared at his receding figure.

―――∞∞∞―――

Sanaischara embarked on his penance in a secluded glade in the heart of the forest. He formulated three *Ashtaakshari mantras* – three incantations composed of eight letters each, addressing Brahma, Vishnu and Maheswara in turn.

Om Chaturmukhaaya namah! Om Mahaavishnave namah! Om Maheswaraaya namah!

Sani meditated on the *Trimurti* simultaneously, reciting his three *mantras* consecutively. Sani's unprecedented, unique method of invocation became a watershed in the history of penance. His *tapas* scaled new heights of spiritual power and intense concentration. They reached out to Brahma, Vishnu and Maheswara with the visceral pull of an infant's cry to his father. Yet, the peculiar circumstance of Sani's penance rendered them helpless to respond!

Sani's invocation of Brahma with the *mantra*, 'Om Chaturmukhaaya namah!' reached the Creator. However, before Brahma could appear before Sani, his next incantation, 'Om Mahaavishnave namah!' intervened to block the Creator's move and kept him firmly on his lotus throne! Brahma was forced to concede that it was Vishnu whom Sani sought to propitiate.

In the same way, whenever Lord Vishnu prepared himself to grant Sani his *darshan*, the *mantra*, 'Om Maheswaraaya namah!' halted him in his tracks. The Lord continued to recline benignly on his serpent-bed of Adisesha's coils, leaving it to Shiva to respond to Sani's call.

Likewise, Lord Shiva was also drawn to answer Sani's insistent invocation. Again, Sani's *mantra* to Brahma overlapped with his own and forced Shiva to remain unresponsive.

Sani's unanswered, unique, three-fold penance rose in tempo. The devouring heat of its intensity engulfed the three worlds: it burst into a conflagration which reduced the forests to ashes, made simmering cauldrons of the oceans and led to a mounting loss of life. The phenomenal heat of Sani's *tapas* reached up to the heavens. The agitated Indra summoned his mentor, Brhaspati, and requested him to determine the cause of this unexpected heat wave.

Before the *deva-guru* could respond, he was interrupted by the familiar chant, "Narayana!"

It was Sage Narada.

"Mahendra," remarked the smiling Brhaspati, "I have been preempted by the arrival of the messenger of the three worlds! He will answer your doubts!"

"Narayana!" said Narada in greeting. "I suppose you refer to the unnatural heat wave which has engulfed all the worlds. As we all know, Indra is responsible for the welfare of the three worlds: that is why I have hastened here to appraise him of the peculiar circumstances prevailing." He continued with his tidings. "The uncommon method of penance adopted by Sanaischara, Surya's son, is the reason for the dire peril faced by the cosmos." ·

Brhaspati and Indra listened to Narada's words and exchanged glances of wonder.

"And what exactly is the reason for this youth's peculiar penance?" asked Indra in exasperation.

"He insists that the three godheads of the Holy Trinity – Brahma, Vishnu and Shiva, appear before him simultaneously," Narada replied.

"Appearance of the *Trimurti* at the same time!" Indra gasped in amazement. "This is nothing but sheer madness!"

"Yes," agreed Brhaspati. "Sani's unnatural desire poses a grave danger to the three worlds."

"I shall cure his madness," firmly declared the irate king of the *devas*. "I will immediately dispatch two exquisite *apsaras* to disrupt his manic penance." Indra smiled sarcastically. "We will ensure that he is too busy pursuing our beauties to find time to resume his *tapas!*"

"Well thought, Mahendra!" Brhaspati applauded the scheme. "Let's not lose any time in putting your plan into action!"

"That Sani is an arrogant and insolent youth ..." Narada inserted a note of caution into the proceedings.

"Never fear, *Maharshi*," Indra was supremely confident. "His arrogance and insolence will vanish with the winds when he sees the captivating beauty of the pair of nymphs I am sending to pay him a visit."

———

Two *apsaras*, attired in seductive, gossamer-thin garments, and adorned with divine ornaments, arrived at the secluded glade of Sani's *tapas*. As their startled eyes took in the ferocious nature of his penance, their hearts quailed and the blood rushed to their heads.

The nymphs stared at Sani in morbid fascination: a feeble, black body; eyes half-closed in meditation; contorted facial features. A dull, crimson glow radiated from his adamantine body, rigid in its seated posture. Menacing, dark tentacles reached out into the surrounding atmosphere. The two watchers were suddenly filled with the same conviction – one glance from this terrifying apparition and they would be reduced to ashes!

The *apsaras* exchanged looks of alarm: at the next instant, they vanished from the scene!

———

Indra was dumbstruck as the excited *apsaras* described their encounter with Sani. The king of the *devas,* keenly aware that his *apsaras* were formidable in their determination to succeed, now conceded that defeating Sani might be beyond his capabilities. Indra turned to Brhaspati for advice.

"Mahendra, I think the *Trimurti* are our only recourse in this predicament," the preceptor said.

"Master," said Indra, "please accompany me. Let us supplicate the *Trimurti* for their aid."

Brahma gave Indra and Brhaspati a patient hearing. However, he shook his head at their request.

"I'm afraid you will have to reach out to Lord Vishnu and Lord Shiva in this situation. Sani's penance is intolerably intense. Each time he invokes my name, I attempt to grant him my *darshan:* however, I am rendered helpless by his subsequent recitation of Lord Vishnu's name."

"For the welfare of the worlds, I implore you to ignore Sani's extraordinary method of penance," Indra bowed to Brahma with folded hands. "In spite of his sequential chant of the *Trimurti's* three names, please appear before him once."

"When he sees Brahma, the Creator, he will forget to invoke the others," Brhaspati added his own words of persuasion.

"Very well," Brahma agreed, "considering the well-being of the worlds, I will grant Sani my *darshan.*"

Indra and Brhaspati expressed their gratitude to the Creator and left on the next step of their mission. They met Lord Vishnu and Lord Shiva in turn and placed the same proposal before the Gods. After deep consideration, both Lord Vishnu and Lord Shiva agreed to comply with their urgent request.

The inhabitants of the three worlds endured untold agony under the glare of Sani's fierce, heat-generating penance.

Keeping his word to Indra, Lord Brahma appeared before Sani and said: "Sanaischara, your penance pleases me greatly!"

Sani folded his hands in salutation and asked: "Where is Vishnu? Where is Shiva??"

Brahma smiled magnanimously. "I am here, my son. I am ready to shower you with boons of your asking."

"Forgive me, *Bhagavan!*" Sani replied determinedly. "Unless the *Trimurti* appear before me simultaneously, I will not ask for anything."

Sani resumed his intense *tapas*. Helpless in the face of Sani's stubborn resolve, Brahma vanished.

After a short interval, Lord Vishnu made his appearance before Sani.

"Sanaischara," called Lord Vishnu, "it is time to end your penance. I am here to grant you the boons you desire."

Sani opened his eyes and offered his respectful greetings to Lord Vishnu. "*Bhagavan*, Brahma and Shiva are not with you."

"They will each give you their *darshan* in turn," Vishnu reassured Sani. "Now, tell me what you want from me."

"The objective of my penance is to receive the *darshan* of the *Trimurti* at the same time." Sani reiterated firmly. "I will not dilute the specifications of my *tapas* at this stage." He bowed to Vishnu. "Please excuse me for my adherence to the parameters of my penance and go away. If you are truly moved to munificence by my *tapas*, please come along with Brahma and Shiva."

Sani closed his eyes and resumed his staunch meditation.

"Sanaischara," Lord Vishnu chuckled softly. "Look here!"

Sani remained indifferent to the Lord's summons. He obstinately persisted in his recitation of his Ashtaakshari mantra:

"*Om Chaturmukhaaya namah! Om Mahaavishnave namah! Om Maheswaraaya namah!*"

"Sanaischara!" Three resonant voices chorused in unison. The majestic tones crashed against his ears like the roar of storm clouds and penetrated into the depths of his trance. Sani opened his eyes – there before him stood the smiling *Trimurti*.

Sani hurriedly rose to his feet and prostrated himself before the Holy Trinity. "I am fortunate to be blessed with the simultaneous *darshan* of the *Trimurti!*" Sani's voice shook with fervor.

"Sanaischara, you are obstinate indeed!" Lord Vishnu smiled at him. "Your unyielding stance has forced us to appear before you as a trio."

"Lord, excuse my adamancy," Sani said in deep humility. "My cousin, Yama, boasted of his feat of obtaining the favour of two of the *Trimurti*. I felt belittled by his attitude. That ignited my zeal to propitiate the *Trimurti* as one entity and compel them to grant me their *darshan* at the same time."

"Very well, Sanaischara," Brahma said. "What do you want from us?"

Sani folded his hands in reverence and said: "My Lords, grant me these boons: let my sight and name inspire fear in all living beings: may they worship me with devotion, mingled with fear. Let my devotees be blessed with longevity. Grant me these boons in one voice."

"So be it, Sanaischara," the *Trimurti* said in unison.

Sani bowed to them and continued: "Grant me a position which is in no way inferior to that of Yama," he asked.

"You will be anointed to such a post in the near future," declared Lord Vishnu.

"We will ensure your appointment to a position of renown," agreed Lord Shiva.

"I am indeed blessed," Sani sang out in delight.

The *Trimurti* vanished as one.

Sanaischara returned home in triumph and prostrated himself at his parents' feet. He then looked round searchingly. "Where is Yama?" he asked.

"After your departure, Yama, following Brahma's instructions, left for Samyamani to assume charge as the *dikpaalaka* of the south," said Samjna.

"I wanted him to hear of my achievement at first-hand," Sani heaved a sigh of disappointment. He turned to Surya and said: "Father, I embarked on a rigorous course of penance to propitiate the *Trimurti* at the same time. As a consequence of my devotion and unswerving determination, Brahma, Vishnu and Maheswara appeared before me simultaneously."

"Can this be true?" Surya exclaimed in astonishment. "Penance directed towards the three godheads at the same time?! Incredible!"

"Yes, father," Sani beamed with pride. "I earned the favour of the three gods and they blessed me with their *darshan* simultaneously. They condescended to grant me all the boons I desired."

Sani elaborated on the boons he had received from the *Trimurti*. Surya, Samjna, Saavarni, Yami and Tapati burst into hearty congratulations on Sani's remarkable achievement.

Sani locked eyes with Surya. "Father," he said, "when Yama boasted that he had succeeded in propitiating both Brahma and Shiva, you praised him at great length: now I have surpassed his achievement, by obtaining the blessings of three gods. Not one ... not two ... but Three Gods! What do you say now, father?"

Surya looked meaningfully at his son. "Sani, you voluntarily took Yama's achievement as a challenge: remember, nobody, including Yama, provoked you to take that stand. Taking up this challenge has earned you rich dividends." A smile lit up Surya's radiant face. "My son, I congratulate you wholeheartedly. I sing your praise. Of course, as Yama's father, I extolled his achievement: now, I commend you too. I do not hesitate to praise you repeatedly: after all, you are the giver of long life to mortals!"

"Yes," agreed Samjna. "*Swami*, our Sanaischara has now matured into a complete individual. It is time we found a suitable bride for him."

"Mother," Sani quickly intervened. "Let me make it clear to you at the very outset: I will not marry just any ordinary maiden. As you know, fear automatically grips anyone who looks at me. I will accept as my bride only a woman of great courage who will be able to look unflinchingly into the terrifying depths of my eyes."

"It shall be as you wish, my son." Samjna reassured Sani. "We will find a brave wife for you."

"Yes," reiterated Sani, "this is my condition for marriage." He walked out of the chamber, accompanied by the admiring Saavarni, Yami and Tapati.

"It will be a difficult task," Surya said thoughtfully to himself.

"What will be difficult, *Swami*?" Samjna asked innocently.

"To find a bride who can fearlessly gaze into our Sani's terrifying eyes!" Surya heaved a sigh.

***

Her name was Jyeshtha. Hers was a fearsome beauty -she had the darkest of complexions and her protruding eyes were tiny balls of fire. Her ugly face was so repulsive that no one could hold her gaze for even a brief moment.

When she emerged from the Ocean of Milk, Vishnu and Shiva turned away from her in instinctive revulsion. However, Brahma, with his four faces, found it impossible to avoid the sight of her repulsive visage. As the hapless Creator continued to suffer this unavoidable torment, Lord Vishnu pitied him and commanded Jyeshtha to remove herself from their presence. Jyeshtha complied and devoted her time to wandering the worlds in constant search of a male who could tolerate her appearance and accept her as his wife.

During her visit to *Swarga* on this quest, Indra saw her at a distance. Even this brief glimpse of her was enough to send the king of the *devas* scurrying for cover to the Nandana garden!

The entire heavenly community, including the *gandharvas, kinnaras and kimpurushas*, could not muster the courage to confront her. Their youth fled at her approach: those unable to make a timely getaway fell unconscious with the shock of her appearance. The *siddhas* and *chaaranaas* reacted to her in the same way.

Even in the nether worlds, the ferocious *rakshasas* ran for their lives at the news of her coming. Jyeshtha moved on to try the regents of the eight directions. The *dikpaalakas* hurriedly closed the gates of their cities and abodes to avoid meeting her. Staunchly refusing to give up hope, Jyeshtha persisted in her search for a male companion.

Jyeshtha now wandered thoughtfully along a narrow path in the depths of a forest. As her futile quest continued endlessly, she was forced to confront the possibility that creation was perhaps incomplete. 'After all,' she thought, 'if creation was indeed entire in itself, I would surely have come across my male counterpart: someone who would dare to gaze into my face and recognize its unique beauty.'

A sudden sound caught her ears. Someone was approaching from the opposite direction. Jyeshtha quickly moved aside and concealed herself behind a tree trunk.

"Narayana! Narayana! Nar ...." Sage Narada abruptly stopped his paean of praise to Lord Vishnu, as Jyeshtha emerged from hiding to block his path. With one startled look at her terrifying visage, the sage turned tail and ran!

"Stop!" Jyeshtha shouted after him.

Narada obeyed but prudently kept his back turned towards the stranger.

"I know who you are," Jyeshtha laughed. "You are the divine Sage Narada – look at me, Narada!" she commanded.

"I do not dare face you ....." Narada stammered.

"And why is that, may I know?" Her defiant question posed a challenge.

"I am afraid that my admiration will cause me to cast the evil eye on you!" exclaimed the sage, past master at witty repartee!

"I like you," Jyeshtha chuckled. "No one has ever paid me a compliment – in fact, no one even looks at me. They avoid me like the plague." She paused thoughtfully. "Everyone is afraid of me: except you! Narada, it is evident that you like me very much. Why don't you marry me?

"Narayana!" Narada was aghast. "I am a born bachelor: this means that I am ordained to remain single all my life!" he explained urgently. "I certainly cannot marry anyone!"

"I refuse to accept any of your lame excuses, Narada." Jyeshtha declared determinedly. "I will not let you evade marriage to me." She moved to the horrified sage and placed her hand on his shoulder in a possessive gesture.

"Jyeshtha!" Narada shuddered. "Listen to me: the person you marry should share your remarkable courage. He should be able to gaze unflinchingly into your beautiful eyes without the least trace of fear. A coward does not deserve to marry you!"

Jyeshtha's hand slipped from Narada's shoulder. "Are you too afraid of looking at my face, Narada?" There was a forlorn note in her voice.

"I will be honest with you, Jyeshtha," the sage's eyes were compassionate. "I belong to the vast majority of males who tremble with fear at your sight! My remark about the evil eye was only a poor attempt at humour." Narada, unable to help himself, turned his face away from her. Keeping his gaze averted, he said kindly: "Continue your search for a male who can tolerate your physical demeanour."

Jyeshtha heaved a sigh of despair. "Narada, I have crisscrossed the worlds in my search for a partner who will not be revolted at my sight. I assure you, in all the expanse of the cosmos, there is not a single soul who can fearlessly lock eyes with me!"

"There is such a person, Jyeshtha – believe me, I know someone who would not hesitate to stare intrepidly into your eyes." Narada was emphatic. "Just as it is almost impossible to look at your face, no one can summon the courage to gaze at his."

"Is this true, Narada!?" Jyeshtha exclaimed in growing excitement.

"Let me describe this person," continued Narada. "His complexion is as dark as a storm cloud. His protruding eyes are a terrifying mix of flaming reds and yellows. It is impossible to look directly into his appalling face. One glance at his eyes is enough to strike panic into the soul!"

"Oh, can there really be such a handsome male in creation?!" Jyeshtha exclaimed in delight. "Who is he? Where does he live?" Her voice quivered in uncontrollable enthusiasm.

Narada, his face still averted from her, asked: "Have you been in the direction of the golden abode in which Surya dwells?"

"No ..." Jyeshtha said hesitantly.

"Then, go in that direction." Narada pointed her towards the correct path. "There you will meet the person I described," he assured her.

"Who is he, Narada?" she implored him. "Tell me who he is!"

"Very well," Narada smiled. "I will give you a few pointers as to how you can identify him: he will stand his ground when he sees you; he will not avert his gaze from your face; just as you look at others fearlessly, he will look into the depths of your protruding eyes without flinching. When you meet such a person, you will instinctively know that he is meant to be your partner for life."

He paused and asked: "Now, will you let me be on my way?"

Only silence greeted his question. Narada looked up cautiously – Jyeshtha was a rapidly moving speck in the distance!

Far ahead of her, Jyeshtha saw a person coming in her direction: his feeble figure was thin, almost to the point of emaciation; he walked gingerly, as though picking his way carefully over sharp stones. Jyeshtha smiled in wry amusement at the stranger who approached her at a snail's pace.

'Hah!' she thought contemptuously to herself. 'One look at me, and he will grow wings under his sluggish feet!'

She came face-to-face with the stranger and stopped defiantly. To her amazement, he stood his ground and gazed intently into her eyes. His own eyes were tiny little goblets of fire, speckled with shades of red and yellow. His unwavering glance was absolutely devoid of fear. The stranger continued to stare at her in unblinking fascination. He seemed to be mesmerized by the glare of her beady, protruding eyes. His face reflected his admiration for the courage of a woman who could look unflinchingly into his own terrifying eyes.

"Who are you, you beautiful woman?" he asked.

Hope illuminated Jyeshtha's dark face. The stranger was not repulsed by her – in fact, he was talking to her! Could this be the person suggested by Narada?

"First tell me who you are!" she countered.

He drew himself up proudly and said, "I am Sanaischara, son of Chaayadevi and Surya."

"And I am Jyeshthadevi," she said in turn. "I emerged from the Ocean of Milk." She locked eyes with him and declared boldly: "You are the one I have been searching for – will you marry me?"

Sani did not hesitate. He extended his hand to her and said, "Come, let us go and obtain my father's permission for our marriage."

Jyeshtha eagerly gave him her hand. They walked together towards Surya's palace.

"Father," said Sani, "this is Jyeshtha. Like me, she has long been in search of a partner who could look fearlessly into her eyes. Now, we have found each other. If you grant us your permission ..."

Surya intervened with a smile. "You both have my blessings to become husband and wife, Sani. We will arrange your marriage at a suitably auspicious time."

Sani's nuptials were celebrated with all happiness in the presence of Kasyapa and his wives and Viswakarma and his wife. Surya, Samjna and Sage Narada joined them in blessing the newly-married couple.

Sani commenced his new life with Jyeshtha.

"We have come to the end of Sani's life history," said Nirvikalpananda. "We will now move on to the life of Rahu."

He continued: "As we know, Rahu, son of Kasyapa's wife, Simhika, and Ketu, who had originated from Mrtyu's sigh, and was brought up by Danudevi, another of Kasyapa's wives, have reached manhood. Rahu and Ketu came into their own at the renowned Churning of the Ocean of Milk. In order to fully understand these developments, it is essential to first comprehend the reasons for the Churning of the Ocean of Milk. The primary cause for the churning was Sage Durvasa ..."

"Master," Chidananda interrupted eagerly. "Wasn't Sage Durvasa Lord Shiva's incarnation – born as Anasuya's son?"

"Yes, my boy," Nirvikalpananda smiled wryly. "He is the one and only Durvasa! He was extremely short-tempered. He was notorious for his tendency to pronounce curses at the least provocation – moreover, he would adamantly refuse to revoke his maledictions! One day, Sage Durvasa was on his way through a forest ..."

The master once again took up his narrative.

THE LIFE OF RAHU

Sage Durvasa made his way rapidly through the dense forest. The cool zephyr caressed his body, making light of his tedious journey. Suddenly, an exotic fragrance wafted to him on the gentle breeze. Durvasa unconsciously slowed his pace, inhaling the sweet perfume which delighted his senses. It pervaded his being and banished all fatigue from his body. The sage stopped, the better to savour the scent.

His eyes widened in surprise as he perceived a beautiful woman coming towards him on the narrow track. It was soon evident that the divine fragrance which enveloped him emanated from her. Durvasa watched in fascination as the damsel approached – her fluid movements transformed her walk into a graceful dance. The sage was now aware of the stranger's identity: it was Menaka, one of the lovely *apsaras* from Indra's court.

Menaka came to stand before Durvasa and saluted the sage respectfully. He noted the source of the captivating fragrance which had heralded her approach: her shapely hands held a garland of divine blossoms.

"May happiness be yours, Menaka!" Durvasa held his right palm in benediction over her bowed head. He continued: "Menaka, I am captivated by the garland in your hand. I wish to have it." His words were not couched in the form of a request – they connoted an obvious command.

"I am indeed fortunate that my handiwork pleases you, *Swami*," Menaka meekly acceded to his demand and held out the fragrant garland. "Please accept this as my humble offering. It has been woven with the divine blossoms from the Nandana garden."

Durvasa took the garland from her impassively and said, "You may proceed on your way, Menaka."

The *apsara* folded her hands in reverence, moved aside and continued on her path.

Sage Durvasa, garland in hand, resumed his own journey.

———— ∞∞∞ ————

Airavata, Indra's royal mount, walked sedately along the broad avenues of Amaravati, capital of the *devas*. The elephant resembled a towering cumulus cloud, sprouting four massive tusks. Indra rode majestically at the head of a procession witnessed by all the denizens of *Swarga*. The *apsaras* danced in the forefront, accompanied by the music of the *gandharvas*, while the *devas* lined the avenues, hailing their king.

Sage Durvasa roughly pushed his way through the spectators and came to stand at a vantage point which offered him an unhindered view of the procession. The king of the gods, smiling impartially at the onlookers, felt the unmistakable pull of a powerful gaze: his eyes came to rest on Durvasa. Indra immediately signaled to Airavata, who came to a halt.

Indra bowed humbly and folded his hands in reverence towards the sage. Pleased with Indra's show of respect, Durvasa flung his garland up at the king. Indra reflexively caught it, touched it to his eyes in devout acceptance and conspicuously inhaled its fragrance. He bowed again to the sage as a mark of gratitude, casually placed the garland on Airavata's forehead, and proceeded on his way.

The constant shift and slide of the garland disturbed the royal elephant. Exasperated by this irritant on its forehead, the animal suddenly grabbed the garland, dashed it to the ground and stomped on it with its foot – the delicate flowers were trampled to a pulp!

Sage Durvasa erupted into a frenzy of rage at this sight. "Indra!" he thundered. "Stop right there!"

Indra froze to a halt and stared at Durvasa in alarm.

"Indra, you insolent fool! Your overweening pride in your kingship has made you arrogant. You have dared to belittle the gift which I bestowed on you as a mark of my special blessing. You have humiliated me: you will now reap the consequences of your behavior!"

The sage drew himself up to his full height and shouted: "Hear me, Indra: May the grandeur of *Swarga* vanish without a trace! May all your trappings of royalty – your elephant, Airavata, your noble stallion, Uchchaisrava, the heavenly cow, *Kaamadhenu*, the *Kalpavrksha*, the precious *Chintamani*, your *apsaras* – may they all be swallowed by the seas! This is the immutable curse of Durvasa!" Durvasa's malediction reverberated like a thunderclap in the skies.

The sage abruptly turned away from the horrified spectators and stalked off in a huff. The shaken Indra jumped down from his mount and hurried after the sage. He prostrated himself before Durvasa and placed his palms on the sage's feet in abject supplication.

"*Maharshi*," Indra lamented. "This unfortunate incident was a pure accident. Placing the garland on Airavata's head was merely a reflex on my part. I beg you to believe me: I would not dream of dishonoring the renowned Durvasa in any way!" He pleaded with the sage. "I implore you, *Bhagavan*: kindly revoke your curse and bless my kingdom."

Durvasa remained unmoved by Indra's humility and protestations of innocence. The sage glared balefully at the king of the *devas* and declared: "The curse is immutable: it was pronounced by none other than Sage Durvasa! Bear in mind, Indra – revoking a curse is contrary to my very nature!" The sage's lips curled in contempt. "You pompously call yourself Indra ... *Devendra* ... *Mahendra* ... Let's see who you are now!"

Durvasa stalked off in high dudgeon, leaving the hapless Indra shuddering in stark terror. The procession came to a standstill. A pall of gloom descended on *Swarga*. Durvasa's curse immediately held sway over Indra's domain. Before the eyes of the aghast gods, Airavata, Uchchaisrava, *Kaamadhenu*, *Kalpavrksha*, *Chintamani*, the *apsaras* – all the treasure of heaven – vanished into thin air. Indra, denuded of all his power, was now just one among the lesser gods.

News of the disaster which had befallen Indra soon reached Bali, the king of the *asuras*. On the advice of their preceptor, the gleeful *rakshasa* army marched on *Swarga* and routed the impotent *devas*. The triumphant Bali declared his sovereignty over the kingdom of heaven.

———

Nirvikalpananda stopped his narration at the bewildered frowns on his disciples' faces.

Vimalananda was the first with his question. "Master, you said that Vrshaparva was the king of the *asuras* ... now you refer to Bali as their king."

Nirvikalpananda smiled indulgently. "The action in our tale of the *Navagrahas* encompasses a tremendous period of time. We have moved from King Vrshaparva's reign to that of King Bali! Both Vrshaparva and Bali were Kasyapa's descendants."

The master elaborated: "Who was Vrshaparva? He was the son of Danudevi, one of Kasyapa *prajapati's* thirteen wives. You will recall Diti, another of Kasyapa's wives: her son, Hiranya Kasyapa, was the father of Prahlada. Bali was born to Virochana, Prahlada's son. This makes King Bali the grandson of Prahlada, the renowned Vishnu devotee.

"Sukra continued to be the preceptor of successive generations of *asuras*. The life of Rahu was contemporaneous with Bali's reign over the *rakshasas*."

He paused for a moment. "Now, let us pick up the threads of our original story!

"Sage Durvasa's curse reduced Indra and his *deva* clan into abject paupers: they became nomads, without shelter or any means of sustenance. On the contrary, the *asuras* flourished and grew from strength to strength. Pushed to the end of his endurance, the hapless Indra, accompanied by Brhaspati, sought Brahma's intercession. Indra described the *devas'* sorry plight and implored Brahma to restore them to their former wealth and glory."

Nirvikapananda was once again in the thick of his narrative ...

———

Brahma heaved a sigh of regret on hearing Indra's recital of the *devas'* woes.

"Sage Durvasa's curses spread like wildfire: I do not have the power to check their relentless advance. Let us seek refuge at the feet of my father, Sri Mahavishnu. Come!" Brahma exhorted his anxious supplicants.

―――⁂―――

Lord Vishnu listened in silence to Indra and Brhaspati.

"Father," Brahma added his voice to their entreaty, "Aditi's sons are in a pitiable state. It is you alone who can restore them to their former glory."

Lord Vishnu remarked, "As a consequence of Durvasa's binding curse, all *Swarga*'s riches and treasure lies at the bottom of the ocean! Even if you succeed in retrieving your lost wealth, it is obvious that the *asuras*, under the leadership of mighty King Bali, will once again snatch it from you. The *devas* are powerless in the face of the Mrtasanjeevani, which the *asuras* alone possess."

The forlorn Indra looked up at the Lord in silent entreaty.

"Indra," Lord Vishnu continued, "the Mrtasanjeevani restores the dead to life ... there is one power which equals that of this redoubtable mantra: *amrita*." He paused for emphasis. "Anyone who drinks the divine *amrita* will attain immortality."

"*Bhagavan*," Indra asked eagerly, "from where can we obtain this *amrita*?"

Lord Vishnu smiled serenely. "It lies in the bowels of the Ocean of Milk. You must churn the ocean to retrieve the lost Airavata, Uchchaisrava, *Kaamadhenu, Chintamani, Kalpavrksha, apsaras* and other treasures of *Swarga*. Your labour will also gain you the divine nectar – the *amrita* will strengthen you and banish death from your bodies."

"We are indeed blessed, *Bhagavan!*" Indra was animated by renewed hope and enthusiasm. "I shall immediately make all preparations for the churning of the Ocean of Milk."

"Indra," Lord Vishnu cautioned, "the gods alone cannot muster the strength needed for this formidable task – it can be executed only by the combined might of the *devas* and the *asuras*." He continued thoughtfully. "You will have to make the Mandara Mountain your churning-staff. The Mandara's summit rears to a height of eleven thousand *yojanas* above the earth's surface – it burrows into the bowels of the earth for another eleven thousand *yojanas*. The mountain, in its entirety of twenty-two thousand *yojanas*, must be uprooted and carried to the shores of the Ocean of Milk. This grueling feat would be impossible for the *devas* without the *asuras'* support."

Lord Vishnu paused to look at his attentive listeners. "The serpent king, Vasuki, may be used as the churning-rope. Preliminary to the churning, it is essential that vast quantities of creepers, herbs, and roots with medicinal properties, be thrown into the ocean depths."

Brhaspati remarked thoughtfully, "It is evident that the churning of the ocean will be no easy task!"

Vishnu nodded in agreement. "Indra, arrange a meeting with King Bali and lay before him your proposal for the joint venture. You must make him an offer which is so attractive that the *asuras* cannot possibly turn it down." He suggested, "Give King Bali your word that you will give the *rakshasas* half of the *amrita* obtained from the ocean. This should be sufficient to motivate Bali into accepting your proposition."

"But ...." Indra was aghast. "*Bhagavan!* The priceless Mrtasanjeevani is already a part of their armour – if we give them a share of the *amrita* as well, they will be completely immune to defeat and death!"

Lord Vishnu chuckled. "Partnering you in your task of churning the ocean, and obtaining the divine ambrosia, is the duty of your cousins, the *asuras*." He paused – there was a twinkle in eyes. "However, distributing the *amrita* among the deserving will be my particular duty!" He urged Indra on his way. "Go to Bali and lay your proposal before him, Indra!" he commanded.

Brahma, Brhaspati and Indra bowed in gratitude before Vishnu and made their departure

---

King Bali welcomed Brhaspati and Indra to *Swarga* and indicated his willingness to give them a hearing.

Indra lost no time in launching into his presentation. "Bali, we have heard from Lord Vishnu that *amrita* – the divine nectar of immortality, lies submerged in the depths of the ocean. We *devas* plan to churn the Ocean of Milk to obtain the ambrosia and conquer death for all eternity. The mighty Mandara Mountain is to be the churning-staff and the serpent, Vasuki, will serve as the rope. However, this is a task of such a gargantuan magnitude that it cannot be accomplished by us alone." He paused and locked eyes with the *asura* king. "It is patently clear that neither the *devas* nor the *asuras* can lay their hands on the *amrita* without the others' assistance. I have a proposal for you: Join hands with us in our venture and we will give you one half of the *amrita* as your share of the prize."

King Bali mulled over Indra's words.

As he hesitated, Indra added persuasively: "Come now, Bali – we are not strangers to each other. When all's said and done, we – the *aadityas, daityas, daanavas, kalakeyas* and others – are the descendants of sisters. We come from common stock. Why then must aggression be our knee-jerk reaction to each other? It may be impossible for us to live together amicably as one family: but, surely, we can unite to scale the heights of adventure to our mutual advantage!"

Brhaspati reinforced Indra's argument: "King Bali, it is eminently fitting that the *devas* and *asuras*, both descendants of Kasyapa *prajapati*, work together for their common benefit." Brhaspati turned confidently to his counterpart, Sukra. "I am sure that the eminent *asura-guru*, Sukracharya, agrees with me on this."

Sukra smiled and nodded in approval. "Mahabali, Indra's proposal is very reasonable and promises to be of definite advantage to us. On the condition that the *asuras* receive one half of the *amrita*, I think we can agree to this."

Bali bowed to the two *gurus*. "When the preceptors of the *devas* and the *asuras* are of one mind, who am I to differ?! Indra and I bow to your counsel." He turned to Indra and said: "I accept your proposal."

The preceptors extended their hands in benediction over the two kings.

"May victory be yours!" said Brhaspati.

"So be it!" echoed Sukra.

Bali and Indra sealed their pact with a warm embrace. Brhaspati and Sukra, in their turn, emulated their kings.

—∞—

Bali informed the *asuras* of his pact with the *devas*. His subjects were divided as to the wisdom of the coming joint venture.

An elderly *rakshasa*, bent with age, voiced the opinion of the dissenters: "Now that we are acquainted with the means of obtaining the *amrita*, why do we need to accommodate the *aadityas*? Let us churn the ocean on our own and secure the nectar. It is best to have no truck with those devious gods."

Another senior *asura* seconded his comrade. "Bali, think it over: if we obtain the *amrita* independently of the *devas*, it will give us a unilateral advantage over the gods – combined with the Mrtasanjeevani, we will never taste defeat again. We will become the immortal masters of the three worlds for all eternity."

King Bali dismissed their scheming with a loud laugh of derision. "Both of you are mature in years – but not in mind! It is unethical to kill those who reach out to us for succor." His voice was firm. "We will contribute equally to the churning .... and we will receive an equal share of the *amrita*!"

Preparations for the churning of the Ocean of Milk commenced on a war-footing. The *devas* and the *asuras* busied themselves with the various tasks assigned to them. At the supplication of the two clans, Adisesha lifted the Mandara Mountain and transported it to the shore of the ocean on his mighty coils.

Indra, accompanied by Bali, Brhaspati and Sukra led a delegation to Vasuki, the serpent king. They requested the serpent to serve as their churning-rope, promising to give him a share of the *amrita* as his reward.

Vasuki smiled at Indra in agreement. "After all, I am the eldest son of Kadru, your mother's own sister – this makes you my brother." He turned to the *asura* king. "And who is Bali? He is my grandson. It will be my pleasure to assist you both in the churning of the ocean!"

To Kasyapa's surprise, Rahu and Ketu came running pell-mell toward the hermitage. They came to a stop before him, excitement writ large on their faces.

"Father," Rahu burst into speech. "I have great tidings! The *devas* and the *asuras* have formed a pact: they plan to collaborate in the churning of the Ocean of Milk in order to obtain *amrita*!"

"Churning of the Ocean of Milk?!" Kasyapa exclaimed in astonishment. "For *amrita*?"

"Yes, father," Ketu reiterated eagerly. "Indra met our King Bali and sought his assistance. They plan to use the Mandara Mountain as the churning-staff. And I heard that *amrita* is a medicine which will make us immortal!"

"We have decided to follow the *asura* army in this venture, father," Rahu declared.

"My sons, do not rush recklessly into adventure. There is no need to crave this *amrita*. Remain here and savour the delights of a tranquil life."

"And what is your objection to my son gaining immortality?"

Kasyapa looked up in astonishment at the sarcastic words – Simhika stood over him, her eyes blazing with fury.

"Simhika …!"

"Rahu and Ketu: you do need to beg anybody for their permission to drink the divine *amrita*!"

Danudevi's lips curled in contempt as she came to stand in solidarity beside Simhika. She urged the duo: "Go ahead, my sons!"

Rahu and Ketu, smiling proudly, left on their eager quest.

On the shore of the Ocean of Milk, the serpent king, Vasuki, coiled himself around the Mandara Mountain: the churning-rod and rope were ready. The *devas* picked up Vasuki's head and lined up against his front torso.

The *asuras* immediately protested: "Why should we belittle ourselves by carrying the snake's hind quarters?!"

The gods peaceably bowed to their demand and moved to Vasuki's tail, leaving the *asura*'s to hold the snake's head.

The gods and the *asuras* commenced to pull the serpent-rope back and forth, churning the waters of the ocean. However, the mammoth Mandara Mountain, lacking equilibrium, began to sink into the ocean bed.

Lord Vishnu immediately assumed the form of a giant turtle and dived into the ocean. He supported the mountain on his broad back, measuring an incredible one lakh *yojanas* in width. The prodigious churning of the ocean now proceeded unhindered, with the *devas* and *asuras* working enthusiastically in tandem.

Suddenly, dense, toxic fumes rose from the water, emitting angry sparks: it was the dreadful poison, Haalaahala. In abject terror, the *devas* and *asuras* dropped the churning-rope and ran helter-skelter in panic. On Brahma's advice, the gods implored Lord Shiva to come to their aid and shield the worlds from this poisonous deluge.

Lord Shiva instantaneously appeared on the scene. The Lord extended his right hand, adorned with the serpent-bracelet, over the ocean and intoned the syllable *Hum*. As the profound vibrations of Lord Shiva's *Humkaara* resonated over the three worlds, the sinister spread of the poison was dammed. The liquid toxin solidified into a vaporous, dark cloud, which quickly metamorphosed into a black elephant. This is turn rapidly assumed the smaller form of a boar and then, a jet-black cuckoo. Finally, the toxic Haalaahala was reduced to the form of a tiny rose-apple, glowing on Lord Shiva's palm.

Shiva – Lord Vaidyanath, the Master of Medicine, swallowed the rose-apple with a serene smile, and immobilized it in his gullet. The globule of poison gleamed like a blue diamond under the translucent, white skin of his throat.

A murmur of awe rippled through the gathered company, which broke into spontaneous chants of "Nilakantha!" "Nilakantha!" glorifying Lord Shiva's feat with a new name. The Blue-Throated One serenely accepted their homage and advised the *devas* and *asuras* to resume their interrupted churning of the Ocean of Milk.

The venture continued rapidly under the deafening roar of the agitated water, which drenched the participants in a cascading spray.

Eventually, a woman emerged from the ocean. The curious spectators were instantly repulsed by her hideous demeanour: red eyes protruded from a black-complexioned, ugly face; her smile was a grimace and her coarse laughter grated on their ears. In one accord, the *devas* and *asuras* turned away from the stranger in patent revulsion.

The woman approached the *Trimurti*, who stood overseeing the churning of the Ocean of Milk. Unable to stand the sight of the repugnant woman, the three Gods, in their turn, averted their eyes. However, the hapless Brahma, with his four faces, was forced to endure her in his view.

"Who am I?" the woman questioned the Holy Trinity. "What is my purpose?"

Lord Shiva and Brahma turned to Lord Vishnu, deferring to him.

Taking the initiative, Lord Vishnu said: "As you are the first to emerge from the ocean, you are Jyeshtha – the eldest. You will henceforth be known as Jyeshthadevi. It is evident that you are the embodiment of ill-omened traits: as such, you will also be known as Alakshmi and Moodevi."

"Jyeshthadevi ... Alakshmi ... Moodevi ..." Jyeshtha grimaced in hideous satisfaction. "And where is my dwelling place?"

"As you are the goddess of inauspiciousness, you will be found in all bleak places where misfortune and adversity reign." Lord Vishnu gestured to her in curt dismissal. "Go and take up your abode in all such places!"

To the relief of all present, Jyeshtha moved silently away, her distorted body fading into the distance.

After another period of prolonged churning, an eight-petalled lotus in full bloom floated up from the surface of the ocean, holding Sri Mahalakshmi tenderly in its folds. All the *devas* and *asuras* bowed reverentially in instinctive response to her exquisite, ethereal beauty. Mahalakshmi gazed at Vishnu with her limpid, lotus-petal-like eyes. Lord Vishnu, exhilarated by this exquisite apparition, held out his arms and received her into his embrace.

A crescent moon now rose from the agitated waters and hovered in the air. Lord Shiva, burning with the toxic fire of the Haalaahala which he had ingested and arrested in his throat, picked the silver arc and placed it on his matted locks. From there, the crescent moon shed its cool light on the Lord.

Next came the precious gem, *Kaustubha*, which Lord Vishnu accepted to adorn his sacred chest.

This was followed in quick succession by the divine flowering plant, the *parijatha, Uchchaisrava, Airavata, Kamadhenu, Kalpavrksha* and all the other heavenly objects. Indra received the *apsaras* who next emerged from the ocean and gladly took possession of all his former wealth, ejected from *Swarga* by Durvasa's malediction.

Enthused by the bounty pouring from the Ocean of Milk, the gods and demons threw themselves into their churning with renewed vigor.

Soon, a divine individual emerged from the ocean. His red eyes gleamed from his blue-complexioned face, framed by lustrous, black tresses. His radiant chest was adorned with a myriad gold ornaments. His hands reverentially carried a *kalasa*. This was Dhanvantari, bearing the pot of divine *amrita*. Dhanvantari walked sedately towards the shore, stepping softly on the tides. He reached the shore, to the dignified applause of the watching *devas*.

Suddenly, an *asura* rushed to intercept him, snatched the precious pot from his hands and took to his heels. A second *asura* set out in hot pursuit, jumped on his fleeing comrade, and forcibly relieved him of the *kalasa*. The demon with the prize himself became the victim of attack by yet another covetous *rakshasa*. The pot of nectar changed hands in quick succession as the demons fought recklessly over it.

Indra and his company of *devas* were aghast at the turn of events. They watched in consternation as the *asuras'* fight deteriorated into a free-for-all. The anxious gods tuned to Lord Vishnu for guidance. Lord Vishnu placated them with a reassuring smile.

Before their astonished eyes, he transformed himself into Mohini – a damsel of extraordinary beauty. The gods were spellbound by her charm: momentarily, it even slipped their minds that this lovely damsel was none other than Lord Vishnu!

On their part, the *asuras* stared entranced at Mohini's captivating grace: to them, she was the very embodiment of all things beautiful. The sight of the lovely damsel was enough to banish all thoughts of the *amrita* from their minds. Lord Vishnu's mesmerizing charm engulfed the *asuras'* psyche like a thick fog shrouding the landscape.

The demon who currently held the pot of *amrita* meekly approached Mohini with an obsequious smile. "It is obvious that you are here solely to look out for our welfare," he said ingratiatingly. "We are all great warriors, descended from the celebrated lineage of Sage Kasyapa *prajapati*. We have obtained the *amrita* by churning the Ocean of Milk. And now, we have been reduced to fighting among ourselves over our share of the spoils." He bowed to her. "We are captivated by your beauty and seek your help. Will you be kind enough to distribute the *amrita* among us?"

Mohini took in the nodding faces of the encircling crowd of demons, who chorused: "Yes, this beauty is the one who deserves the honour of distributing the nectar of immortality!"

Mohini darted a coquettish look at the excited *asuras* milling around her and said sweetly: "As a woman, I cannot show any partiality in the serving of food. The *devas* and the *asuras* are equal in my sight. I am aware that both of you are descendants of Kasyapa *prajapati*. You have also shared in the prodigious labour of churning the ocean. I will distribute the *amrita* among all of you."

She went on to bestow a ravishing smile on the demons and cajoled them into an orderly file. Seduced by her charm, the *asuras* acceded to her proposal and docilely seated themselves in a row. They graciously beckoned the gods to come forward and sit in a parallel row.

Letting her upper garment fall sensuously from her shoulder in apparent carelessness, Mohini took the pot of nectar from the hands of the compliant *asura*. Completely bewitched by her seductive grace, the demons drank in her beauty with hungry eyes – while the discerning gods drank the *amrita* she surreptitiously served them!

However, Rahu and Ketu were not taken in by Mohini's devious charade. Their keen eyes saw Mohini dispensing the nectar of immortality to the gods. Rahu bent his head and whispered suggestively to Ketu, who sat beside him. In a twinkling, the duo assumed the guise of *devas* and stealthily joined the row of gods. Their transformation passed unnoticed, escaping the attention of both gods and demons and of Mohini, preoccupied with the distribution of the *amrita*. However, Surya and Chandra, more perceptive than their comrades, spotted the clever machinations of the two *asuras* and alerted Mohini.

Lord Vishnu immediately resumed his true form and beheaded Rahu and Ketu with his Sudarshana *chakra*. However, by the time the whirling golden discus reached them, the nectar consumed by the *asuras* had passed into their throats. Consequently, their heads remained alive – even when separated from their lifeless torsos.

The scales fell from the *asuras'* eyes. Aware that they had been cheated, they went on the rampage and attacked the *devas*. A terrible battle ensued, in which the demons suffered heavy casualties. Securing the pot of *amrita*, the gods, under Indra, triumphantly returned to *Swarga* with their recovered wealth and treasure.

Sukra invoked the Mrtasanjeevani to bring the dead *asuras* back to life. King Bali gathered his dejected subjects and returned to his own *asura* kingdom with a heavy heart.

Rahu and Ketu made their way back to the hermitage, minus their bodies. Kasyapa and his wives were aghast at the sight of Rahu and Ketu's arrival in the form of talking heads.

Rahu elaborated on the course of events which had resulted in their sorry plight. His mother, Simhika, and Danudevi, Ketu's foster mother, burst into loud lamentation, while their wives, Simhi and Chitralekha, gave way to a paroxysm of sobs. The women could not digest the fact that Rahu and Ketu had irrevocably lost their torsos. Kasyapa, Aditi, Diti and the others in the family tried in vain to comfort the grief-stricken women.

Rahu's only son, Meghahasa, flew into a towering rage at the misfortune which had befallen his father and uncle.

Kasyapa attempted to placate him: "Meghahasa, this is the will of the Supreme God. Lord Vishnu ordains the unfolding of every development in the three worlds. It must be conceded that Rahu and Ketu were at fault: like everyone else, they should have awaited their turn to receive the amrita. It was their rash behavior which led to their doom."

Diti glared accusingly at her husband. "To hear you talk, one would think that you are the father of Aditi's children alone! Supported by Vishnu, Aditi's sons constantly slaughter my sons, along with the sons of Danu and my other sisters." She lashed out furiously at Kasyapa. "After all, Rahu and Ketu are Surya's cousins through his mother: was he not at fault in implicating them?"

"Yes," Danu added her angry criticism, "It was Surya and Chandra who were instrumental in Vishnu's beheading of Rahu and Ketu!"

"Tell me – who is to take care of Simhi and Chitralekha?" Simhika upbraided Kasyapa. "How will they live with husbands who do not have torsos?"

At these words, Simhi and Chitralekha burst into a fresh bout of weeping.

"My dear mothers, do not abandon yourselves to despair – dry your tears." Meghahasa straightened his shoulders in determination and looked into his mother, Simhi's eyes. "Mother, I, Meghahasa, Rahu's son, am very much alive. Furthermore, I still have a torso with a head attached to it! I will not close my eyes in slumber until I restore their bodies to my father and uncle!"

"Meghahasa ...." Rahu was dumbstruck, his eyes brimming with tears of pride and happiness.

"Megha," Ketu exclaimed, "your words give me renewed hope!"

"I will perform penance to propitiate Lord Shiva of Kailash!" Meghahasa declared. "I will implore him to restore your bodies to you." Meghahasa hurried from the ashram on his urgent quest.

Simhidevi and Chitralekha tenderly gathered their husbands' heads, which were suspended in the air, and pressed them to their breasts.

Meghahasa commenced his penance. On hearing about this development through Sage Narada, the anxious Indra sought Brhaspati's advice.

"Master," Indra said, "Lord Vishnu beheaded Rahu and Ketu as punishment for disguising themselves as devas."

"Yes, Mahendra," agreed Brhaspati. "That is something which is widely known."

"Sage Narada now informs me that Meghahasa, Rahu's son, is engaged in penance to bring about the restoration of their torsos." He paused. "I say we disrupt his *tapas* before it is too late. What do you think, *gurudev?*"

"Indra, the entire clan of *asuras* remains our arch-enemy – and all of them have their complete bodies. In the event of Rahu and Ketu regaining their lost bodies, this will in no way enhance the threat they pose to the *devas*." Brhaspati smiled reassuringly at the king of the gods. "By all means, let Rahu and Ketu become whole again: it will not affect us in any way!"

Indra heaved a sigh of relief. "In that case, I find Meghahasa's *tapas* admirable!"

Meghahasa's penance grew in intensity until the extraordinary heat generated by it compelled Lord Shiva to grant him his *darshan*.

"My boy," Shiva asked, "what do you desire from me?"

"*Bhagavan*, kindly restore to my father, Rahu, and his brother, Ketu, the bodies which were sundered by Vishnu." Meghahasa folded his hands in supplication. "Also grant them power which surpasses the might of Surya and Chandra, who were instrumental in their decapitation and subsequent misery."

"Meghahasa," said Lord Shiva, "it is impossible to restore Rahu and Ketu's torsos, which were severed by Sri Mahavishnu with his Sudarsana *chakra*." He paused. "However, I will make an amendment to ameliorate their present condition: in the eyes of all onlookers, Rahu and Ketu will appear to be whole."

"I am indeed blessed!" exclaimed Meghahasa in delight.

"As for your second wish," continued Shiva, "I grant it in its entirety." Lord Shiva raised his hand in benediction and disappeared.

Rahu and Ketu's wives, Simhidevi and Chitraleka, erupted into happiness at the sight of their husbands entering the hermitage with their heads once again appended to their bodies.

"My son has succeeded in his penance!" Simhika said proudly, eyes brimming with tears of joy.

"Sister, Meghahasa is my son, too!" exclaimed Chitralekha, wiping her tear-streaked face. "My husband and I are indebted to him for eternity!"

Meghahasa returned to the hermitage to bask in his happiness at the sight of Rahu and Ketu with their whole bodies.

"Father ... Uncle ..." he said in triumph. "Lord Shiva has granted you both the potential to surpass the might of Surya and Chandra. He has also ordained that you will soon attain a status equal to theirs!"

"Son, your tidings gladden my heart!" exclaimed Rahu. His eyes darkened. "We will avenge ourselves on Surya and Chandra for the wrong done to us: this will make the boon you obtained on our behalf truly meaningful."

<hr />

Rahu and Ketu sat on the banks of the river watching the rays of the setting sun paint the sky in vibrant hues of purple and gold. They remained oblivious to the beauty lavished on them. Rahu's eyes were hard and his flushed face mirrored the fire of vengeance which consumed his soul.

"Ketu," he said in cold determination. "It is time to wreak our vengeance on Surya."

"Brother, what can we do?" Ketu asked.

"Lord Shiva has granted us manifold powers. We will use them to make Surya invisible to the worlds – and the worlds invisible to him!" He continued angrily. "He prevented us from swallowing the *amrita*: now, we will swallow him!"

"That would be befitting punishment, indeed!" Ketu applauded.

The sun sank into the horizon and darkness blanketed the three worlds. Rahu and Ketu remained silent, engrossed in schemes to satisfy their burning desire for revenge.

"Brother ..." Ketu said hesitantly. "Is it possible for us to consume and digest Surya?"

Rahu shook his head vehemently. "Digesting him would be irrevocable: that is not sufficient punishment for him. He must undergo continuous torment!" His eyes gleamed in hatred. "Surya flaunts his power only during the daytime – that is when we must bring him to his knees! We will swallow him during the day and vomit him at night!"

"Bravo! What a wonderful plan!" Ketu jumped up in enthusiasm. "That would indeed be suitable punishment for Surya." He pointed to the rising moon in the west. "And what about Chandra?" he asked.

"We will deal with him in the same way: we will wreak vengeance on them by swallowing Surya by day and Chandra by night!"

"Great! We will demonstrate our combined might by taking chances in swallowing them," Ketu said defiantly.

"I will swallow Surya: Chandra is yours!" Rahu stood up determinedly.

Ketu looked up at the moon and gnashed his teeth. "Surya and Chandra will endure eternal torment: we will teach them a fitting lesson for the injustice meted out to us!" "

They will suffer agonies in our abdomens!" Rahu declared in smug menace.

Sage Kasyapa, in the midst of his morning ablutions at the river, looked up in surprise at the sky – there was a definite decrease in the sun's radiance! He kept his fascinated eyes glued to the sun as an extraordinary scene unfolded before him ....

A dim patch appeared on one edge of the golden orb. The dark silhouette spread inexorably over the sun's surface and engulfed it in its entirety. The sun was now completely masked by a black disc. The rising sun had vanished, taking with it its heat and light!

Kasyapa, completely at sea as to this abnormal phenomenon, walked rapidly back to his hermitage in the unnatural darkness.

The unexplained, abrupt disappearance of the rising sun threw the three worlds into premature darkness. Time came to a standstill, with routines in shambles and nature herself coming to a confused halt. The lotuses which unfolded in response to the warmth of the sun's gentle rays shrunk and wilted.

Kasyapa's hermitage was in an uproar, as the sun's disappearance was excitedly discussed.

Simhika, Danu, Simhidevi and Chitralekha soon recovered from their initial shock. Once Ketu explained the cause of Surya's absence from the daytime sky, they exulted in Rahu's triumph over his nemesis.

Aditi, overhearing their excited talk, rushed to Kasyapa to report that Rahu had swallowed Surya in vindictive fury. Aditi, eyes brimming with tears, implored her husband to go to Surya's aid.

Kasyapa heaved a sigh of regret. "Aditi," he said, "What you ask of me is beyond my power." His pitying eyes reflected his helplessness. "This disastrous state of affairs will not be confined to one day: Rahu and Ketu will persist in their vendetta. Remember, they possess the inherent *tamasic* qualities of *rakshasas*: as such, they will not give up their aggressive tactics."

"Do you mean to say that nothing can be done while the one who bestows life-giving heat and light to the worlds is ...."

Kasyapa hushed her indignant outburst with a conciliatory smile and said, "Aditi, the Supreme God, Vishnu, who blessed you with Surya, will deal with this – let us leave matters in his eminently capable hands!"

———

As night fell, Rahu released Surya from his confinement. Surya emerged, disoriented and drowsy.

Rahu looked at Surya in gloating triumph and crowed: "You made Vishnu decapitate us with his discus once – just once!" Rahu laughed harshly. "But our vengeance will inflict unrelenting torment on you. Rahu and Ketu will punish you through all eternity!"

———

Compressed in the dark recesses of Rahu's abdomen all day, Surya was now debilitated and completely depleted of energy. His crushed body screamed out in agony at the unprecedented, cruel punishment it had endured. He deduced the primary reason for his alarming condition: his body had been ravaged by the contaminated saliva in Rahu's mouth. His sense of humiliation and outrage added salt to his wounds.

Samjna rushed to meet him as he entered his palace. "*Swami!*" she cried out anxiously. "What ill has befallen you? Why was it dark during the day? What is the meaning of this?"

"Samjna," replied Surya wearily. "You know that I pointed out Rahu and Ketu to Lord Vishnu when they attempted to obtain the *amrita* in the guise of *devas*. It appears that they have been nursing a deep resentment against me." He continued with a wry smile. "Rahu has warned me that today was but the first day of his revenge – he will persist in swallowing me every day!"

"Swami!" Samjna gasped in alarm. "Do they truly possess such power?"

"Yes, they do," Surya was forced to concede. "Rahu proved it by swallowing me today."

"But, Swami ..." Samjna was distraught. "What will happen to you if they repeatedly swallow you as they threaten to do?"

Surya shook off his lethargy and straightened his shoulders. "They will not succeed, Samjna." His voice was resolute. "Today, Rahu demonstrated his might – tomorrow I, Surya, will demonstrate mine!"

⚬⚬⚬

The next morning, the sun rose in sedate glory. Rahu, concealed behind a bank of clouds, burst out of hiding and gave a bark of sarcastic laughter. His cavernous mouth yawned open to reveal terrifying rows of vicious teeth. His moist red tongue seemed to be dripping blood.

"Surya!" Rahu taunted. "What an auspicious morning! Come, it is time for you to enjoy your usual repose in the cool darkness of my stomach!" Rahu approached Surya with his mouth open wide.

Suddenly, the sun's core underwent a dramatic transformation. Phenomenal heat radiated outwards to the corona – the sun was now a raging ball of fury. Tongues of flame streaked out to lash the atmosphere. In the twinkling of an eye, the east became an ocean of fire.

Rahu's headlong rush towards Surya grinded to an abrupt halt. The blast of the inferno hit him head-on. The acrid odour of his own singed hair assaulted his nostrils. He hung in the air, frozen in terror, unable to believe the evidence of his eyes.

The ball of fire grew redder by the moment. The outraged Surya erupted into a frenzy of hot rage, hurling heatwaves in every direction. Rahu felt himself being engulfed by the fiery tides and pulled relentlessly towards the heart of the inferno. Breaking into a sweat of panic, Rahu, fearing that he would be reduced to ashes if he lingered, turned tail and fled to safety.

"Come on, Rahu! The day remains auspicious: come and swallow me!" Surya taunted the asura. "Let us see your vengeance!"

Surya's loud, mocking laughter followed Rahu as the asura made his ignominious retreat.

⚬⚬⚬

Surya, wearing his intense heat as a protective armour against Rahu's depredation, sedately continued on his routine diurnal journey, beaming in triumph.

However, the abnormally high temperature, which fended off Rahu, also ravaged the entire cosmos. The waters of the oceans and rivers evaporated in the shimmering heat. Rocks, and the exposed mountains themselves, developed cracks and splintered in self-combustion. Surya's rampant fury brought the universe to the brink of fiery catastrophe.

———

Indra and Brhaspati were bewildered by the strange absence of Surya one day, and the alarming magnification of his heat on the next. As they struggled in vain to comprehend the reasons for these dangerous developments, they heard the chant: "Narayana!"

They turned with eager relief to Sage Narada who explained: "Rahu has been nursing a grudge against Surya right from the day of his decapitation by Lord Vishnu for attempting to obtain the *amrita* in disguise. In revenge, Rahu swallowed Surya, shrouding the worlds in darkness. Surya, having experienced a day's agony in the confines of Rahu's stomach, has now transformed himself into a fiery ball to repel the *asura's* attacks."

"What about the dangerous repercussions of this feud on all living beings in the three worlds?" Indra asked in agitation. "What will happen?"

"Narayana!" exclaimed Narada in helpless chagrin. "That is a question you must direct to my father, Brahma!"

Indra rose hurriedly to his feet saying, "*Gurudev,* there is no time to be lost: let us go!"

———

In urgent tones, Indra gave Brahma his account of the catastrophe facing the worlds as a result of Surya's defensive reaction to Rahu's offensive.

"Sage Narada advised us to seek your aid, your eminence," Brhaspati added.

"Hmm …" Brahma mulled over the circumstances. "We seem to be caught on the horns of a dilemma: if Surya reduces his intensity to normal levels, he faces the risk of being swallowed by Rahu yet again; on the other hand, if he maintains his protective stance, the animate and inanimate worlds are in danger of annihilation." Brahma heaved a sigh. "This is beyond me – I can see no way out of this predicament!"

The Creator came to a quick decision: "Our only option is to seek Sri Mahavishnu's intercession."

Indra bowed in acceptance of this proposal. "We will go at once to Sri Hari, *Bhagavan*."

"Mahendra," Brahma said. "This is a very grave situation. I will accompany you."

———

Lord Vishnu gave the delegation a patient hearing. He smiled serenely and said: "If Surya does not reduce the intensity of his heat, the worlds and their inhabitants are in danger ... if he does decrease his temperature, he himself is in danger. Under these circumstances, Surya has no choice but to maintain his fiery form. At the same time, the three worlds must be shielded from the intolerable radiation. This calls for a force to be permanently deployed in front of Surya in order to filter the heat emitted by him and reduce it to bearable levels."

"Father," said Brahma humbly. "You alone can tell us where such a powerful shield can be found."

"*Bhagavan*, what is that force?" Indra asked eagerly.

Lord Vishnu's eyes twinkled. "Not 'what,' Indra, but 'who': ask me 'who' that force is!"

Brahma, Indra, Brhaspati and Narada looked at the Lord expectantly.

"That force is none other than Aruna, the thigh-less!" proclaimed Lord Vishnu.

"Aruna!" Brahma exclaimed in astonishment.

"Yes," said the Lord. "He is Kasyapa's son by his wife, Vinata. In spite of lacking lower limbs, Aruna's body possesses the strength to absorb and filter Surya's heat. Brahma, it is your duty to convince Aruna to take up his permanent station before Surya on his chariot."

Brahma obediently saluted Lord Vishnu. The rest of the company followed suit and took their leave of Sri Mahavishnu.

———

"Master!" Chidananda pointed out eagerly. "You have not related the story of Aruna's birth."

"Aruna's birth had no relevance to our earlier narrative," Nirvikalpananda replied. "Now that he enters the picture, I will give you the complete details of his origin and life.

"I have already told you how Kasyapa *prajapati's* wives, Vinata and Kadru, asked him for children. While Kadru wished for a thousand Naga sons, Vinata desired two sons of formidable strength.

"Sage Kasyapa granted their wishes. In due course, Kadru delivered one thousand eggs and Vinata, two. The sage cautioned them to keep the eggs carefully in pots of ghee and protect them. After a few days, Kadru's eggs hatched and Vasuki, Sesha, Iravatha, Takshaka and other serpents emerged from them. However, to Vinata's disappointment, her eggs remained unchanged.

"As the days passed, Vinata grew increasingly anxious. Her younger sister was now a mother, but she herself continued to be childless! She watched her eggs with growing impatience. Finally, reaching the end of her endurance, she removed one of eggs from the pot of ghee and dropped it on the ground. A baby boy emerged from the broken shell: to Vinata's horror, as a result of her impetuosity, the infant was only half-developed and had no limbs beneath his waist. This boy was Aruna. He is also called Anoora – the thigh-less one.

"Aruna was furious with his mother for rashly breaking the egg before the complete development of his body. Blaming her for his deformity, Aruna cursed her to become her sister Kadru's slave. He strictly commanded her to leave the other egg in the pot of ghee. He assured her that it would hatch in its own good time and a brother of great strength would emerge from it. This son would procure her freedom from her slavery. With this advice, Aruna stoically bid his mother farewell and flew into the vast expanse of the sky," Nirvikalpananda said.

"Master, did Aruna get married?" asked Vimalananda.

"Yes, Vimalananda," Nirvikalpananda said. "Aruna accepted Syeni as his wife and had two sons." He smiled at his four listeners. "You know who they are: one is Sampaati and the other is Jataayu. Both these eagles feature in the *Ramayana.*"

"Master," Sanananda asked curiously, "what happened to Vinata's other egg?"

"As Aruna predicted, a golden bird of awesome strength emerged from the second egg: it was none other than Garuda!" The master paused as the disciples exclaimed in wonder. "After freeing his mother from slavery, Garuda left to become Sri Mahavishnu's vehicle. And now, let us return to Rahu's life story! Bowing to Lord Vishnu's command, Brahma appeared before Aruna ..."

———∞∞———

Aruna prostrated himself before Brahma.

"May happiness be yours!" said Brahma in blessing.

"*Bhagavan,*" Aruna retorted, "how can this deformed being experience happiness?"

"Aruna," smiled Brahma, "I am here for the express purpose of showing you the path which leads to happiness and universal respect."

Aruna waited expectantly for the Creator to continue.

"Lord Vishnu has sent me here to command you to sit before Surya on his chariot. I hereby appoint you Surya's charioteer."

"*Bhagavan!*" exclaimed the surprised Aruna. "May I know the reason for this sudden appointment?"

Brahma acquainted Aruna with the prevailing circumstances: "Rahu swallowed Surya in an act of vengeance. In order to protect himself from further threats, Surya has increased his temperature to unendurable heights. Consequently, the worlds are buffeted by dangerous heat waves." Brahma urged his listener: "Aruna, you alone have the strength to filter Surya's heat. That is why we choose you to be his charioteer. Bow to my request and ..."

Aruna intervened quickly. "*Bhagavan,* I willingly accept your command as a boon bestowed on me – it is a mark of honour! After all, Surya is the son of my mother's elder sister, Aditi – I am fortunate to serve my elder brother as his charioteer. I am grateful to you for your grace." Aruna folded his hands in reverence.

Syeni, Aruna's wife, came to pay her respects to Brahma. Bowing to the Creator, she said: "*Bhagavan,* I beg you to bless my husband by making him whole."

Brahma's eyes were compassionate. "Syeni, your desire stems from your deep affection. However, any achievement by a person who is whole in body does not stand out – it is not a victory in the true sense of the word!"

Brahma's next words rang with conviction: "Aruna will prove to the world that a physical deformity is neither a curse nor an obstacle to achievement. Your husband will stand as the role model for all handicapped mortals and inspire them to great heights of accomplishment!"

"Your will is our treasure, my Lord!" Syeni said.

"Aruna," Brahma extended his hand. "Come, my son."

Aruna took the Creator's hand and both of them vanished together on their urgent mission.

⊗⊗

Surya strode briskly towards his chariot, heating himself up for the day ahead. He stopped in his tracks at Brahma's sudden appearance. To his surprise, the Lord held a stranger by the hand: it was a person with a partially developed body.

Surya folded his hands in reverence and saluted Brahma, who raised his own hand in benediction.

"Surya," Brahma introduced the stranger. "This is Aruna: he is none other than your younger brother."

"Younger brother?" Surya frowned in bewilderment.

"Yes, brother," Aruna replied. "I am the son of Vinata: your mother's younger sister. I am Aruna – also called Anoora." Aruna greeted Surya with respectfully folded hands.

Surya embraced Aruna warmly.

Lord Brahma explained the circumstances. "Surya, you are under constant danger of being swallowed by Rahu and Ketu at the first opportune moment. On the other hand, the flaming protective shield you have assumed in defense is wreaking havoc on the atmospheric balance. The worlds are reeling under the onslaught of your phenomenal heat." He continued, "Your brother, Aruna, has the strength to regulate your temperature – he will absorb your rays and filter them to endurable levels. Your life-giving rays will then reach the three worlds and bless them with prosperity as before. Position Aruna before you on the yoke of your chariot and accept him as your charioteer."

Surya folded his hands and bowed in acceptance. "I am indeed blessed!" he said.

As commanded by Brahma, Surya installed Aruna as his charioteer and took his own place behind him. Immediately, Surya's excessive heat was tempered by Aruna, who sat before him as a protective shield.

Brahma smiled contentedly at the pair and raised his hand in benediction over them.

⊗⊗

The astonished Rahu and Ketu noted the abrupt drop in Surya's temperature.

"Brother Rahu!" exclaimed Ketu. "It looks like the tide is turning in our favour! Come, let's not waste time in swallowing Surya – it's my turn now: I will show him what I'm made of!"

Rahu was more circumspect. "Let's first find out what's happening and then decide on our course of action," he said.

Concealing themselves behind a thick cloud in Surya's path, the *asuras* eagerly awaited his arrival. Soon, his glittering chariot appeared in the distance. To their surprise, an individual with an obviously deformed physique sat on the chariot's yoke, blocking Surya from their view. And, to their further amazement, Surya's heat was now reduced to normal levels.

Gradually, it dawned on the bewildered *asuras* that it was the strange charioteer who was instrumental in filtering and absorbing Surya's abnormal radiation.

"Brother," urged Ketu, in impetuous excitement. "Let's quickly swallow them both!"

Rahu cautioned his brother. "Ketu, we cannot attack the charioteer. He is the shield which protects all the beings of the worlds, including you and me, from the threat of Surya's intolerable heat waves. It is essential to the survival of the universe that Surya's heat remains confined to bearable levels." He continued thoughtfully: "We will have to bide our time and wait patiently until we can catch Surya unguarded and at his normal temperature."

Ketu was bitterly disappointed. "When can I swallow him? How I want to punish him right now!"

"We'll do one thing!" Rahu consoled his brother. "We will show ourselves to Surya in an indirect show of strength and make it clear to him that we are constantly on the alert to attack him: he will not have a moment's peace of mind!"

Rahu and Ketu waited in ambush for Surya. As the chariot drew near, the *asuras* burst out of hiding and heckled the vehicle's two passengers with loud jeers and raucous laughter.

Aruna turned to Surya in interrogation. Surya remained coolly self-possessed. "Aruna," he said in imperturbable composure. "Keep going. Do not halt the chariot."

Aruna, obeying his instructions, asked, "But, brother ... who are they?"

"They are also our father's sons." Surya replied. "Keep going now – I will explain everything to you later."

Surya gave Rahu and Ketu an impassive stare as he passed on.

———∝≋∝———

Kasyapa *prajapati* stood in the *ashram* grounds, surrounded by a happy crowd: Aditi, Vinata and Kadru, relief writ large on their faces, rejoiced at Surya's escape and his return to his normal condition.

"*Swami*," Aditi addressed her husband. "Surya has reduced his temperature to regular levels."

"As always, your son considers the welfare of the three worlds," Sage Kasyapa smiled benignly at her.

Aditi did not return his smile. "*Swami*, Surya has lowered the abnormal intensity of his radiation. He is now vulnerable to attack once more. I am worried that Rahu and Ketu may go on the offensive again!"

"Narayana!" Everyone looked up at Sage Narada's familiar chant.

"Now, now," Narada reassured Aditi. "There is nothing to worry about! In practical terms, Surya has not lowered his guard: he remains well-protected by the fiery defense mechanism he has assumed." He smiled at the assembled gathering: "As ordained by Sri Mahavishnu, Brahma has positioned an individual of formidable strength in front of Surya as his charioteer. It is this living shield which regulates the heat waves radiating from Surya and defends the worlds from the ravages of his fiery rays."

"Oh, this is good news indeed, Sage Narada," said Kasyapa. "By the way, who is this mighty person who shields the cosmos from our son's destructive heat?"

Narada's eyes twinkled. "That great person is none other than this great person's son!" The sage pointed laughingly at Kasyapa.

"What?!" exclaimed the bewildered Kasyapa.

"Yes," Narada said with a smile. "It is Vinatadevi's son, Aruna, born with an unformed body."

Kasyapa, along with Aditi and her sisters, turned to Vinata in one accord.

"Can this be true?" Vinata asked tremulously. "Is my son his elder brother, Surya's, charioteer?"

"Yes, Vinatadevi," Narada reiterated emphatically. "Your malformed son is fortunate indeed!"

"I did my son grave injustice by cutting short his development through my reckless impatience. It was I who made Aruna deformed." Vinata wiped the tears of joy which coursed down her cheeks. "But the Supreme God, in his mercy, has redressed the wrong done to my son!"

Kasyapa congratulated his wife: "Vinata, you are indeed fortunate: one son is Lord Vishnu's vehicle; the other is Surya's charioteer."

"Let us add another blessing to that – Aruna will be the one to grant his *darshan* to the entire cosmos before they glimpse Surya himself. Aruna's dawn will herald Surya's rising!" Narada smiled complacently at this eminently satisfactory state of affairs.

Subsequent to Sage Narada's visit, Simhika, Danu, Simhidevi, Chitralekha and Meghahasa held a private conclave in a secluded corner of the hermitage. Danu, who had eavesdropped on Narada's conversation with Vinata, acquainted the group with the information regarding Aruna.

"It is all Vishnu's doing!" raged Simhika. "He persists in fanning the flame of enmity among our children!"

"Yes," Danu reinforced her accusation. "He has deliberately made Surya's step-brother his charioteer. It is a ploy to foil Rahu and Ketu's scheme to wreak vengeance on Surya!"

"Now, our husbands will be unable to make Surya and Chandra pay for their treachery!" lamented Simhika.

"Why not?" The group looked up in surprise at these defiant words: Rahu stood before them, with Ketu by his side as usual.

"Aruna's presence, or absence, from Surya's side is immaterial to the execution of our plan." Ketu proclaimed arrogantly. "Our hunger for vengeance is immutable and we will not rest until it is appeased."

"Yes," added Meghahasa. "And the boons I have obtained for my father and uncle from Lord Shiva are formidable weapons in our armoury!"

"Well said, Meghahasa!" Rahu swelled in approval of his son's words. "Our power is unmatched! Surya thinks he has evaded capture by hiding behind Anoora." He snorted in contempt and continued. "Never fear – I will soon trap him and swallow him again."

"But, Anoora sits right in front of Surya," Simhidevi reminded them. "If he meets with harm, our mother-in-law, Vinatadevi, will endure untold agony!"

"*Devi*," Rahu reassured her. "Anoora will not suffer in any way. The poor boy has no legs – I would not dream of harming him." He continued confidently. "I can reach Surya in spite of Anoora shielding him. I will pull Surya into my mouth. Once he is inside, his heat will die." There was a proud gleam in Rahu's eyes. "He is merely Bhanu: the radiance – I am Swarbhanu: the splendor of radiance! Moreover, I am also armed with Lord Shiva's priceless boons."

"*Swami*," Chitralekha addressed her husband curiously. "Are you both planning to take turns in wreaking vengeance on Surya and Chandra?"

Ketu's terrifying gales of laughter assailed their ears. "Both of us harbor a grudge in our souls ... both of us burn with the desire for vengeance ... and both of us will swallow Surya and Chandra in alternate succession! We will reduce them to a state of abject helplessness and alarm: they will live in constant fear, trying in vain to guess when, and from whom, the next attack comes!"

"I pay obeisance to the feet of my father and mother!" Sage Narada stood before Brahma and Saraswati with respectfully folded hands.

Saraswati's eyes twinkled. "Narada, my son, and what juicy tidbit do you bring to your father's ears?"

"Narayana! Narayana!" Narada exclaimed in apparent innocence. "And what makes you suspect that I bring fresh tidings, mother?"

"My son, we all know that you would not honour anyone with your presence unless you have some information to impart or gather!" Brahma smiled in wry amusement. "Do you think Saraswati, the goddess of speech, cannot deduce your motive? Come, now: tell us the purpose of your visit. Why are you here – to collect information, or to disseminate it?"

"Father," Narada smiled back in surrender. "You know that I can do neither without it being decreed by you! Grant me the pleasure of telling you what I have seen and heard." He continued: "At Lord Vishnu's command, you positioned Aruna before Surya and successfully regulated the heat waves emanating from him – but you have overlooked the need to regulate Rahu!"

Brahma nodded thoughtfully at Brahma's words.

"Without Aruna as a protective shield, Surya's fiery demeanour kept Rahu at bay. But now... the situation has changed," Narada emphasized.

Goddess Saraswati chuckled. "It looks like father and son wracked their brains and came up with a solution to one problem – but failed to take into consideration the other! You controlled the menace posed by Surya's insufferable heat – and neglected to deal with the menace posed by Rahu!"

"Saraswati, that cannot be termed neglect," Brahma protested mildly. "It is more of an oversight. Moreover, Vishnu and I cannot resolve this issue unilaterally without Lord Shiva's contribution: remember, it was he who granted Rahu and Ketu boons through Meghahasa."

"*Swami*," Saraswati smiled complacently. "Of course, I am aware of that." She paused meaningfully. "It is obvious that the *Trimurti* must meet and hammer out a consensual solution."

"Well said, mother!" Narada was enthusiastic at this proposal. "I come here straight from Sage Kasyapa's hermitage – and Kasyapa and Aditi are of the same opinion. They insist that something must to be done to restrain Rahu, as he will not be deterred by Aruna's mere presence."

Brahma nodded in agreement. "Yes, Narada, your mother is right. It is high time the *Trimurti* came together to deal with this predicament once and for all!" He ordered his son: "Until a permanent solution is found, keep a watchful eye on Rahu."

"It shall be done, father. It is essential that the *Trimurti* resolve this issue as fast as possible!"

Narada saluted his parents and hurried away.

⸻

Rahu streaked eastwards across the sky, intent on his mission of vengeance. He mulled over his plan of action. Today he would capture Surya and keep him confined in his stomach from dawn to dusk. It should be simple enough to approach Surya and swallow him quickly.

Aruna would not prove an obstacle to his goal. After all, Rahu had single-handedly vanquished Surya himself – surely a deformed Aruna, lacking lower limbs, could not mount any defence worth the name!

The exultant Rahu, confident in the success of his coming offensive, weaved playfully among the clouds: he floated serenely above them, fitfully concealed himself within their fluffy interiors and then banked to flash underneath their cover. He frolicked in glee, scattering the clouds into tatters of laughter. He emerged from a thick bank of cumulus and braked to an abrupt halt. His eyes widened in surprise, mixed with growing suspicion.

The *Trimurti* blocked his path. There before him stood Lord Vishnu, who had beheaded him, Lord Shiva, who has bestowed wondrous boons on him, and Lord Brahma, his own grandfather.

"I salute Lord Shiva's holy feet!" Rahu bowed in reverence to his benefactor.

Lord Shiva extended his hand in benediction over Rahu's bowed head and gently reprimanded the *asura*: "Rahu, it is not right to show overt partiality. Offer your salutations to Vishnu and Brahma too."

Rahu folded his hands perfunctorily in Lord Brahma's direction and turned toward Lord Shiva. *"Bhagavan,"* he said indignantly, "you know that Vishnu demonstrated his own partiality towards the *devas* by serving the *amrita* exclusively to them. He then beheaded Ketu and me for having had the presence of mind to sit with the gods!" Rahu pointed an accusing finger at Lord Vishnu, his words simmering with anger.

"Rahu," Vishnu smiled serenely. "Even before I could serve the *amrita*, you and Ketu, fearing that the *asuras* would not get their share, committed the grave mistake of disguising yourself as *devas*. Every crime merits its punishment."

"That does not excuse your **own** crime!" Rahu retorted.

Lord Vishnu asked in his turn: "When Dhanvantari emerged with the pot of *amrita*, an *asura* snatched it from him and fled. Was that not a crime? Why did you not condemn your fellow-demons' improper action?"

Rahu, at a loss for words, looked away peevishly.

Lord Shiva intervened emphatically: "Rahu, all this is water under the bridge. Let us forget the past. Your festering resentment against Surya goaded you into inflicting punishment on him by swallowing him. It is acceptable to retaliate against one's enemy: however, your action impinges on all the worlds." Lord Shiva locked eyes with the *asura*. "Rahu, the effect of your vengeance is not confined to Surya alone. You must put a stop to it!"

"Swami ..." Rahu faltered.

"In response to your son's penance, I lavished boons on you. These boons will earn you fame and secure your advancement." He smiled wryly. "Surya and Chandra merely pointed you out to Vishnu – it was Vishnu who beheaded you. Why then does your vengeance not extend to Vishnu? Is that not strange?"

"Rahu," Brahma spoke in conciliatory tones. "Your desire for revenge was born from impetuous anger, not from calm contemplation. You may subject your adversary to torment – but not at the cost of the well-being of the entire cosmos. You know that Lord Shiva is right."

"Rahu," Sri Mahavishnu said. "You were born as Sage Kasyapa's son, as ordained by me. Your birth has a purpose: and that is certainly not to inflict vengeance on Surya and Chandra!" He continued persuasively. "Soon, you will be anointed to take your place in a renowned company of the gods. At that time, the boon bestowed on you by Lord Shiva will come into effect. You will be worshipped by the three worlds. Prepare for that eminent role and banish your vendetta from your mind."

"Rahu, this is the wish of the *Trimurti*," Brahma emphasized.

Rahu looked silently at Lord Shiva, who added: "Rahu, it is in your interest to accept our proposal." He smiled reassuringly at the *asura*. "You will be endowed with a palatial abode in space and invested with special powers and duties."

Rahu folded his hands in reverence and addressed the Holy Trinity as one. "I swore an oath to my family to avenge myself on Surya and Chandra. I will keep my promise to them – at the same time, I will bow to the command of the *Trimurti*."

The three gods frowned in bewilderment.

"Contrary to our earlier resolution to exact revenge on them daily, Ketu and I will content ourselves with swallowing Surya and Chandra a few times each year. Again, instead of keeping them confined to our abdomens for an entire day, we will eclipse their power momentarily and then expel them." He insisted to the listening gods. "You must accept this compromise and bless us. Leave it to me to convince my brother, Ketu."

Lord Shiva mulled over the implications of this proposal. "In effect, your vengeance will be confined to a well-delineated, limited time." He came to a decision. "Rahu, we accept your proposition."

"So be it!" chorused Vishnu and Brahma in unison.

Rahu circumambulated the *Trimurti* with devoutly folded hands and came to stand before them again.

"Return to the hermitage, Rahu!" Lord Vishnu said with a smile.

"And that brings us to the end of Rahu's life story." Nirvikalpananda looked questioningly at his attentive listeners. "Any doubts? If so, let me hear them!"

"Master, did Rahu faithfully keep the promise he made to the *Trimurti*?" Sadananda asked.

"Certainly, my boy," the master was emphatic. "We all see Rahu and Ketu swallowing Surya and Chandra a few times a year for a limited period of time.

"Rahu and Ketu decided to swallow Surya during the day of a new moon and Chandra during the night of a full moon. We will elaborate on this when we move on to Ketu's life story. As I told you earlier, Ketu grew up with Rahu in Kasyapa's hermitage. He joined Rahu in disguising himself as a *deva* in order to obtain the *amrita* and, along with Rahu, was decapitated. Now, let us listen to the other significant events in Ketu's life ..."

Vimalananda respectfully intervened. "Master, wouldn't it be better if we first cleared our doubts regarding Ketu's origin?"

"That would certainly be best, Vimalananda," Nirvikalpananda agreed. "What is on your mind?"

"Master, according to you, Ketu emerged from the heated breath of Mrthyu and was brought up in Sage Kasyapa's hermitage ..."

"Yes, my boy," Nirvikalpananda interrupted him. "I have also given you my explanation for this. We have already arrived at a rational conclusion regarding Ketu's birth and upbringing."

"Yes, master – but some scriptures assert that Rahu was the only one to disguise himself as a god, and be beheaded, during the churning of the Ocean of Milk. According to those texts, while Rahu's head survived as Rahu, his body became Ketu."

"Ah," exclaimed Nirvikalpananda, "I see your confusion. I will address it in detail.

"Have you taken into consideration the form in which Ketu is worshipped in temples, along with the other *grahas*? This must be done in order to give due regard to the *Navagrahas'* believers and devotees. Their sensibilities must be respected before drawing any conclusion.

"Like the other eight *grahas*, Ketu is represented with a distinct body and features. Though many consider Rahu and Ketu to be shadow planets, it is generally accepted that they possess their own unique traits and personalities.

"Ketu boasts of a singular from. His prescribed worship and special eulogy are markedly distinct. His glow can be easily differentiated. He has specific features. In this context, it is logical to accept that he had his own particular identity right from the beginning."

The master continued in this vein. "Some scriptures specifically state that Ketu was born as an individual in his own right. The *Vishnudharmothara Purana* holds that Ketu was not a part of Rahu, but a separate entity. Again, the *Skaanda Purana* asserts that Rahu and Ketu were seated side by side during the distribution of the *amrita* by Lord Vishnu as Mohini. The *Ranganatha Ramayana* also supports this stand and says that Rahu and Ketu have their own separate physiques and unique characteristics. The last text unambiguously claims that Vishnu beheaded both Rahu and Ketu.

"Based on the established practice of worshipping Rahu and Ketu as different idol forms at temples, we can safely accept them as two distinct *grahas* right from their births," Nirvikalpananda explained.

"Master," Shivananda bowed in respect. "As always, your analysis is well reasoned and eminently satisfactory."

"So, let us resume Ketu's narrative using the same logical viewpoint. Everyone in Kasyapa's hermitage approved of the truce forged by Rahu with the *Trimurti*, except Ketu ..."

Nirvikalpananda launched his narrative once more.

THE LIFE OF KETU

The garden behind the hermitage was deserted except for one very angry, inconsolable individual – Ketu agitatedly paced up and down its narrow paths. A terrifying crimson hue animated his burning face and sparks of fury flashed from his red eyes.

Rahu's account of his pusillanimous treaty with the *Trimurti* echoed mockingly in Ketu's ears. It was evident that Rahu had been deceived by the sweet-talking Holy Trinity: why else would his brother have so easily agreed to give up his vendetta against Surya and Chandra, who had instigated Vishnu to behead him and Ketu? How could Rahu have ignored the oath they had taken to wreak continuous vengeance on Surya and Chandra?

Vishnu's charade during the distribution of the *amrita* was an insult, not only to him and his brother, but to the entire *rakshasa* clan. The gods undoubtedly deserved to be punished.

After Rahu's tame surrender, it would be best if they both parted ways. Ketu himself would single-handedly inflict punishment on Surya and Chandra – he would hold them captive by eclipsing their light. Surya would suffer under his hold on every day of the month. In Chandra's case, it would suffice to punish him on fifteen nights in a month – he would anyway wane under the influence of his chronic tuberculosis on the other fifteen nights.

Proud of his own determination and courage, Ketu laughed aloud.

"*Swami* ..." Ketu stopped short and turned in the direction of the faltering voice. His wife, Chitralekha, and his mother, Danudevi, were coming towards him.

"Son," Danu asked, "why are you here alone, laughing to yourself?"

"He is happy," Chitralekha remarked naively. But once they stood beside him, they looked askance at his thunderous countenance.

"Mother," Ketu exclaimed. "how can I be happy? Are we to be conciliated with a few paltry boons for all the hatred and insults of the past?! Mother, your son's heart burns!"

"I understand, my son," Danu consoled Ketu. "Surya and Chandra were responsible for your decapitation at Vishnu's ruthless hands. It is not right that they be allowed to get away scot-free for their heinous crime – they must be punished! You must regain your past glory!"

"*Swami* ..." Chitralekha said hesitantly, "the treaty forged by your brother, Rahu, seems to be just ..."

"Chitralekha!" Chitralekha and Danu froze in alarm at Ketu's roar of warning.

He continued angrily: "Rahu was bewitched! He has forgotten his vow to exact vengeance!"

Danudevi locked eyes with her furious son and asked, "Very well, Ketu, what do you plan to do, now?"

"I will burn Aditeya and Aatreya in the everlasting fire of my vengeance!" Ketu gnashed his teeth. Chitralekha looked at her mother-in-law in alarm.

"How would you accomplish that, son?" Danudevi calmly asked.

"How?!" Ketu laughed in derision. "Surya will vanish during every day of the month – Chandra will vanish during the first fifteen nights of the month. They will disappear into the dark cavern of my stomach!"

"Very well, Ketu," Danu said. "But, have you stopped to think about the consequences of your action on the three worlds?"

"Mother," Ketu said haughtily, "the worlds can be annihilated for all I care!! Tell me, mother, did any one of those worlds shed tears when our heads were sundered from our torsos?"

"If you swallow Surya, the worlds will languish in the absence of heat and light. Famine will raise its ugly head."

"Mother," Ketu shrugged callously, "I am indifferent to the suffering of the three worlds."

"And when you swallow Chandra," Danu persisted, "there will be no moonlight. The herbs which flourish in the cool light of the moon will perish. Without medicines, all diseased beings will inevitably die."

Ketu burst into cruel laughter. "I would be very happy if such an outcome came to pass! What a triumph that would be for my vengeance!"

Danudevi smiled enigmatically. "Son, the sunlight and the moonlight are not essential to the three worlds alone: certain other people are also dependent on them for survival."

"And who might they be, mother?" Ketu asked curiously.

"I, your father, your wife, my sisters, your *rakshasa* kin and, finally, you yourself, all need the light of the sun and the moon as a precondition for life! Have you forgotten this simple truth, Ketu?"

Danu's words cut him like a whiplash. Ketu stood with his mouth agape, his eyes fixed on his mother.

"*Swami*," Chitralekha said gently. "What your mother says is true: all of us at the hermitage grew weak when the sun failed to shine for just a single day!"

"My son, here is another fact you should keep in mind," Danudevi's voice was filled with compassion. "In order to take revenge on Surya, you must remain in good health – and in order to remain healthy, you require both sunlight and moonlight."

"Mother ..." Ketu faltered.

"Son, inflicting suffering on another makes sense only when it gives you joy. It would be self- defeating if your vengeance ruined your own welfare."

"How then can I taste vengeance, mother?" Ketu was disconsolate.

"Just emulate your elder brother, Rahu," Danu was serenely confident.

Ketu stared at his mother. 'Yes,' he thought, 'Mother is right! If one plans to push someone into a ravine, one must first have his own feet firmly planted on the overhanging cliff!'

Ketu nodded slowly in agreement. "Mother, you are right," he said. "I will follow brother Rahu's lead. He is yet to swallow Chandra – perhaps he has left him to me! I will swallow Chandra tonight!" Ketu exclaimed enthusiastically.

"Ketu," Danudevi said in wry amusement, "enthusiasm alone is not enough to ensure success. It should be complemented with intelligent thinking. Right now, Chandra is a crescent – soon he will grow to his full rotundity. On the night of the full moon, he will be at the peak of happiness and pride. That is when you must strike – the enemy's suffering will be multiplied if it shatters existing happiness." Her voice rose in command. "Son, attack Chandra on the night of the full moon!"

"Mother, your wisdom is past compare! I bow to your advice." He paused thoughtfully. "There are many days to go for the full moon. In that interim, I will concentrate on Surya!" Ketu gave a malicious cackle of laughter. "I will ensure that Surya is haunted by my constant presence!"

"Are you planning to swallow Surya?" Danudevi asked.

"No, mother," Ketu smiled. "In future, Rahu and Ketu will faithfully take turns to deal with Surya."

"Son, obtain Rahu's blessings before you leave," were Danudevi's affectionate words of parting.

⌘

Surya reclined complacently on the seat of his chariot. He was supremely secure in the confidence that he need no longer fear Rahu: the *Trimurti's* intervention had put paid to that threat. He was blessed with a charioteer who could instinctively comprehend the intentions of both the chariot's master and the steeds drawing it. This made Surya's diurnal journey across the daytime sky a pleasure.

Suddenly, he sat up in alarm. A hoot of blood-curdling laughter came to taunt him from the roaring clouds. Surya looked round him searchingly. The hideous sound seemed to emerge from a thick bank of clouds in his path. Who could this be? What was the reason for this jeering laughter? Was it Rahu?

The gales of merriment scattered the clouds with their ferocity, revealing Ketu's face: it hung in the air like a glistening, wicked clot of blood.

Aruna instinctively turned to his master. "Surya *Bhagavan*," he asked, "who is this demon?"

Surya's eyes were glued to the hideous face. "It is Ketu, Rahu's younger brother," he replied.

Ketu's cavernous mouth yawned open and the *asura* gestured at Surya to come forward. His red tongue was a bright flame inside the deep cavity. Wickedly pointed incisors and canines formed barriers framing the entrance to this abyss of doom. His taunts and terrifying laughter conveyed the warning: 'I am waiting to swallow you – be prepared!"

However, Surya noticed that Ketu remained equidistant from the chariot, even when he persisted in his chase. Rahu and Ketu had both nursed their resentment into full-blown hatred towards him and Chandra. Why had the *Trimurti* dealt with Rahu alone and ignored Ketu? Had they mistakenly assumed that Ketu bore no grudge against Surya? Were Rahu and Ketu in cahoots over some scheme to take turns in attacking him? Why did Ketu keep at a distance? These and a thousand other niggling doubts buzzed through Surya's anxious mind: his earlier complacence vanished into the blue sky.

As Surya continued on his passage, Ketu's mocking laughter followed him inexorably, echoing through the vast reaches of the atmosphere. It seemed as though the chariot was surrounded by an invisible crowd of jeering *asuras*.

At long last, it was the time of sunset. Surya heaved a sigh of relief. Aruna's face glowed with a serene smile and calm repose spread across the sky.

Surya looked back: Ketu remained at his fixed distance behind the chariot, leering at them.

Surya wondered: 'Was Ketu conveying a warning?' Surya reached out to the *Trimurti* in silent prayer.

Chandra, liberated from the curse pronounced on him by his father-in-law, Daksha *prajapati*, recovered from the dreadful tuberculosis which had decimated him for fifteen days. Over the next fifteen days, he waxed into his full glory and reached his zenith. On the night of the full moon, Chandra's twenty-seven wives gazed in admiration at his unblemished, complete radiance and bid him a fond farewell as he set out on his journey across the night sky.

Chandra made his serene way through the cloudless night, bathing the worlds in his silver light. Suddenly, a deafening thunder-clap shattered the silence of night. Thunder – in a clear sky?!

Chandra looked round in bewilderment. He gave a gasp of surprise at the strange apparition standing before him: a crimson face ... cavernous mouth .... sharp, pointed teeth ... wild, matted hair ...

"Why do you stare at me like that, Chandra?" the stranger asked. "Don't you recognize me? You were perfectly capable of identifying me earlier in a *deva's* disguise!" He broke into wicked laughter.

Chandra came to a halt and continued to stare at the demon in puzzlement.

"It seems you have conveniently forgotten the moment you had my head severed from my body!"

Realization dawned belatedly on Chandra. "You ... you are Ketu!" he gasped.

"You may forget me," Ketu screeched, "but, rest assured, I will never forget you! I will keep you constantly in my mind. I will ensure that I meet you every night. I will swallow you unceasingly!"

Ketu dashed towards the unsuspecting Chandra with a speed which threw the winds into a roaring turmoil. Ketu's cavernous mouth opened wider and wider until it was a repulsive, gargantuan cavity of gore. Catching Chandra unawares, Ketu quickly pulled him into his gaping maw. With deliberate, unhurried movements, Ketu effortlessly swallowed the hapless Chandra, delighting in every movement of his jaws.

Chandra disappeared into the fiery pit of Ketu's mouth as if into a dark storm cloud. His brilliant radiance diminished gradually. Soon, the moonlight vanished from the night sky and darkness shrouded the three worlds.

Indra strolled with Sachidevi in the divine Nandana garden. The cool breeze carried the fragrance of the heavenly *paarijaatha* flowers and the *kalpaka* trees. The light of the full moon painted the garden in ethereal beauty.

Sachidevi was bathed in silver. In Indra's eyes, his wife surpassed the *apsaras* in loveliness. The king of the *devas* drank in her beauty as she lifted her face towards the moon like a night-blooming lily.

Suddenly, a shadow crossed her face and blurred its exquisite contours and her body was engulfed in darkness. Indra frowned in bewilderment and looked around him. Darkness had crept not only over his wife, but over the entire garden! Indra looked up at the sky: Had a cloud blocked the moon? No ... the sky remained clear.

Indra's eyes widened in shock at the drama unfolding in the night sky. Someone was swallowing Chandra! Who was it? Was it Rahu? Had the *asura* broken his compact with the *Trimurti*? In a flash of sudden realization, Indra guessed that it was none other than Ketu!

Rahu had retired behind the curtains and let Ketu take center-stage! After all, Ketu was also an injured party during the distribution of the *amrita*.

"*Swami*," Indra snapped out of his introspection at Sachidevi's anxious call. He peered into the darkness and saw his wife groping her way towards him as a vague shadow. He reached out for her hand.

"*Swami*," her voice mirrored her bewilderment, "what is the cause of this sudden darkness on a full moon night?"

"A new threat has reared its ugly head." Indra said angrily. "It is black magic: Ketu has swallowed Chandra. I must rush to meet the Holy Trinity!"

Indra walked rapidly towards his palace, shepherding his wife before him.

⌘

Having kept Chandra confined in his stomach all night long, and subjecting him to agonizing punishment, Ketu spat him out at dawn. Like a grotesque artist gloating over a canvas painted with a demonic brush, the *asura* gazed in smug satisfaction at his bedraggled, feeble, dim captive. .

"Chandra, hear me: this is but the first of an unending series of punishment for the wrong you did me and brother Rahu." Ketu crowed in malicious triumph. "I will come for you at my whim and pleasure and wreak my vengeance by swallowing you!"

As Chandra remained in forlorn silence, Ketu burst into gleeful laughter at his miserable state. The *asura*'s face grew even more hideous with the flash of his cruel teeth. Head bent under the heavy burden of abject defeat, Chandra rose to make his departure. Ketu's malicious laughter pursued him relentlessly.

Chandra could not recover from Ketu's merciless pummeling – even under the tender ministrations of his twenty-seven wives! A bath in scented water failed to relax his rigid muscles. He was petrified with fear: he was fated to endure Daksha's curse of tuberculosis for the first half of the month – now, to compound his misery, he had to suffer being eclipsed by the *asuras* in the second half of the month! He was surrounded by hardships beyond his wildest imagination!

"*Swami,*" asked a concerned Aswini, "how will you escape from Rahu and Ketu's clutches?"

"Their demonic strength is incredible ... and it is augmented by Lord Shiva's boons!" Chandra heaved a sigh of despair. "Aswini, my heart aches at being subjected to such torment. All I did was to ensure that the *asuras* did not lay their hands on the *amrita.*" He closed his eyes in pained recollection: "Oh! The foul odour in that hideous stomach ... the revolting saliva ... I shudder to think of the torture!"

"How are we to escape from this great danger, *Swami?*" Rohini's eyes melted in compassion.

"There is only one way: I will have to stay at home and abdicate all my ordained tasks and duties," Chandra said resignedly.

"But, *Swami,*" Bharani pointed out: "the worlds will suffer in the absence of moonlight!"

"Sister, there are only two options for our husband: remaining in the security of our abode or enduring untold suffering in that hideous *rakshasa's* stomach. There is no way he can risk travelling in the night sky," Krthika argued.

Chandra nodded in sombre agreement with Krthika. "If I am destined to deny the worlds my light by being cooped up somewhere, let it be here with you! I refuse to walk into that demon's stomach – I will not go out!" Chandra declared emphatically.

"Narayana! Narayana!" Sage Narada had arrived with his familiar invocation to Lord Vishnu.

The anxious gathering rose to salute the sage. Chandra folded his hands weakly in wordless greeting and sank back onto his couch.

"May happiness be yours," blessed Narada. The sage took an appreciative sniff. "Aaaah ... what a pleasant fragrance!'

"Our husband was trapped in that *rakshasa's* abominable stomach for the entire night. He returned home dripping with revolting fluids and reeking of a foul odour," Aswini explained indignantly. "We have given him a bath in water, scented with divine perfumes."

"Lucky you, Chandra!" Narada eyes twinkled. "All these beautiful ladies bathing you in scented water!"

"Sage Narada!" Chandra, not in the least amused, protested weakly. "You cannot imagine my terror and agony!"

"Narayana," said the irrepressible sage. "I heard you elaborate on them at length from the door!" He continued, "So, you have decided not to go out tonight to discharge your duties?"

"*Maharshi*," Chandra said gravely, "I am thinking of retiring permanently!"

"Narayana!" Narada exclaimed. "You will wane under the debilitating influence of tuberculosis during the first half of the month. If you refuse to cross the night sky for the other fifteen days, what will the repercussions be? How will the herbs flourish without the light of your cool rays? Without herbs, how will medicines be prepared? What will be the fate of the sick?"

"Do you advise service at the cost of personal suffering, *Maharshi*?" Chandra countered plaintively.

"Narayana!" retorted the sage. "It was precisely because they feared that you would abdicate your duties with such thoughts that the *Trimurti* sent me here!"

"The *Trimurti*?!" Chandra sat up straight.

"Chandra," there was a faint note of rebuke in Narada's voice. "The Holy Trinity is constantly on the alert to deal with problems which crop up in the three worlds. I relay their command to you – resume your daily tasks instead of hiding at home among your wives! They will keep Ketu in order, just as they did with Rahu."

"Is that so, *Maharshi*?" Chandra asked eagerly.

"Yes," Narada reassured him. "Set out fearlessly on your journey: the *Trimurti* will keep Ketu at bay!"

"I am blessed indeed, *Maharshi*!" Chandra exclaimed happily.

⚬⚬⚬⚬

Ketu frowned up at the night sky in puzzlement. "Brother Rahu, it looks like Chandra is exulting in his daily travel ..."

Meghahasa, who had accompanied his father and uncle on their nocturnal raid, shared his bewilderment. "Uncle, it was just last night that you tormented him in the depths of your stomach. How come he is now lording it over the sky as if he does not have a care in the world? How can Chandra be so courageous?"

"All the better for us, Meghahasa," Rahu gave a sinister smile. "Surya and Chandra are vulnerable to attack only when they roam about fearlessly in the sky. Also remember, they are obliged to carry out their daily duties without fail."

"Very well," Ketu rubbed his hands in glee. "Let me at them!"

Rahu and Meghahasa embraced Ketu and cheered him on.

Ketu zoomed into the sky and turned back to wave jauntily at the father and son.

"May victory be yours, brother! May victory be yours!" Rahu shouted after him.

Ketu streaked towards Chandra like a dark banner of smoke.

Ketu reached Chandra's ordained path and lay in ambush behind a thick, white cloud. He peered out furtively at the approaching *graha*.

Chandra continued on his way across the sky, putting up a brave front to conceal the stark fear in his heart. He held on desperately to his faith in the *Trimurti*. Try as he might, he could not forget his terrible agony at Ketu's hands the previous night.

"Proceed fearlessly on your journey. The Trinity will keep Ketu at bay ..." Narada's remembered words of courage were lost in the hideous echo of Ketu's taunting laughter. Chandra looked about him in alarm – like fire billowing from a curtain of smoke, Ketu's dark face grimaced at him from behind a white cloud!

Ketu jumped out of hiding and dashed towards Chandra: only to come to a screeching halt! There before him stood the *Trimurti*, forming a vast, impenetrable barrier between the *asura* and Chandra. Their serene smiles surpassed the light of the moon in radiance.

"Ketu," said Lord Brahma, without prelude. "It is time to reveal the secret of your birth. You are a demigod with the traits of a *rakshasa*. Your mother is the goddess Mrthyu. We are here to anoint you as a *Navagraha*, along with Surya, Chandra and the others."

"Ketu," Lord Shiva's words carried implicit warning, "do not waste the boons I granted you through Meghahasa by rashly swallowing Surya and Chandra!"

Lord Vishnu spoke up in his turn: "Your decapitation at my hands was ordained. Lord Shiva's boons have addressed your loss and restored your head to your body. Being consumed by hatred will in no way contribute to your future status. Set aside your obsession with swallowing Chandra and Surya."

"Forgive my interruption," Ketu asked ominously, "what about my sworn oath to exact vengeance on Chandra and Surya in perpetuity?

What about my promise to my mother and my wife?"

"We are willing to arrive at a compromise so that you can keep your promise to your mother – just as we did in the case of your brother, Rahu." Sri Mahavishnu said. "You may also satisfy your desire for revenge by swallowing Surya and Chandra for a limited period of time a few times a year – of course, without endangering the three worlds."

"Ketu, this compromise is our unanimous decision." Lord Shiva advised the *asura* with a reassuring smile.

"Accept it and be happy," Lord Brahma added his persuasion.

Ketu bowed before the Three. "I accept your proposal with respect. My brother and I will take turns to swallow Surya on a new moon day, and Chandra on a full moon night."

"So be it!" the *Trimurti* chorused in benediction.

Ketu saluted them devotedly. He then turned to Chandra with a triumphant gleam in his eyes and departed with the satisfaction of having carved a victory for himself.

The Holy Trinity vanished and Chandra was left to continue on his journey, spreading his cool light over the dark skies with renewed vigor.

∞

Ketu returned to an affectionate welcome from Rahu, Meghahasa, Simhika, Danudevi, Simhidevi and Chitraleka, who stood waiting expectantly at the entrance to Kasyapa's hermitage.

Rahu rushed to embrace Ketu. The two *asuras* clapped each other on the shoulder and erupted into loud guffaws of triumphant laughter. The sound of their merriment, as they celebrated their victory, resounded like the thunder clap caused by the friction between two dark storm clouds. The duos' exultant glee was contagious: soon, the entire company of seven was roaring with uncontrollable mirth and Kasyapa's *ashram* shook with their laughter.

Kasyapa *prajapti*, accompanied by Aditi, Vinata, Kadru, Diti and his other wives, came running at the loud commotion. The merry-makers were so absorbed in their mirth that they were oblivious to the arrival of the newcomers.

"Danu …. Simhika!" Aditi called out to her younger sisters.

Aditi's sharp reprimand brought Danu and Simhika to abrupt sobriety and they turned to her in one accord. One by one, the others ceased their laughter. Kasyapa *prajapati* frowned at the merry group in bewilderment.

Ketu had returned from his mission without swallowing Chandra, who continued to glow complacently in the sky above: why then this raucous celebration?

"Meghahasa," Kasyapa summoned his grandson.

"Grandfather," Meghahasa obediently came to stand before Kasyapa. His cheeks were wet with tears of glee.

"Why are you all in fits of laughter, my boy?"

"Grandfather, like my father, uncle Ketu has also obtained boons from the *Trimurti*," Meghahaasa replied with a satisfied smile.

"Is that so?" Kasyapa turned to Ketu. "What boons have you received, Ketu?"

Ketu, beaming with happy pride, obligingly recounted the course of events which had culminated in his agreement with the *Trimurti*.

"This means that you two will swallow Surya and Chandra for a limited period, a few times each year," Aditi said thoughtfully.

"This pact is an excellent compromise" exclaimed Kasyapa in relief. "You are both my sons ... and so is Surya! I have spent sleepless nights worrying that I am poking my eyes with my own fingers!" Kasyapa smiled. "Again, Chandra is also kin to us: he is the son of Sage Atri, who is a *maanasaputra*, and one of my father's brothers."

"Father," Rahu said solemnly, "we took all aspects of the situation into consideration before we accepted the *Trimurti's* proposal."

"That gives me great satisfaction, my son! Like Surya and Chandra, you two have attained eminent positions. You will be worshipped by the three worlds. I wholeheartedly appreciate your achievements and bless you!" Kasyapa *prajapati's* eyes brimmed with affection.

"I deserve your appreciation too, *Swami*," Simhika said with a smile. "After all, it is my son who has proved his worth!"

"So has my son," Danudevi embraced Ketu.

Not to be left out, Meghahasa came forward to hold his grandfather's hands. "Bless me too, grandfather," he said. "It was I who propitiated Lord Shiva with my penance and obtained boons for your sons."

Kasyapa drew Meghahasa into his warm embrace. "My sons and grandsons are earning fame and greatness! It is the will of the Supreme God and my own good fortune!"

Rahu and Ketu burst into pleased laughter once more.

"And that, in short, is the story of Ketu's life." Nirvikalpananda wound up this segment of his narration.

"It is rather brief, master," Chidananda remarked with a smile.

"I have given you all the available information on Ketu, my boy." Nirvikalpananda pointed out carefully: "Though his life history may not be as long as that of the other *grahas*, he definitely holds his own with them in the power he possesses."

"Master," asked Shivananada, "have we come to the end of the history of the *Navagrahas*?"

"Shivananda," Nirvikalpananda retorted with an indulgent smile, "do you think so?"

The four young disciples looked at their master in expectant curiosity.

"We have seen the *Navagrahas* born, reach maturity and equip themselves with the various strengths which qualify them for their status. But, there is much more to it: their specific positions have to be determined; their duties ordained – they must be anointed!" Nirvikalpananda explained. "The history of the *Navagrahas* will not be complete without these details."

Vimalananda looked at his friends in excited anticipation. "So, our master will now describe the anointing of the *Navagrahas*!"

"Bowing to the *Trimurti's* command, Sage Narada invited all the gods to the Anointing of the *Navagrahas*.

"Surya, Chandra, Kuja, Budha, Brhaspati, Sukra, Sani, Rahu, Ketu and their wives were the special invitees. The *Navagrahas'* parents were also there, of course. Narada summoned the *daityas* and *daanavas* too. At Brahma's suggestion, Narada invited Svaayambhuva Manu and his faithful wife Satarupadevi ..."

Nirvikalpananda continued his discourse.

THE ANOINTMENT OF THE NAVAGRAHAS

Cool breezes from the sparkling waters of the Ocean of Milk wafted pleasantly over the august assembly gathered on its shores. The company's innate radiance lit up the ambience like the glow of a thousand lamps. A tide of cheerful good-will washed over the gods and their consorts as they waited to witness the anointment of the *Navagrahas*.

The mammoth court was filled to capacity. Sri Mahavishnu and Goddess Lakshmi occupied places of honour on the court's elevated dais, with Brahma and Saraswati on one side, and Shiva and Parvati on the other. Indra and the other *devas*, along with their consorts, sat in a long row below the dais. Facing across from them were the Brahma *maanasaputras* and their wives, with the sages forming the third line of the triad.

The protagonists of the coming ceremony – Surya, Chandra, Kuja, Budha, Brhaspati, Sukra, Sani, Rahu and Ketu, sat apart in a row of their own. Their wives – Samjna, Aswini and her twenty-six sisters, Saktidevi, Ila, Taara, Urjaswati, Jyeshtaadevi, Simhidevi and Chitralekha, were in the gathering, beaming on their husbands in happy pride.

Near the Holy Trinity stood nine ornate gold thrones, waiting expectantly for their special occupants.

Brahma closed his eyes in silent meditation. He then turned to Lord Vishnu. "Father, the auspicious moment has dawned. Please begin."

Lord Vishnu embraced the great council with the warmth of his radiant smile. His deep voice caressed the ears of the gathering, drowning out the tides dashing on the shores of the Ocean of Milk.

"The incarnation of the *Navagrahas* in physical form is a significant step in the rich progression of creation which flourishes in every *kalpa*. At the start of creation, it occurred to me that it would be beneficial if the *Navagrahas*, who were in their astral forms, were to be born with gross physical bodies: this would facilitate their tangible worship by humans who seek their mercy and favour."

Sri Mahavishnu paused and gestured regally with his right hand. "In accordance with the dictates of my will, I present to you the new physical manifestation of the Nine *Navagrahas!*" The entire assembly of gods, *maanasaputras* and sages turned in one accord to gaze in silent admiration at Surya and his company of *grahas* who, in turn, folded their hands in respectful salutation to the gathering.

Again, Lord Vishnu's rich voice resonated above the crashing of the ocean waves. "The *Navagrahas'* order of significance has been determined by taking into consideration Brahma and Shiva's suggestions. Individual powers and duties have been assigned to them, corresponding to their respective strengths and abilities." He continued. "I will now invite them to the dais, one by one, in that ordained order. Each *graha* will come up and occupy his golden throne according to his sequence of merit."

An excited murmur ran through the mammoth court. Vishnu smiled benignly at the sea of upturned faces and launched into his dignified summons.

"The first among the *Navagrahas* is Surya!"

The enthusiastic applause of the audience sounded a triumphant background score, as Surya rose, folded his hands in salutation to the assembly, and walked in sedate dignity towards the gleaming row of golden thrones. He seated himself majestically on the first throne.

"The second of the *grahas* is Chandra!" Vishnu's voice echoed along the shore of the Ocean of Milk.

"The third is Kuja!" "The fourth – Budha!" "The fifth – Brhaspati!" "The sixth – Sukra!" "The seventh – Sanaischara!" "The eighth – Rahu!" "And the ninth – Ketu!"

The eight *grahas* answered Vishnu's summons in turn and took their assigned places on the dais. All eyes were glued to the *Navagrahas*, now seated in splendid array on their golden thrones, adorned with the nine precious gems.

"In recognition of his position as the preceptor of the gods, and his

towering intellect, Brhaspati shall be popularly known as the 'Guru,'" Sri
Mahavishnu announced to warm applause.

"Nine grains and nine gems stand out in importance in nature's
design. Each *graha* will be awarded sovereignty over a particular grain
and a specific gem."

Sri Mahavishnu turned to Brahma and Shiva. "I call upon Brahma to
announce the jurisdiction of the respective *Navagrahas* over each grain
and Shiva to proclaim their dominion over each of the Nine Gems."

Brahma bowed to Vishnu and proclaimed: "Surya will assume
sovereignty over wheat, Chandra over paddy and Kuja over red gram.
Green gram will come under Budha, other grams under Guru, and
awnless barley under Sukra. Sani will exercise his dominion over
sesame, Rahu over black gram and Ketu over horse gram." He paused.
"Each of these will be the preferred grain of the respective *grahas* – who
in turn will command their favourite grain. This is will of the Holy
Trinity!"

"I will now list the particular gems over which each *graha* will
exercise authority ..." Shiva spoke up in his turn, extending his hand in
benediction over the *Navagrahas*. "Surya – Ruby, Chandra – Pearl, Kuja –
Coral, Budha – Emerald, Guru – Yellow sapphire, Sukra – Diamond, Sani
– Blue sapphire, Rahu – Hessonite and Ketu – Cymophane."

Shiva gestured with his hand. A gasp of wonder ran through the
spectators at the miracle which unfolded before their astonished eyes:
precious gems rained down on the *Navagrahas*! A shower of rubies fell on
Surya, while Chandra was covered with pearls. Kuja, Budha, Guru and
Sukra were bathed in streams of corals, emeralds, yellow sapphires and
diamonds, respectively. Blue sapphires cascaded down on Sani, hessonite
on Rahu and cymophane on Ketu.

Thunderous claps and cheers roared through the court. The
Navagrahas sparkled in multi hued splendor under their sparkling coats
of precious gems. Vishnu and Brahma smiled appreciatively at Shiva's
dazzling display of the *navaratnas*.

Shiva turned to Vishnu. "Srihari, every group must have a leader: do
decide who is to govern the *Navagrahas*."

Lord Vishnu nodded in agreement. "Shiva is right: the *Navagrahas*
must be ruled by a king. At this auspicious moment, I would like to
decide who among them is worthy of being elevated to this position of
command ..."

Vishnu let his eyes measure each of the *grahas* in turn. An expectant hush fell over the gathering. The *Navagrahas* waited in silence. Rahu and Ketu bent forward attentively.

Sri Mahavishnu's words split the silence like a thunder-clap. "I hereby appoint Surya as the king of the *grahas*: he will enjoy the title, *Graharaju!*"

Surya rose to the sound of deafening applause and bowed respectfully towards the *Trimurti*. With two notable exceptions, the other *grahas* joined in the general acclamation of Surya as their king. Rahu and Ketu remained unmoved by the ovation.

Chandra shouted, "Victory to Surya, the King of the *Grahas!*"

"Victory to Surya, the King of the *Grahas!*" The entire assembly joyously echoed Chandra's acclamation. Rahu and Ketu shut their ears to block out the hails of triumph which rent the air.

Suddenly, unable to tolerate it any further, Rahu jumped to his feet and shouted: "Stop it!" His face was dark with fury. "Enough of your senseless cheers!" Rahu strode angrily towards the Holy Trinity, with Ketu fuming at his heels.

"Rahu!" Lord Shiva called him to order. "What is the meaning of this behavior?"

"Yes, *Bhagavan*," Rahu cried out in a rage. "My rude behavior has significance: it highlights Vishnu's partiality."

"Rahu ..." Vishnu's eyes widened in surprise.

"Don't play the innocent with me, Vishnu," Rahu spat at him. "You have favoured Surya and made him the king of the *grahas* only because he was born from your attribute!"

"Rahu, this is a preposterous accusation!" Brahma intervened quickly. "The king of the *grahas* was chosen on the strength of his merit, strength and capabilities – not out of any kind of favoritism."

Ketu's loud laughter dripped with sarcasm as he said: "Of course you would jump to Vishnu's defence – after all, he is your father!"

"If we were also Aditi's sons, we would not have been subjected to this discrimination and humiliation," Rahu complained.

There was pandemonium in the assembly as the *asuras'* accusations became the subject of animated discussion.

Lord Vishnu rose and held out his hand for silence. "Rahu," he said gravely, "Your allegation of bias has no foundation. My decision to appoint Surya as the king of the *grahas* was based on his proficiency and the all-encompassing affection he lavishes on the three worlds." He continued emphatically: "Surya is the central force of the *Navagrahas*. He is the power which provides the energy essential for the growth of food and life in all the worlds ..."

"We, Rahu and Ketu, are powerful in our own right, Vishnu," Ketu interrupted angrily. "Lord Shiva has blessed us with power and status equal to that of Surya and Chandra."

"Careful, Ketu!" Shiva stood up. "Do not demean your power and position. In the eyes of the *Trimurti*, and indeed that of the entire universe, all the *grahas* enjoy equal stature."

"*Bhagavan*," Ketu shouted, "that is what you say ... but, contrary to your stand, Vishnu insists on demonstrating his partiality towards Surya!"

"I for one refuse to bow abjectly to Vishnu's decree," Rahu proclaimed defiantly. "I will not accept Surya as our king. If, in your opinion, he is best suited to be the king, prove that he is more powerful than us ... or else, prove that we are powerless!"

"I agree with my brother, Rahu," Ketu declared haughtily. "Give us conclusive proof of Surya's superiority!"

"Yes," challenged Rahu. "Give us proof of Surya's strength ... the Surya who is so afraid of us that he cowers behind the handicapped Aruna, shamelessly using him as a shield!"

"Surya gives energy for food ... Surya gives energy for life ... Ha, ha ha ..." Ketu laughed in derision. "We too have those powers. We proved our might by swallowing him!" Rahu joined his brother's sarcastic mirth.

Sage Kasyapa, distressed by Rahu and Ketu's blatant display of arrogance, rose to intervene. However, Aditi dissuaded him with a meaningful pressure on his hand.

"Very well, Rahu," Sri Mahavishnu said serenely, "we agree to your proposal."

"It is not a proposal, Vishnu," Rahu said contemptuously. "It is a challenge!"

"Have it as you will," Vishnu remained unruffled. "Now, I will give you an opportunity to demonstrate your power and skills."

Vishnu turned to Brahma. "Brahma, create a sapling for Rahu and Ketu."

Closing his eyes in obedience to Sri Mahavishu's command, Brahma extended his hand and exercised the power of his will. Instantaneously, a small sapling appeared in a golden pot. Its tender, green leaves quivered in the breeze from the Ocean of Milk.

"Rahu and Ketu," Vishnu said gravely, "you see the sapling before you. You have claimed to have the power to generate the energy essential for life and sustenance. Here is your chance to prove your worth: emit rays of energy and make the sapling grow. This is the test you must pass."

Ketu laughed loudly and gave a snort of contempt. "Such a trifling task does not require our combined effort. My elder brother, the formidable Rahu, is perfectly capable of accepting and winning your challenge singlehandedly!"

Rahu patted Ketu's shoulder in affectionate approval and laughed uproariously.

"Brother," urged Ketu, "prove your mighty strength – let waves of energy gush forth from you!"

The entire assembly leaned forward in one accord, holding their breaths in anticipation. Rahu approached the sapling. With a look of disdain at Vishnu, he gave the sapling a penetrating glance. Rays of energy burst from the *asura*'s eyes and bathed the tender leaves in harsh ultraviolet light. Right under the gaze of the fascinated onlookers, the sapling wilted – the green quickly leached away from its leaves, leaving the withered plant bent feebly over the rim of its golden pot.

Ketu gave a hiss of regret and placed his hand in sympathy on Rahu's shoulder. Rahu turned from his brother to look at the sapling which was slowly dying. His eyes mirrored the defeat in Ketu's eyes.

As Rahu's defeat sank in, the assembly was in an uproar.

"Ketu," Vishnu called out gravely to the *asura*. "Now, you may attempt the test."

Rahu staggered towards his throne, head bent under the heavy burden of defeat. Ketu, sticking to his brother like a dark shadow, continued to follow him, turning a deaf ear to Lord Vishnu's challenge. The assembly buzzed with the excitement of the *asuras'* ignominious defeat.

Vishnu turned to Surya and commanded, "Surya, nurture that sapling with your life-giving energy. Let your rays shine forth!"

Surya rose to his feet obediently. He respectfully saluted the Trinity and turned to the plant. Gentle beams of light fell on the sapling ... minutes passed ... a current of energy pulsated through the feeble, withered plant. A flush of pale green spread over the tiny, faded leaves. The sapling straightened, and stood tall and fresh, glowing with the absorbed vigor of sunlight. Surya ceased his outpouring of energy.

"Victory to Surya, the King of the *Grahas*! Victory to the *Graharaju*!" the gathering erupted into rapturous cheers of acclaim. The *Trimurti* smiled benignly at the thousand voices raised in emphatic ratification of their decision.

Rahu and Ketu bowed their heads in shame. As the cheers subsided, sage Kasyapa went up to the two brothers and gazed compassionately at their downcast faces.

A gentle smile played across Kasyapa *prajapati*'s face. His voice was kind. "Rahu ... Ketu, lift your chins and stand tall. Salute the Trinity and apologize for your arrogance. Gracefully accept your brother and fellow-*graha*, Surya, as your rightful king and accord him due respect. By this, you will keep intact your honour as one of the demigods."

Rahu and Ketu paid heed to their father's wise counsel. They respectfully saluted the Trinity. Next, they approached Surya and expressed their regrets with folded hands. Surya favoured them with a radiant smile. The chastened brothers quietly returned to their assigned thrones.

"The objective of this contest was not to glorify Surya, or to demean his brothers, Rahu and Ketu." Lord Vishnu was explicit. "All the *Navagrahas* are imbued with equal importance, with each of them possessing his own unique power and strength. The Nine *Grahas* will have tremendous significance on the life of all beings in the universe."

"Brahma and I are in accord with Vishnu," Shiva added with a smile.

"Rahu and Ketu, blinded by jealousy and anger, could not understand the basis of our decision." Sri Mahavishnu elaborated. "Surya's light and heat are essential for life and he is the source of all nourishment. Trees, creeper and crops absorb his light to retain their life-sustaining green foliage. Sunlight is the fount of health and sustenance. This is the reason we have appointed Surya as the king of the *grahas*." Vishnu decreed: "Henceforth, humans will adopt the ritual of offering the food grains cultivated by them to Surya first and foremost."

"Surya, who bestows his rays of light on all the creatures of the three worlds without any discrimination, is best fitted to be the king of the *grahas*," Shiva emphasized benignly.

"He is the unanimous choice of the *Trimurti*," Brahma added his voice to that of the other two.

Chandra, Kuja, Budha, Guru, Sukra, Sani, Rahu and Ketu joined to applaud the *Trimurti*.

"Father," Brahma reminded Vishnu, "the time of consecration is fast approaching."

"Indra!" Vishnu summoned the king of the *devas*. Indra responded promptly and came to stand before Lord Vishnu with hands folded in reverence.

"Indra," continued Vishnu, "the consecration ceremony will begin with the anointment of the *Navagrahas* with milk from the Ocean of Milk. Brahma will conduct this auspicious rite."

"*Bhagavan*," Indra bowed solemnly. "In line with your command, the nymphs are ready with golden pots brimming with milk."

At Indra's signal, *gandharvas* and *vidyaadharas* broke into glorious strains of auspicious music. The tides of the ocean danced in rhythm to the divine melody.

Under the aegis of Brahma, the consecration of the *Navagrahas* commenced. The Seven Sages chanted the *Vedic mantras*, as decreed by the Creator. The *Maharshis* anointed the *Navagrahas* with the milk brought by the heavenly *apsaras*.

As commanded by Indra, the nymphs anointed the *Navagrahas'* foreheads with the auspicious *tilak*, composed of red chalk collected from the shores of the Ocean of Milk. The *Navagrahas'* wives looked on in fascination at the unfolding grandeur of their spouse's consecration. The lovely *apsaras* danced in procession to the dais, holding fragrant garlands of flowers from the *kalpavrksha*. At Brahma's nod, the nymphs gracefully arranged the garlands about the *Navagrahas'* necks.

The *Trimurti*, along with their consorts, stepped forward to shower their blessings on the *Navagrahas* with the ritual *akshata*. The *grahas* accepted the rain of auspicious grain and flowers with reverentially folded hands and bowed heads.

"Srihari," Shiva said magnanimously, "I will anoint Surya as the king of the *grahas* with *amrita*."

"Surya is fortunate indeed," replied Vishnu with a smile.

Soon, everything was in readiness for Surya's elevation as the king of the *grahas*. Surya sat on an ornate gold throne, under the canopy of a pristine white umbrella. He was flanked on either side by the other eight *grahas*, seated on a level lower to his own throne.

The *Trimurti* and their consorts took their places on the dais beside Surya. Indra, with his wife at his side, climbed the steps to the platform, bearing the pot of *amrita* in his hands.

Lord Shiva solemnly anointed Surya with the divine nectar, accompanied by the chant of *Vedic mantras* in the background. He adorned Surya's neck with the garland of lotus blossoms which Sachidevi handed him. Vishnu and Mahalakshmi, Brahma and Saraswati, Shiva and Parvati and Indra and Sachidevi came forward in turn to shower him with *akshata* as a symbol of blessing.

The assembly erupted into cheers, acknowledging the newly anointed king of the *grahas*. The waves of the Ocean of Milk seemed to echo their jubilation as they dashed joyously on the shores.

The seated gods came to their feet to form two rows facing each other. The parallel lines of *devas* and their consorts were like strings of multi-hued blossoms. In their hands were fragrant flowers. Suddenly, everyone pricked up their ears: the sound of horses' hooves sounded in the distance, gradually becoming louder. All eyes turned towards the golden chariot which materialized in the distance and made its way majestically towards them.

Seven green stallions drew the vehicle. Miraculously, the chariot glided by smoothly on a single wheel. Surya was ensconced in stately dignity on a lotus-shaped seat in the center of the chariot, Aruna glowing before him as his charioteer.

Surya's glittering chariot approached the lines of waiting gods. The red umbrella above the chariot added its sparkle to the lustre of the equipage. A crimson flag fluttered bravely in the wind. The *Trimurti* and their consorts, who stood in the vanguard of the two rows, raised their hands in benediction towards Surya, who was radiant in red garments and wore a garland of red lotuses. The brilliance emanating from his body enhanced the gleam of the chariot.

The Seven Sages stepped forward to chant *Vedic mantras* and shower flowers on Surya.

> *"Japaakusuma samkaasam Kaasyapeyam Mahaadyutim!*
> *Tamorim Sarvapaapaghnam pranatosmi Divaakaram!"*

> *I offer my salutations to Divaakara (Surya), who shines like the japa flower,*
> *who is the son of Kasyapa, who is resplendent, who is the enemy of darkness,*
> *and who is the destroyer of all sins.*

A host of voices sang of Surya's glory, while all eyes drank in the delight of his radiant person and equipage. Surya's chariot passed regally between the two lines of gods and came to a standstill at a designated spot beyond. Silence once again filled the arena.

All heads turned towards the clip-clop of horses' hooves, which grew increasingly louder.

A three-wheeled, golden chariot appeared in the distance, drawn by ten white horses, their manes streaming in the wind like a froth of milk. A white umbrella crowned its top and a pristine white flag waved in the wind blowing from the Ocean of Milk.

Chandra, clothed in gleaming white and wearing a garland of white blossoms, sat in the chariot. The spectators were captivated by the charming picture he presented.

The Seven Sages took up their verse in praise of Chandra, who was as white as curd ... as the conch-shell ... as snow!

"Dadhi sankha tushaaraabham ksheerodaarnava sambhavam!
Namaami sasinam Somam Sambhormakuta bhooshanam!"

I offer my salutations to Sasi who is known as Soma (Chandra) who shines like curds, the conch and snow, who rose from the Ocean of Milk, who is the ornament on Sambhu's (Lord Shiva) crown.

The assembly of gods echoed Chandra's glory and showered multi-coloured flowers on him, as he made his stately passage of honour between them. Chandra's golden chariot halted beside Surya's.

To the onlookers' delight, the next golden chariot quickly hovered into view. Eight horses, sparkling red like rubies, pulled the two-wheeled vehicle. The umbrella at its peak was a gleaming red and a red ensign fluttered in the breeze. Kuja, the son of the earth goddess – he who had received the eternal name, Angaaraka, sat in this chariot. Attired in blood-red garments, Kuja's fiery complexion was complemented by a garland of scarlet flowers. A shower of blossoms fell on Angaaraka Kuja, who appeared to the spectators' eyes as a precious ruby embedded in gleaming gold. A pleasing radiance emanated from him, bathing the surroundings in a warm glow of light.

"Dharanee garbha sambhootam vidyut kaanti samaprabham!
Kumaaram sakti hastham tam Mangalam pranamaamyaham!"

I offer my salutations to Mangala (Kuja) who is born from the womb of the Earth, who is resplendent like lightning, who is (called) Kumara, and who holds the weapon, Sakti, in his hand.

The gods and their consorts devotedly repeated the *sloka* recited in Kuja's homage by the Seven Sages. Angaaaraka made his solemn way past the admiring gods, to stop beside Surya and Chandra.

Next, a gleaming, orange-brown, two-wheeled equipage emerged from the distance, sporting an ornate, yellow umbrella. Eight tawny horses galloped in perfect unison under its shaft. Its turmeric-coloured standard waved proudly in the wind.

Budha held his position in this chariot, a benign smile on his face. His captivating good looks, which surpassed even Chandra in handsomeness, drew an admiring gasp from the spectators. He wore garments of sparkling yellow.

> *"Priyangu kalikaasyaamam roopenaa apratimam Budham!*
> *Sowmyam Sowmyagunopetam tam Budhaam pranamaamyaham!"*

> *I offer my salutations to Budha who is of dark blue complexion like the Priyangu bud, who is wise, who is of incomparable beauty, who is (called) Soumya and who is of benevolent quality.*

The glorious invocation to Budha was recited by the Seven Sages, to be echoed in chorus by the assembled gods. A rain of flowers accompanied Budha on his passage, as he sedately moved on to join the *grahas* who had preceded him.

In quick succession, Guru's chariot of mellow gold claimed everyone's attention. A panoply of golden hues greeted their wondering eyes: Guru sat in his seat, attired in gold … a golden halo of wisdom emanated from him. His aureate flag glimmered above the brilliant umbrella which sheltered him. The two-wheeled vehicle was drawn by eight, perfectly matched stallions of unblemished white. The chariot passed between the two rows of waiting gods.

The Seven Sages sprinkled the auspicious *akshata* and flowers on him as they intoned:

> *"Devaanaamcha rushinaamcha Gurum kaanchana sannibham!*
> *Buddhimantam trilokesam tam namaami Brhaspatim!"*

> *I offer my salutations to Brhaspati, who is the preceptor of the gods and sages, who is resplendent like gold, who is the personification of wisdom and who is the lord of the three worlds.*

The *devas* responded with special enthusiasm to their preceptor's ceremonial passage. The shower of flowers increased to become a veritable downpour of affection. As they stood looking fondly after his equipage, the sound of unknown wheels compelled their attention.

Ten white horses cantered ahead of a glorious chariot, shining like molten gold. Sukra, all in white, sat majestically on his seat of flaming aureate. A garland of white flowers glowed round his neck. His ensign and umbrella were dazzling white, rivalling the waves of the Ocean of Milk in their pristine purity.

The Seven Sages received Sukra's equipage with their paean of glory to him:

> *"Himakunda mrnaalaabham daityaanaam paramam gurum!*
> *Sarvasaastra pravakaaram Bhaargavam pranamaamyaham!"*

> *I offer my salutations to Bhargava (Sukra) who shines like snow, like the Kunda flower and lotus fiber, who is the great preceptor of the demons and who is the expert orator of all the scriptures.*

The gods rained their flowers on the chariot and responded to the *sloka* with one accord. Suddenly, their response was drowned by the thunderous roar of a mighty horde of *rakshasas*. To the gods' astonishment, thousands of *asuras*, invisible up to then, stood revealed in lines contiguous with those of the *devas*.

The very shores of the Ocean of Milk trembled with the *rakshasas'* resonating cheers for their preceptor, Sukra. Sukra smiled fondly on his disciples, who showered him with blood-red blossoms. Sukra moved past the lines to join the other *grahas* arrayed before him.

Next came a coldly gleaming iron chariot, drawn by ten horses whose mottled bodies were smeared with a jarring mixture of dark hues. The jet-black canopy and ensign struck terror in the hearts of the spectators, who peered fascinatedly at its hideous rider.

Sanaischara, with his pitch-dark complexion, dressed all in black, sat regally in this chariot, garlanded with black flowers. The dappled steeds menacingly galloped towards the waiting crowd, making their blood run cold.

> *"Neelaanjana samaabhaasam Ravi putram Yamaagrajam!*
> *Chaayaa Maartaanda sambhootham tam namaami Sanaischaram!"*

> *I offer my salutations to Sanaischara who shines like dark blue collyrium, who is the son of Ravi (Surya),who has Yama as his elder brother and who is born of Chaaya and Maartaanda (Surya).*

The Seven Sages performed their ritual sprinkling of the *akshata* and flowers on Sani, while reciting the *sloka* acknowledging his glory. The *devas* and *rakshasas* hurriedly followed suit with rather excessive fervor! Sanaischara made his ceremonial passage through the lines of gods and demons and came to a halt beside Sukra at the other end.

It was now Rahu's turn to make his furious appearance. He arrived in a two-wheeled chariot, ash-cold in colour. Its eight horses surged forward like gargantuan black bees, whirling through the air. Rahu's black canopy and standard streamed in the wind, a fitting foil to his dark blue attire and the blackish-blue flowers garlanding his neck.

At Rahu's approach, the Seven Sages dutifully sprinkled their *akshata* and flowers and launched into their invocatory chant in his praise.

"Ardhakaayam mahaaveeram Chandraaditya vimardanam!
Simhikaa garbha sambhootam tam Raahum pranamaamyaham!"

I offer my salutations to Rahu who is half-bodied, who is distinguished and valiant, who is the oppressor of Chandra and Aditya and who is born from Simhika's womb.

The *suras* and *asuras* followed the sages in their acclamation of Rahu's glory. Rahu stormed ahead in his chariot, majestically acknowledging the shower of flowers in his honour. He drew to a halt beside Sanaischara.

At once, the crash of Ketu's chariot wheels rose above the resounding voices of the *rakshasas* hailing his elder brother, Rahu. Eight red horses charged forward furiously, pulling a chariot which flashed by like a vaporous trail of smoke, streaked with wisps of black and fiery red.

A garland of strangely coloured flowers gleamed round Ketu's neck, above his motley attire. His pennant and umbrella mirrored the incongruous hues of his attire. Ketu's body, in quirky and disparate garments, was a grotesque picture painted in bright *palaasa* colour.

"Palaasa pushpa sankaasam taarakaagrahamastakam!
Roudram roudraatmakam ghoram tam Ketum pranamaamyaham!"

I offer my salutations to Ketu who shines like the palaasa flower, who is foremost among the stars and planets, who is Roudra, whose form is fierce and horrible.

The Seven Sages broke into their invocatory chant in praise of Ketu and showered him with *akshata* and flowers. The gods and demons followed their lead and chorused Ketu's glory. Ketu gravely drove past his *rakshasa* brothers, who greeted him with raucous cheers, while raining flowers on him.

Rahu beamed proudly at his younger brother, Ketu, who stopped his chariot beside his own.

Now, it was the turn of the *Navagrahas'* wives to walk down the ceremonial passage formed by the gods and demons. The *apsaras* danced before them, sprinkling flowers on the ground as a soft carpet for their feet. The *Navagrahas,* seated in regal splendor on their chariots, smiled fondly at their approaching spouses.

Surya's wife – Samjna, Chandra's wives – Aswini, Bharani, Krthika, Rohini, Mrgasira, Aardhra, Punarvasu, Pushyami, Aaslesha, Makha, Purva Phalguni, Uttara Phalguni, Hasta, Chitta, Swaati, Visakha, Anuradha, Jyeshta, Moola, Poorvaashaada, Uttaraashaada, Sravanam, Dhanishta, Satabhisham, Poorvaabhaadra, Uttaraabhaadra and Revati, Angaaraka's wife – Sakti, Budha's wife – Ila, Guru's wife – Taara, Sukra's wife – Oorjaswati, Sani's wife – Jyeshtaadevi, Rahu's wife – Simhidevi, and Ketu's wife – Chitralekha, walked in joyous procession towards their husbands, newly anointed as the *Navagrahas.*

The radiant women, beaming with pride, joined their husbands on their respective chariots. The onlookers broke into spontaneous applause at the glorious sight of the *Navagrahas* bestowing their *darshan* in unison with their spouses. The *Trimurti* commended Viswakarma who had crafted the *Navagrahas'* divine chariots, each one faithfully mirroring the traits of their respective owners.

Vishnu addressed the *Navagrahas:* "Go now and take up residence in the abodes built for you by Viswakarma at your ordained positions in space. Exercise your authority over the lives of all beings, in line with the execution of your duties and obligations." Vishnu paused for emphasis. "Be especially magnanimous to humans, by accepting their worship and blessing them."

"Your wish is our command, *Bhagavan!*" the *Navagrahas* chorused in unison.

"Surya and Chandra are already established in their beautiful palaces, where they live with their families," Vishnu continued. "Kuja, Budha,

Guru, Sukra, Sani, Rahu and Ketu – you will now take up abode in your own palaces, located at the coordinates in space which your astral bodies occupy." Vishnu smiled and gestured to the Creator. "Brahma will now detail the positions of your respective abodes."

Brahma bowed to Vishnu and turned to the *Navagrahas*. "Surya, the king of the *grahas*, occupies pride of place with his abode at the very centre of the universe. This is called Surya's sphere. Chandra's sphere lies to the south-east of Surya's orb. Angaaraka's sphere is in the south. Budha stands in the north-east. Guru's sphere lies to Surya's north, while Sukra's orb is located at Surya's east. Sani's sphere stands to Surya's west. Rahu has his sphere in the south-west and Ketu lies in the north-west." Brahma looked at them gravely. "These are the permanent positions laid down for the nine *grahas*." Brahma looked meaningfully at Shiva.

Shiva, in his turn, addressed the *Navagrahas*: "All of you possess the power to carry out your ordained tasks. You have been invested with sovereignty over the kingdoms of Bharatakhanda and Bharatavarsha. You are perfectly aware of all the relevant details of your position in your subtle astral forms." Shiva continued seriously. "However, in your present gross manifestations, your natures demonstrate certain inherent flaws. This is because your physical senses exert an inevitable influence on your thoughts and actions – pride is an overweening defect in you. Such shortcomings will cloud your wisdom and dilute your divine attributes. In this context, it is essential to explicitly delineate your duties, powers, positions ..."

"I beg your forgiveness, Lord Shiva," Rahu interrupted haughtily. "We are divine forms, consecrated as the *Navagrahas*. We remain gods, even in our gross bodies. Yet, you accuse us of being flawed!"

"Pride?! ... Flaws?! ... In us?!" Ketu lifted his eyebrows in an exaggerated parody of surprise and gave a bark of laughter.

Surya, Chandra, Kuja, Budha, Guru, Sukra, Sani and Rahu – in enthusiastic approval of Ketu's words – joined his merriment.

"So, you are perfect, is it?" Lord Shiva smiled. "Well, let's see ... Surya was unable to see through Chaaya when she impersonated his wife, Samjna. Is that not a flaw in Surya, the omniscient witness to all the actions of living beings?"

The chastised Surya bent his head in shame.

"Coming to Chandra," Lord Shiva continued, "he was born to Atri and Anasuya, the ideal parents. However, he eloped with his master's wife. Again, he favoured Rohini and discriminated against his other twenty-six wives, subjecting them to painful humiliation. Finally, he became the victim of his father-in-law's curse which sees him afflicted by chronic tuberculosis. Are these not defects in his character?"

Chandra hid his mortified face from the others.

"As for Kuja ..." Shiva said, "Kuja was born from a drop of my perspiration and grew up under Bhudevi's care. He presumed that he had been abandoned by me, his father, and ignored me deliberately. He propitiated Parvati, my wife, and obtained boons from her. He did not recognize the truth that I am Ardhanaareeswara – Parvati and I share one, indivisible body. He failed to comprehend that Parvati's blessings encompass my own. Is that not ignorance?"

Shiva turned to Kuja. "Angaaraka, my son, what do you have to say to that?!"

A hot flush of shame suffused Kuja's face. He folded his hands in respect and said, "Father, I admit the truth of your words. My pride made me turn away from you. I ask your forgiveness."

"And what about Budha?" Shiva asked with a smile. "Budha, the son of Chandra, and grandson of Atri and Anasuya, is undoubtedly exceptionally wise and intelligent. Yet, he was unable of perceive that Ila was actually Sudyumna in female form: his lust blunted his wisdom."

Budha nodded slowly in regret and bowed his head.

"Let's take Guru." Shiva was implacable. "Brhaspati is an intellectual prodigy. Yet, he made himself a slave to lust. He raped Mamata, his brother Utadhya's wife, in her husband's absence. Mamata was pregnant at that time. When she subsequently gave birth to two boys, Brhaspati accepted the second son as the product of his rape. That boy is none other than Bharadvaaja. Is Brhaspati's heinous crime not an evident flaw in his nature?"

Brhaspati's downcast eyes remained glued to the floor.

Shiva turned to Sukra. "And now we come to the preceptor of the *asuras*. Sukra, an acknowledged poet and intellectual, was addicted to wine. Is that not a defect?" Sukra nodded regretfully.

"There is more: Sukra abused his yogic power to rob Kubera, the cosmic treasurer, of his wealth. That is also an irrefutable crime."

"As for you, Sanaischara," Lord Shiva addressed Sani, "you did not commit any crime – however, you hated Vaivasvata, Yama and Yami – children of Samjna, your father's lawful wife. You were consumed by jealousy towards Yama, your elder brother. I hope you all agree that hatred and envy are certainly not divine virtues!"

Saniaschara bowed his head in silent acknowledgment of Lord Shiva's accusation.

Lord Shiva confronted Rahu and Ketu and locked eyes with them. "You have persistently questioned and criticized my opinion. Let me remind you of your numerous transgressions. You attempted to obtain the *amrita* fraudulently in the guise of *devas*. You swallowed Surya and Chandra, depriving the three worlds of their life-giving rays. Your obsession with vengeance adversely affected the welfare of all living beings. I think you will admit that these are not actions worthy of godheads who are to be universally worshipped."

The discomfited Rahu and Ketu could not meet Lord Shiva's piercing gaze.

Sri Mahavishnu stepped forward to address the embarrassed *Navagrahas*. "I commend you for your humble acceptance of Lord Shiva's analysis."

"After all, Father," Brahma said, with a twinkle in his eyes, "Lord Shiva is the architect of the definitive treatise on punishment. I'm sure his analysis is absolutely correct!"

"My analysis does not seek to emphasize the *Navagrahas'* past misdeeds," Shiva smiled serenely. "My only intention is to point out how the physical senses can wreak havoc on inherent virtue." Lord Shiva raised his arm in benediction over the *Navagrahas*. "Today, your consecration under the aegis of the *Trimurti* has cleansed you of all your past sins. You stand before us now as divine forms, equipped with appropriate qualities. You are the awesome *Navagrahas*: gods wielding formidable powers!"

"That was well said," Vishnu smiled at Shiva. "The kingdoms of humans, Svaayambhuva Manu's progeny, are spread across the sacred land of Bharatakhada. The *Navagrahas* will have dominion over these kingdom too. Shiva will elaborate on the boundaries of your respective realms."

Shiva nodded in agreement and announced: "The foremost of the *Navagrahas*, Surya, the *Graharaju*, will rule over the Kalinga Kingdom. Chandra will exercise authority over the Yaamuna Kingdom and Angaaraka over the Kingdom of Avanti. Budha is given sovereignty over Magadha, and Guru over the Sindhu Kingdom. Sukra is to reign over the Kingdom of Kambhoja, while Sanaischara gets command of the Sowraashtra Kingdom. Rahu will rule the Barbara Kingdom and Ketu, the Kingdom of Antarvedi.

"The writ of the *Navagrahas* will prevail largely on the inhabitants of their respective kingdoms." Lord Shiva paused. "There are twelve zodiac signs corresponding to the constellations of stars in the sky." Shiva smiled at the Creator. "Lord Brahma will now specify the constellations which each of the *grahas* will command."

"All beings, particularly humans, have strong connections with the twelve zodiac signs, depending on their time of birth. Each sign of the zodiac will come under the command of a particular *graha*. The zodiac sign of every being is allotted according to the star under which he is born. As the rulers of the zodiac, you will effectively control the lives of humans and all other beings."

Brahma completed his introduction and continued. "Please pay attention as I enumerate the specifics of your authority over the zodiac ... Surya commands the zodiac sign Leo, and Chandra, Cancer. Angaaraka Kuja will exercise authority over Aries and Scorpio, and Budha over Virgo and Gemini. Guru rules Sagittarius and Pisces, and Sukra, Libra and Taurus. Sanaischara has dominion over Capricorn and Aquarius. Rahu's command will alternate between Libra, which comes under Sukra, and Virgo, which Budha rules. Ketu will sometimes take charge of Gemini, which is under the command of Budha, and sometimes of Pisces, which is Guru's fief." Brahma concluded: "In short, the zodiac signs will exert a strong influence over all beings and you will have a powerful impact on the zodiac."

"Aditya, Soma, Mangala, Budha, Guru, Sukra, Sani, Rahu and Ketu," Sri Mahavishnu looked at each of them in turn. "I have a directive for you ... I willed the astral *Navagrahas* to be incarnated with gross bodies to facilitate your worship by all beings, especially humans. Consequently, you were born with physical bodies to ideal parents and have been anointed as the *Navagrahas*.

"The humans whose lives depend on your influence, will worship, serve and honor you devotedly, in order to ensure that you look upon them favorably. In the days to come, they will erect magnificent temples in your honour and install you there in idol form – imbuing these idols with the power of your invocation. They will attempt to appease you with ablutions and rites. I command you to accept their offerings and bless them in return. Fulfill my will which gave you your glorious gross manifestations."

Sri Mahavishnu raised his hand in benediction: "You may now depart for your abodes. May good fortune be yours!"

"May good fortune be yours!" Brahma and Shiva echoed in unison.

"So be it!" chorused the Seven Sages, *maanasaputras* and *devas*.

Surya folded his hands and saluted the *Trimurti*, his parents and elders. Anoora prompted the horses – Surya's chariot moved forward resolutely. The other *grahas* in turn bowed in gratitude, folded their hands in reverence and signaled exultantly to their steeds. The *Navagrahas'* chariots moved in solemn procession and then diverged towards the direction of their respective spheres.

The fascinated onlookers stared at the gleaming chariots until they became distant beams of light.

———

Nirvikalpananda smiled at his four disciples. "That completes our account of the *Navagrahas'* consecration. While listening to the *Puranas*, it is normal to question many things." One of the boys stirred. "Sadananda, if you have any doubts, do not hesitate to voice them."

"A small doubt, master," Sadananda replied. "The first seven *grahas*, from Surya to Sanaischara, command their own exclusive zodiac signs. However, Rahu and Ketu do not have independent sovereignty over any sign. How can this be, if all the *grahas* are supposedly equal?"

"Excellent reasoning!" applauded Nirvikalpananda. "Except in the matter of lacking independent command over the zodiac signs, Rahu and Ketu are equal to their peers in all other respects. It must be admitted that many astrologers and sages insist that they are shadow-planets – this may be the reason for not allotting them authority over their own zodiac signs."

He continued: "Another relevant factor here is that, based on geography, there are various conflicting theories regarding Rahu and Ketu's dominion over the zodiac signs. The Telugu people believe that Rahu commands Libra, and Ketu commands Gemini. But, in fact, Sukra rules Libra and Budha, Gemini. On the other hand, the people of Karnataka believe that Rahu has sovereignty over Virgo, and Ketu over Pisces. But, the truth is that Budha commands Virgo, and Guru commands Pisces."

Nirvikalpananda smiled serenely at his disciples. "By right, it is the astrologers' duty to analyze these divergent theories and arrive at a logical conclusion – we'll leave it to them, shall we?!"

"Master," Shivananda said. "You have given us a gripping account of the *Navagrahas'* consecration. We have also heard about their sovereignty over the Nine Gems and Nine Grains. However, people say that the *Navagrahas* also have dominion over particular trees – is this correct?"

"Yes," the master admitted, "the *Navagrahas* rule over nine kinds of trees. It is generally acknowledged that one has a soft corner for things under one's command: so, these trees are recognized as being the favourites of the respective *grahas*. In fact, our scriptures hold that the Navagrahas also have their favourite metals and tastes, along with the gems, grains and trees.

"Coming to the trees, Surya's favourite is the Jilledu (gigantic swallow wort) and Chandra's is the Moduga (butea frondosa). Angaaraka prefers the Chandra (mimosa catechu), and Budha the Uthareni (prickly chaff flower plant). The Aswattha (Peepal tree) is dear to Guru, and the Udumbara (fig tree) to Sukra. The Jammi (bulrush tree) is special for Sanaischara, and the Garika (bent grass) and the Darbha (sacrificial grass) for Rahu for Ketu respectively. Among these, Garika and Darbha are not trees, but grasses."

"Master," asked Sadananda, "is there any particular reason to consider these trees and grasses as the *Navagrahas'* favourites?"

Nirvikalpananda said thoughtfully, "Perhaps the medicinal properties of these plants is the underlying reason for their selection. The special quality of the air which touches these plants, the medicinal benefits derived from the smoke, and the smell they emit when burned in the *homam* – these could explain their elevated status.

"This is the greatest glory of our spiritual inheritance, our way of thought and our traditions. Each god has a particular animal as his vehicle; each god has a particular tree as his favourite. What is the unspoken significance behind these messages?

"We unanimously worship and adore the gods. In the same way, we should cherish those animals which serve as their vehicles. In effect, we are subtly told not to hunt animals for food, or as a pastime. We are exhorted to refrain from destroying the trees which the gods hold close to their hearts. This is the golden message conveyed by our inimitable scriptures and traditions.

"Now, let us look at the various metals with respect to the *Navagrahas*: Surya's favourite metal is copper and Chandra's, bronze. Kuja prefers gold, and Budha, brass, bronze and pewter. Gold and silver are special to Guru, and silver to Sukra. Saniaschara favours iron, and Rahu and Ketu, lead.

"When we consider the various tastes, it is spicy for Surya, salty for Chandra, bitter for Kuja, savory for Budha, sweet for Guru, sour for Sukra, and bitter for Sanaischara, Rahu and Ketu."

"Master," asked Chidananda, "am I correct in assuming that we must worship the *Navagrahas* with offerings of their favourite tree or grass, their preferred metal and the foods that reflect their particular tastes?"

"Yes, my son," Nirvikalpananda emphasized. "Let us take a practical example: suppose I am fond of cheese and creamy curd … whenever you find them, you are likely to bring them to me. Why would you do this?"

"Obviously because you like cheese and curds, master!" Shivananda smiled.

"Very well," said Nirvikalpananda, with a twinkle in his eyes. "If you give me something I cherish, what will I give you in return?"

The disciples remained in expectant silence.

"I will give you what you like!" the master chuckled. "Yes, master!" his pupils chorused happily.

"It is the same with our spiritual beliefs. When a devotee worships god by offering him his favourite things, god will reciprocate by granting the devotee what he likes. It is a simple matter of mutual exchange. This is the reason why our wise and virtuous ancestors noted the favourite flowers, foods, plants, etc. of the respective gods and passed on this precious knowledge to succeeding generations."

"Master, you have indeed enlightened us!" Vimalananda's face glowed with joy.

"Our narrative has covered the birth and life of the *Navagrahas*." Nirvikalpananda returned to his subject. "We will now go on to hear of the glories of the Nine Planets. With that, our *Navagraha Purana* will be completed.

"The *Trimurti* blessed the *Navagrahas* abundantly and bestowed power and status on them – along with corresponding duties and obligations. Each and every living being in the three worlds was subject to their influence. Eminent historical and *Puranic* personages, towering intellectuals – why, even the incarnations of the very Gods themselves, were swayed by their impact. No one is exempt from the implacable influence of the *Navagrahas*.

"We will now acquaint ourselves with those whom the *Navagrahas*, in their mercy, blessed with happy, prosperous lives." He paused. "We will also get to know those unfortunate individuals who earned the *Navagrahas'* wrath and experienced untold misery and hardship in consequence. Let us begin with Surya, the king of the *grahas*."

Nirvikalpananda closed his eyes, folded his hands in devotion, and broke into his chant glorifying Surya:

*"Saptaasva rathamaaroodham prachandam Kasyapaatmajam!
Swethapadmadharam Devam! Tam Suryam! Pranamaamyaham!!"*

*I offer my salutations to Surya who rides the seven horse-chariot, who is very
passionate, who is the son of Kasyapa, who holds the white lotus and who
is God.*

After a pregnant pause, the master slowly opened his eyes and looked
somberly at his disciples.

"We have reached the finest part of the *Navagraha Purana*. We will see
how the *grahas'* lives and greatness exert their inevitable influence on us.

"*Surya Bhagavan*, the king of the *grahas*, and the foremost of the Nine
Planets, constantly lavishes two priceless gifts on the three worlds – heat
and light. All living beings depend on these gifts for their health and
sustenance. In addition to heat and light, Surya is also the dispenser of
knowledge when he pleases.

"There are some notable individuals from the *Puranas* who propitiated
Surya and were blessed with the gift of exceptional learning. Their stories
demonstrate Surya's glory."

"Who are they, master?" asked Sadananda, bursting with curiosity.

Nirvikalpananda smiled indulgently at his enthusiasm. "They
are many: *Maharshi* Yaajnavalkya, Anjaneya, Sri Rama, Dharmaraja,
Kunti, Draupadi and numerous others were the recipients of Surya's
magnanimity. Let us begin with the story of *Maharshi* Yaajnavalkya …"

Part 3

xxxxxxxxxxxxxxxxxxxxxxxxxxxxx

The Glory of
the Navagrahas

THE GLORY OF SURYA

*Japaakusuma Sankaasam kaasyapeyam mahaadyutim
Tamorim sarva paapaghnam pranatosmi Divaakaram!*

*I offer my salutations to Divaakara (Surya), who shines like the japa flower,
who is the son of Kasyapa, who is resplendent, who is the enemy of darkness,
and who is the destroyer of all sins.*

"Sage Yaajnavalkya was King Janaka's renowned preceptor. The sage himself gave the monarch an account of how his own *guru* had denied him instruction in *Vedic* knowledge …" Nirvikalpananda began.

"Master," Shivananda interrupted, "who was sage Yaajnavalkya?"

"According to our mythology, Yaajnavalkya was the son of Aalambini devi and Devaraata. Let us see what particular knowledge he wished to acquire, why he could not acquire it and how he managed to obtain

it later. One day, Yaajnavalkya was summoned by his *guru* ..."
Nirvikalpananda resumed his story.

∞∞∞

Yaajnavalkya prostrated himself before his *guru* and stood waiting with folded hands. "*Gurudev*, I am here at your command."

"Yaajnavalkya, you have come to the end of your course of study – you may leave," the master said.

Yaajnavalkya's eyes widened in surprise at this abrupt dismissal. "*Gurudev*, you have not yet blessed me with *Vedic* knowledge and the *Saamkhya Yoga*!"

"You are not eligible to receive such knowledge," his master replied peremptorily.

"*Gurudev*," Yaajnavalkya asked anxiously, "have I unknowingly erred in my actions? If so ..."

He was cut off angrily by his master. "Clever riposte will not make you eligible, Yaajnavalkya! You talk too much! Your actions have nothing to do with my decision. It is your unfortunate fate, as ordained by planetary alignment."

"*Gurudev* ..."

"Enough!" his master snapped. "Be on your way!"

With one last look into his master's implacable, burning eyes, Yaajnavalkya folded his hands and turned away. Weighted down by disappointment and grief, he mechanically made his departure from the hermitage.

∞∞∞

Heart-sore and weary, Yaajnavalkya wandered aimlessly through the forest. The scorching sun beat down on him mercilessly, as he followed a narrow track, roughly hewn by the passage of wild animals. He had no idea where it led, nor did he have a destination. His master's harsh words echoed in his ears: "You are not eligible to receive such knowledge!"

Yaajnavalkya stopped short. Why was he not eligible for advanced study? On what criteria had his master based his decision? Again, his *guru*'s voice thundered in his ears: "It is your unfortunate fate, as ordained by planetary alignment."

Planetary ... alignment ... Yaajnavalkya came to a halt once more. If the reason for his premature dismissal was the unfavourable alignment of the planets, was there more to his master's words than met the eye? Had his *guru* given him a hint? Was one of the *Navagrahas* unfavourably disposed towards him? Was one of the planets eyeing him malignantly?

The chirping of birds roused him from his reverie. Suddenly conscious of his sweat-drenched body and raging thirst, Yaajnavalkya made his way towards the bird-song, which heralded the presence of water. After quenching his thirst and bathing in the pool he found there, Yaajnavalkya sat under the shade of a tree on the bank.

Like a coiled snake lifting its hood, the question of the adverse influence of one of the *Navagrahas* rose to his mind. Yaajnavalkya closed his eyes and recalled his horoscope, his nimble fingers moving in quick calculation. His eyes reopened with a new gleam – yes, his master was right: Surya, the king of the *grahas*, was ill-disposed towards him.

Surya's favour was a precondition to the acquisition of the *Vedic* knowledge Yaajnavalkya craved. Very well – in that case, he would propitiate Surya and earn his favour; he would invoke Surya and obtain his *darshan*. Yaajnavalkya refused to be dissuaded by his preceptor's abrupt dismissal. He looked around him: dusk was fast approaching. He decided to commence his penance at an auspicious hour the next morning. His spirits lifted and he smiled to himself. The magnanimous Surya would surely bless him and help him gain the knowledge he desired. Mind at rest, Yaajnavalkya settled down for the night under the tree.

<hr />

The eastern sky flushed pink and gold with the light of dawn. The sun rose, embracing the world with radiant arms. Yaajnavalkya, standing waist-deep in the waters of the pond, offered his *arghya*, or ritual ablution, to the sun god. He folded his hands in respectful salutation and recited the *Mahasankalpa mantra*. Touched by the soft rays of the rising sun, the lotus buds around him unfurled their tender petals. Yaajnavalkya smiled, considering this to be a good omen for the success of his venture. Leaving the pond, he chose a spot exposed to the sun's light from dawn to dusk and commenced his *tapas*.

The days passed. The sun continued its diurnal journey from east to west, but Yaajnavalkya remained oblivious to the transition of day and night. His single-minded determination to succeed in his objective enabled him to immerse himself in transcendental meditation instantly.

Yaajnavalkya lost all awareness of his physical senses: he was immune to hunger and thirst, heat and cold, light and darkness.

Ultimately, the passage of time saw Yaajnavalkya triumph. A new glow touched his half-closed eyes. His lids fluttered open tentatively, only to shut in reflex at the blinding glare which assaulted his eyes.

"Yaajnavalkya!" A vibrant voice compelled his attention.

Yaajnavalkya slowly opened his eyes in response to the summons. An awesome spectacle unfolded before him. A one-wheeled chariot, drawn by seven green steeds, emerged from an orb of incredible radiance. On the shaft was Aruna, the charioteer. Behind him, the god of a thousand rays sat in majestic splendor, holding a pure white lotus in his hand. Attired in gleaming red, his complexion resembled a crimson lotus in bloom. His smile outdid the orb in brilliance.

"Om Suryaya Namaha! Om Suryaya Namaha!" Yaajnavalkya chanted the Aaditya mantra with devotedly folded hands.

"Yaajnavalkya," the voice was honey-rich in timbre. "The keen ray of your tapas has exerted its magnetic pull on my own thousand rays and brought me here to grant you my darshan. What do you want from me?"

"Bhagavan, your adverse influence has resulted in my master refusing to impart instruction to me. As a consequence, I have failed to gain the knowledge I crave. Now, I ask you to grant me the invaluable Vedic wisdom and the prose mantras of the Yajus. Let your benign face be turned towards me," Yaajnavalkya prayed.

Surya smiled munificently and said, "Let's first take up your second wish – I now withdraw my inimical influence and look on you auspiciously."

"Bhagavan," Yaajnavalkya exclaimed, "I am indeed blessed!"

Surya continued: "Coming to your first wish, I hereby invoke the goddess of words and knowledge and direct her to enter your body ... open your mouth and grant her access."

Gazing adoringly at Surya, Yaajnavalkya obediently opened his mouth. In an instant, Goddess Saraswati appeared there before them. Mahaswetha smiled at Yaajnavalkya, assumed a subtle form, and entered his mouth.

Yaajnavalkya shuddered uncontrollably as his body was consumed by a fiery heat. In an instinctive bid for survival, the terrified Yaajnavalkya dashed towards the pond, intending to jump into its cooling waters.

"Yaajna, stop!" Surya's thunderous warning halted him in his tracks. "Goddess Saraswati's incomparable store of knowledge and writing has entered your body. Its awesome power is the cause of the heat which wracks your physique: it will soon pass. Endure it and meditate on Goddess Saraswati."

In accordance with Surya's instruction, Yaajnavalkya folded his hands in prayer. In a few moments, the fire which consumed him abated and a cool wave engulfed his body, like a healing second skin over his burns.

"Yaajna," Surya said, "I am greatly pleased by your devotion, confidence and penance. You have succeeded in turning my malignant influence into one of magnanimity. You will acquire the *Vedic* knowledge which you crave – the storehouse of the *Yajus*. Furthermore, I grant you knowledge of the *Saamkhya Yoga* and the *Satapatha Brahamana*. Yaajna – your intellect will bloom like the lotus in my hand. Goddess Saraswati will always abide in you. Go your way – your wishes will be fulfilled."

Yaajnavalkya, moved to tears by Surya's abundant mercy, folded his hands in reverence and said, "I am blessed, *Bhagavan* ... truly, I am blessed."

Surya's chariot merged into the sky. In its place stood the glowing orb of the sun.

As directed by Surya, Yaajnavalkya completed his morning rites and sat in meditation on Goddess Saraswati in those sylvan surroundings.

Presently, the dulcet notes of a lute caressed his ears. The instrument echoed the *Nada Brahma* – the Supreme God of Sound. Yaajnavalkya opened his wondering eyes to find Goddess Saraswati, draped in pristine white, standing before him. The primordial letter, *Om*, adorned her head as a crown. She wore the letters of the Sanskrit alphabet as her ornaments. Yaajnavalkya gazed in deep awe at the goddess, the personification of letters, radiant in the light of learning. He prostrated himself at her holy feet and rose to worship her with folded hands.

"Oh, Mother of Knowledge," Yaajnavalkya implored, "grant me the knowledge of the *Vedas*."

"My son," Goddess Saraswati replied, "it was due to Surya's adverse impact that you could not acquire the knowledge you desired. Now that you have gained the favour of the king of the *grahas*, I am eager to impart that knowledge to you."

"I am truly blessed, mother," Yaajnavalkya said. He worshipped her with the ritual offering of water through the *arghya*, and sat devotedly at her feet.

Goddess Saraswati smiled benignly at him and said, "Yaajna, close your eyes and focus on your meditation. Through my grace, all the learning of the *Vidyas* will become clear to you."

Yaajnavalkya was blinded by the rays of splendor emanating from Goddess Saraswati's large eyes. He closed his own eyes in instinctive obedience and immersed himself in meditation. A deep swell of knowledge pervaded his inner self like a divine fragrance. The fifteen branches of the *Yajurveda* took up residence in his mind. Under *Saamkhya Yoga,* the flower of wisdom bloomed in him. The riches of the great *Satapatha Brahmana* became his. All this happened in one glorious flash.

Yaajnavalkya, filled with a sense of fulfillment, opened his eyes. Saraswati, the Goddess of Knowledge, smiled at him as tenderly as a mother suckling her babe. Lifting her right hand in benediction over him, Mahaswetha disappeared.

Yaajnavalkya's eyes brimmed with tears of joy.

<hr />

"Thus, as a result of Surya's benevolence, the goddess of knowledge herself came in person to bless Yaajnavalkya with the knowledge of the *Vedas* and *Saamkhya Yoga.* She bestowed on Yaajnavalkya the essence of the *Yajur Veda,*" Nirvikalpananda said. "The unparalleled wealth of knowledge acquired by Yaajnavalkya through Goddess Saraswati's grace, under Surya's benevolent influence, earned him a seat in the hall of fame.

"It is known that Visvavasu, a *gandharva* who had long struggled to find logical answers to fifteen extremely difficult questions, was able to obtain satisfying answers from Sage Yaajnavalkya. In time, Yaajnavalkya authored a new version of the *Satapatha Brahmana.* Yaajnavalkya has also written a treatise titled *Yaajnavalkya Smrti,* which is a veritable treasure-trove of knowledge, and of immense value to mankind.

"So, it is evident that, without Surya's beneficial influence, it is impossible to acquire a good education," concluded Nirvikalpananda.

"Master," Vimalananda said thoughtfully, "to be explicit, it was Goddess Saraswati who imparted *Vedic* knowledge to Yaajnavalkya. Is it fair to give Surya the credit for this?"

Nirvikalpananda smiled indulgently. "Now, Vimalananda, let's take you as our example. Let us assume that you are a six-year old boy. You want a rupee. Your father is the custodian of the household finances.

However, you ask your mother for the money. She, in turn, tells your father to give you a rupee – which he does. Now, tell me: who deserves the credit for this – your mother or your father?"

"My mother, of course!" replied Vimalananda promptly. "It was only at her instigation that my father gave me the rupee!"

"That's a logical reply, Vimalananda," the master said approvingly. "Similarly, if not for Surya's grace and his benign influence, Goddess Saraswati would not have given Yaajnavalkya her *darshan* and the *Vedic* knowledge he deserved.

"We must keep in mind one significant fact: the gods and demigods will strictly confine themselves to the discharge of their designated duties alone. Surya, the king of the *grahas*, was well aware of the level of knowledge he was entitled to grant. Yaajnavalkya desired advanced education in the priceless *Yajur Veda*. Surya acknowledged that this was beyond his brief. Saraswati, goddess of the word and education, the manifestation of letters, was the one equipped to impart such knowledge.

"However, Surya voluntarily imparted such knowledge as fell within his own ambit to a particular student who approached him ...." The master paused on a note of suspense.

"Who was that student, master?" Chidananda was agog with curiosity.

"Anjaneya," said Nirvikalpananda. "As a consequence of Surya's adverse influence, Anjaneya had no one to instruct him. He was forced to beseech Surya, whom he had earlier humiliated by attempting to swallow, to be his preceptor."

"Master," said Shivananda enthusiastically, "please narrate this episode."

"Very well. Let me first tell you about Anjaneya's parents and his birth. We shall then go on to his education. Do you all remember Punjikasthala?" Nirvikalpananda asked.

"How could we forget, master?" Sadananda smiled wryly. "Your narrative technique is so captivating that the details are etched permanently on our memories! Punjikasthala was the nymph who served as a servant maid at Brhaspati's *ashram*."

"Excellent!" Nirvikalpananda smiled. "Brhaspati, infuriated by Punjikasthala's shenanigans, cursed her to be born as a she-monkey. Consequently, Punjikasthala was born to a heroic monkey, Kunjara, who named her Anjana. Anjana grew to adulthood under Kunjara's tutelage. Kunjara had a nephew, Kesari, who was valiant and phenomenally strong.

Approving of Kesari's fondness for Anjana, Kunjara gave her in marriage
to his nephew ..."

Nirvikalpananda was back in the thick of his narrative.

⸺◦∞◦⸺

Kesari reached the cave he shared with Anjana, his arms loaded with the
fruits he had collected in the forest. To his surprise, Anjana did not come
to meet him at the entrance, as was her wont. Calling out to her, Kesari
peered into the cave's unlit interior – Anjana was crouched in a dark corner.

Kesari looked at her in concern and asked, "Anjana, what is the
matter? You look listless and ill!"

Anjana heaved a sigh. "My physical health is good enough! I am sick
at heart!"

"Anjana!" Kesari gasped in bewilderment.

"My friend, Haritaki, has become a mother ... her infant son is so
beautiful! He has an adorable red face!"

"That makes you sad?"

"I am not sorry that Haritaki has a son – I am sorry for myself for not
having one!" Anjana said disconsolately.

"What can we do?" Kesari sighed in his turn. "Our married life has
not been fruitful."

"How can our marriage be truly fulfilled without progeny!" Anjana
lamented.

"Come out of the darkness, Anjana," Kesari said tenderly, "Let's talk
outside."

Kesari held out his hand to his wife. Anjana pulled herself up. Kesari
put his arm around her slender waist, led her into the sunshine and seated
her on a boulder. Sitting beside her, he gently caressed her head and
listened patiently as Anjana waxed eloquent on Haritaki's motherhood
and her newborn son's beauty.

"Let's meet our monkey physician," Kesari said consolingly. "I'll ask
him to give you some medicines which will facilitate your pregnancy."

"There is no need for a physician!"

"Anjana!" Kesari exclaimed at her vehemence.

"We need someone who is more powerful than a mere physician,"
Anjana said emphatically. "We will seek Sage Maatanga's *darshan*
tomorrow morning."

⸺◦∞◦⸺

A divine tranquility embraced Sage Maatanga's *ashram*. The heady fragrance of multi-hued blossoms pervaded the air. Anjana and Kesari made their quiet entrance and saw Sage Maatanga seated on a dais in the shade of a tree. A luminescent halo shone round his head and his eyes were closed in deep meditation. Anjana, moved to devotion, extended her arm to pick a flower to lay at his feet.

"Anjana!" the sage's voice suddenly lashed out in warning. "Do not pluck the flower!"

Anjana jumped back in startled alarm and looked at the sage: his eyes remained shut! Maatanga could see them even through his closed eyes!

Holding his wife's hand, Kesari guided her towards the dais, where they came to a respectful halt before the sage.

Sage Maatanga opened his eyes and greeted the couple with a welcoming smile. "You are here after a long interval! Come ...." Sage Maatanga beckoned them near.

Anjana and Kesari prostrated themselves before him and touched his feet in worship.

"May happiness be yours," Sage Maatanga said. "Anjana, do you know why I warned you not to pluck the flowers?"

Anjana shook her head in bewilderment.

"In this *ashram*, the flowers remain eternally fresh, as if they have just bloomed – they will never wither! Once, my disciples returned with vast quantities of fruits for me. Due to their heavy burden, they were drenched in sweat. At the moment of their entry into the *ashram*, the drops of perspiration from their bodies fell on the flowering plants – the plants were instantly transformed into beautiful, fragrant blossoms! In my eyes, these are not mere flowers: they are living symbols of *guru bhakti* – devotion towards the *guru*."

"Your disciples are indeed fortunate!" Kesari remarked.

"I am also fortunate, Kesari – it is a master's good fortune to have sincere disciples." The sage turned to Anjana. "I haven't set eyes on you for a long time, Anjana," he said. "How is your father, Kunjara?"

"Father is well ... but ..." Anjana faltered and lowered her eyes to the ground.

"But ...?" the sage frowned. "Come on, Anjana – out with it! I am very fond of Kunjara."

"Father is sad as I continue to remain childless."

"The father mirrors his daughter's sorrow!"

"Well said, master!" Kesari exclaimed. "How can we be happy without children? Our life has become meaningless."

"*Swami* ..." Anjana addressed the sage.

"Yes, Anjana – what is it?" Sage Maatanga gazed into her tear-filled eyes. Anjana bent her head and the tears overflowed to drop on the sage's feet. Sage Maatanga placed his palm in blessing on her bowed head. "Anjana!"

Anjana looked up into his eyes. "*Bhagavan,* bless me with a son who will surpass his father, Kesari, and his grandfather, Kunjara, in strength and valour!"

Sage Maatanga smiled wryly. "I do not possess such power. However, I shall bless your effort to beget such a son. You were in my thoughts earlier this morning. I wished to bless you and to give you my advice regarding your course of action in this matter."

"*Bhagavan!*" Anjana gasped in wonder.

"Yes, Anjana," the sage said, "I can foresee your future in my mind's eye. Propitiate Vayudeva who is also known as the *Maha Praana* and *Mukhya Praana* – the Great Life Force. In his mercy, he will grant you the son you desire."

"Oh .... *Bhagavan* ..." Anjana was speechless with joy.

"Tomorrow is a very auspicious day," the sage continued. "Go to the summit of this mountain and commence your penance." He turned to Kesari. "Kesari, it is your duty to see that Anjana's penance is not disrupted."

"I will guard Anjana and her *tapas*," Kesari declared staunchly.

Anjana and Kesari folded their hands, touched Sage Maatanga's feet in respect and took their leave.

───────

The next morning, Anjana and Kesari reached the summit of the mountain and Kesari cleared a spot under the spreading branches of a tree. Anjana bathed in a nearby pond and touched her husband's feet in reverence. She swore a solemn oath to beget a son endowed with extraordinary strength, vast intelligence, nobility and valour, and commenced her penance to propitiate Vayudeva, the god of wind.

Kesari faithfully collected fruits, and washed and cleaned them in readiness for Anjana to eat. However, steadfast in her penance, Anjana did not open her eyes for food or water – the fruits remained untouched.

Anjana rose above the physical senses, and oblivious to hunger and thirst, lost all consciousness of self. Kesari, transfixed by the sight of Anjana's ardent penance, gazed in astonishment at her resolute concentration and devotion. He mused: a mother's agonized yearning for a child cannot be fully comprehended by a father!

As Anjana's penance continued uninterruptedly, there was a sudden change in the atmosphere. The soft zephyr which had wafted over them, gradually turned into a strong wind. Within moments, it picked up further momentum and became a furious gale. Trees bent under the force of the violent whirlwind, which shrieked through the mountain caves and lashed at the shrubs. The massive tree under which Anjana sat, lost in penance, creaked and bent menacingly, its branches lashing out in frenzy. The alarmed Kesari prayed it would not be uprooted in the gale.

Anjana, immersed in a transcendental state beyond time, space and reason, remained oblivious to the raging pandemonium around her. Kesari stood astounded by her concentration.

Gradually, the gale lost its force and subsided into a gentle breeze once more. The furious shriek of the tempest which shook the trees, animals and the very mountain itself, receded into the depths of the forest. Kesari, who had taken shelter in a cave, emerged into the calm and looked at Anjana – his wife remained lost in in serene contemplation.

⸉⸊

"Salutations to the primeval couple!" Vayudeva, the god of wind, prostrated himself before Lord Shiva and Parvati on Mount Kailash.

"May happiness be yours," Lord Shiva blessed him. "How are you, Vayu?"

"How can I be anything but in the best of health and spirits when I bear Lord Shiva's awesome *tejas* in my stomach?!" Vayu smiled in reply.

"Lord Shiva's awesome *tejas*? ... in your stomach? What do you mean, Vayu?" Goddess Parvati asked in bewilderment.

"Yes, mother," Vayu said, "have you forgotten the time when you and your divine spouse frolicked together in the assumed form of monkeys?"

"Oh ... that monkey business!" Lord Shiva smiled at Parvati with a twinkle in his eyes.

"At that time," Vayu continued, "Lord Shiva entrusted me with his semen, commanding me to keep it safely in my stomach. Since that day,

I have faithfully carried your charge on my head – and the luster of your *tejas* in my stomach!"

"Very well, Vayu," Lord Shiva asked, "but why are you bringing this up now?"

"*Bhagavan*," Vayu explained, "Anjana, daughter of the warrior-monkey, Kunjara, and wife of Kesari, another warrior-monkey, is immersed in *tapas*, propitiating me for the gift of a son. I am pleased by her penance. I am here to request your permission to bestow the great *Rudra Veerya* on the virtuous Anjana."

"Certainly, Vayu," Lord Shiva agreed promptly. "Anjana was an *apsara* in her previous birth. She was reborn as a monkey due to Brhaspati's curse. Anjana is undoubtedly worthy of begetting a son with my *tejas*."

"Anjana, who shows such fortitude in her *tapas*, will definitely nurture the child and rear him to reach his full potential," Goddess Parvati added.

"Go, Vayu," Lord Shiva commanded, "bestow the fruit of my *tejas* on Anjana." He continued, "Anjana's son will achieve great fame and will be renowned as your son too!"

"I am blessed, indeed!" Vayu said humbly, with folded hands.

⚬⚬⚬

Kesari sighed at the heap of untouched fruits. Anjana remained engrossed in her unrelenting *tapas*. He had no idea when her penance would end – but he would steadfastly continue to guard her and bring her delicious fruits and honey, in the hope that she would break her fast. Praying to Vayu, the god of wind, to grant his wife's wish soon, Kesari went to forage in the forest.

The wind blowing on the summit abruptly took on the fierce aspect of a tempest and whirled around Anjana, who remained like a stone statue, oblivious to its force. Gradually, the whirlwind subsided into a gentle breeze.

"Anjana!" the voice roared like a lion in its den. Anjana shuddered in response to the thunderous summons, which reverberated in her ears. Her eyes slowly fluttered open to see a gargantuan form hovering before her. Its contours were vague, as if shrouded by a thin veil of gauze. The body gleamed a dull gold behind the shimmering curtain. The apparition held a huge, golden mace on his left shoulder. Anjana stared at him in awe.

"Anjana," the voice resonated in all directions from that divine, colossal form, "I am Vayudeva, the god of wind."

"My lord ... you heard my prayer!" Anjana exclaimed in delight and offered her humble salutation to the wind god.

"I am pleased with your flawless penance. You yearn to become a mother. I will now bestow the all-powerful *tejas* on you. Its mighty luster will engulf your body and enter your sacred womb, to grow within its protective walls. In due course, it will be born as the son you long to cradle tenderly in your lap." As he spoke, Vayudeva raised his palm over her in benediction.

Rays of shimmering gray radiated from his palm and swamped Anjana's entire form. In an instant, the divine emanation vanished, having been absorbed into Anjana's body.

"Anjana," Vayudeva smiled magnanimously, "you will bear a son with the *amsa* of Lord Paramashiva. He will be endowed with extraordinary strength and intelligence and shine as a mighty warrior and exemplary scholar. Through him, your name will be immortal. He will achieve renown as Vayuputra, Vatatmaja and Maruti. He will be the shining example which proves that the *vanara* (monkey) is greater than the *nara* (human)."

"*Bhagavan,*" Anjana said with tears in her eyes, "I am blessed – my life has become truly meaningful." She folded her hands in reverence.

In the next instant, Vayudeva disappeared with the roaring sound of wind whooshing into a cave. Anjana, emerging from her transformational encounter, looked round eagerly for her husband.

"Anjana!" she heard him call, as he returned from the forest with his collection of fruits.

Anjana flew to him with the glad tidings.

The seasons came and went. The goddess of time changed her attire to suit each season, laying on a continuous feast for the eyes. Buds blossomed into flowers, flowers into unripe fruits and then into succulent, mature fruits.

Anjana's womb swelled with her pregnancy, like the waxing moon. She shone like a lotus bud, as a strange, new, radiant beauty suffused her entire being. Her divine loveliness was a delight to every heart and eye. It was a transcendental beauty, which went deeper than the merely physical. Kesari lavished his affectionate care on his glowing wife.

On the tenth day of the dark half of the month of *Vaisakh*, at an

auspicious time, Anjana delivered a baby boy. The infant was golden
complexioned, with a red face. A yellow robe was wrapped round his
tiny waist. Golden ornaments, studded with precious gems, adorned
his little body: sparkling necklaces and earrings, and bracelets clinking
on his arms. The sacred thread of the *yajnopaveetam* was tied across his
shoulders. Anjana and Kesari were astonished to see the newborn baby
thus richly attired and adorned.

Suddenly, a gentle zephyr, laden with sweet fragrance, crept into the
inner reaches of the cave. In its wake came Vayudeva – the god of wind.
Anjana and Kesari offered their salutations to him.

"*Bhagavan* Vayu," Anjana greeted him with tears of joy, "your boon
has fructified. I am the blessed mother of a baby boy!"

"I am also blessed, Anjana!" Kesari added with a broad grin.

"Yes," Vayudeva smiled at them. "Yours is an exemplary marriage!"
He tenderly gathered the infant into his arms. "Lord Shiva's holy force
has taken birth as your son. This child will be the manifestation of
phenomenal strength. He will be renowned as Anjaneya, Anjanakumar
and Kesarinandan. As Vayuputra, Maruti and Paavani, he will immortalize
my name. All three of us are very fortunate!"

"*Bhagavan*," Anjana implored, "be my son's protector."

"Certainly, Anjana: it will be my pleasure. No harm will befall your
son as long as I, Mahaprana, am present!" Vayu placed a tender kiss on
the baby's forehead and said, "Name him Anjaneya." He passed the infant
to Kesari, who gathered him into his warm embrace. Blessing the parents
and child, the god of wind vanished into the blue sky.

<hr />

As a flower dispenses its inherent fragrance as it blossoms, the infant
Anjaneya demonstrated his prodigious strength as he grew. His antics
were a source of continuous delight and pride to his parents. Time passed.

One day, Anjana and Kesari emerged from the cave in search of
Anjaneya. Suddenly, flowers and unripe fruit rained down on them from
the thick foliage of a nearby tree. They peered up to see the young
Anjaneya perched on a branch, biting into the raw fruit, before throwing
them uneaten to the ground.

"Anjaneya, my boy! Climb down from the trees, son! Come to me!"
Anjana walked towards the tree, as her little boy jumped down, throwing
away the last of the gnawed fruits.

Anjana lifted the child into her arms and hugged him. "Now, now, my son ... is it right to pluck the fruit and throw them away like that?!" she exclaimed in gentle reprimand.

"They do not taste good, mother," Anjaneya replied with a grimace.

"That is because they are raw, my son. You should pluck only ripe fruits, which are red in colour: they will be tasty."

"Oh ... ripe fruits are red, is it, mother?" Anjaneya asked curiously.

"Yes, my son," Anjana emphasized. "Unripe fruits are green and ripe fruits are red. You should be careful not to waste the fruit buds and the green fruits."

"Yes, mother," Anjaneya said obediently, before slipping from her arms to run towards his father, Kesari, who carried a pile of red fruit in his arms.

❦

Anjaneya stood at mouth of the cave, looking after his mother's receding back. Anjana was off to the forest to forage for food. It was dawn. The eastern horizon blazed with light as the rising sun spread its first rays over the earth. Anjaneya gazed in fascination at the blazing play of colours in the sky. The red orb of the sun slowly glided above the horizon. Suddenly, a frown marred Anjaneya's brow – the rising sun was just like the round, red fruits his parents gave him.

"You should pluck only ripe fruits, which are red in colour: they will be tasty." Anjaneya recalled his mother's words. He stared at the eastern horizon. The ripe red fruit slowly climbed higher into the sky – his mouth watered at the succulent sight!

Anjaneya peered into the cave: to his relief, his father, Kesari, was nowhere to be seen. He turned back to the east. Holding his breath, he leaped into the sky, held his tail erect and flew unerringly like an arrow towards the 'red fruit' hanging temptingly before him. A cool wind caressed his face as he accelerated and sped towards the east. He looked down at the thick forests and mighty mountains which clothed the earth and rushed backwards as he continued on his passage across the vast expanse of the sky.

Anjana, busy collecting fruits for her beloved little boy, looked up instinctively to see him whizzing across the sky. She turned and ran in panic to their cave. Kesari stood at the cave entrance, staring open-mouthed at the sight of his son flying past in the sky. Anjana came to stand close beside him, cold dread gripping her heart.

Anjaneya continued to accelerate, gradually reducing the distance between him and the 'red fruit.'

Indra, enjoying the spectacular sunrise from the Nandana garden, gave a gasp of astonishment on seeing a little monkey flashing towards the sun's orb. Assuming that some evil force, in the guise of a monkey, was bent on swallowing Surya, the alarmed Indra immediately set out for the mountain of the sunrise on his royal elephant, Airavata. The divine architect, Viswakarma, and the guardians of the eight directions, followed the king of the *devas*.

Even as Indra and his agitated entourage hurried on, Anjaneya reached dangerously close to Surya.

"You monkey child! Stop right there!" Indra roared his warning. "Turn around and go back from where you came."

The young Anjaneya snarled at Indra before turning away indifferently. Indra was enraged at the little monkey's insolent defiance. In a trice, Indra hurled his weapon, the *vajrayudha*, towards the monkey, who was on the verge of swallowing Surya. The *vajra* hit Anjaneya on his jaw. At its tremendous impact, Anjaneya hurtled to the earth, where he fell unconscious on the ground.

Vayudeva, the god of wind, erupted in fury at Indra's callous failure to acknowledge and respect Vayu's relationship with the young Anjaneya. How dare Indra attack his son with the *vajrayudha*?

Assuming his gross form, the wind god tenderly picked up the unconscious Anjaneya in his arms and rushed to Kesari's cave. On entering the cave, Vayudeva deliberately withdrew his action on the three worlds – at once, the wind died down completely. Consequently, the animate world drew to a standstill and became inanimate. Indra, the guardians of the directions and all the other *devas* stood as still as statues. Unable to glide on the wind currents, birds lost the power of flight and hovered immobilized in the air. All the worlds were poised on the edge of extinction, as beings gasped for breath and struggled to overcome death through suffocation.

Brahma, aware of imminent catastrophe, rushed to Kesari's cave.

"Vayu," Brahma asked, "where is your beloved son?" He gathered the boy into his arms and delicately caressed him with his right hand. Under the divine touch of the Creator, the unconscious Anjaneya emerged from his coma.

"Vayu," Brahma urged the wind god, "release your life-giving breezes and let the worlds live. I assure you that your son is safe and will remain safe forever!"

Bowing to Brahma's wish, Vayudeva released his force and reanimated the three worlds. Every being regained its movement and inhaled the life-giving air in grateful relief.

Brahma summoned Indra, the *astadikpalakas* and Viswakarma to the cave. At the same time, Lord Shiva also appeared there on his own volition.

Indra looked ruefully at the deep scar inflicted on the boy's jar by his *vajrayudha* and said, "My *vajrayudha* has left a cleft on the boy's jaw, or *Hanu*. I therefore declare that, henceforth, he will be known as Hanuman. I grant Hanuman this boon: he will never again be vulnerable to my *vajra*."

Brahma came forward to lay his palm on the boy's head. "My divine missile – the *Brahmastra*, will have no impact on Hanuman. I grant him the boon of longevity. He will be a *Chiranjeevi*: an immortal."

It was Lord Shiva's turn. "I ordain that Anjaneya will never be wounded by my Trident or the *Rudra-astra* and *Pasupatha-astra* missiles."

Varuna, the god of the waters, decreed that Hanuman would remain immune to his power.

Agni, the god of fire, granted Hanuman protection from fire.

Kubera, the god of wealth, gifted Hanuman with his mace.

The other *devas* followed suit and showered boons on the young Hanuman.

⚬⚬⚬

The child, Anjaneya, empowered by the munificent gifts of the gods, grew up in Anjana's care. Kesari taught him the science of wrestling: in an incredibly short span of time, Anjaneya became a past-master in combat.

When Anjaneya expressed his desire to study the scriptures, Anjana immediately thought of Brhaspati, the preceptor of the gods.

"My son," Anjana said, "Brhaspati, the *deva-guru*, is a powerhouse of knowledge. There is no scripture which he does not know, or which he cannot teach – furthermore, he believes in imparting free education to all. Go to his *ashram* and request him to accept you as his disciple."

After obtaining his parents' permission and blessings, Anjaneya set out for Brhaspati's hermitage.

⚬⚬⚬

Brhaspati looked up from his explication of a *Vedic sukta* and gazed intently at the young monkey who approached him.

Anjaneya stood at a respectable distance, folded his hands in salutation and said, "*Gurudev*, my *pranam*. I am Anjaneya, the son of Anjana and Kesari. My mother, Anjana, advised me to approach your eminence for my education. Please accept me as your pupil and impart to me the knowledge of the scriptures."

Brhaspati, his eyes half-closed, remained in thoughtful silence. Anjana ... Anjaneya ... Punjikasthala ... Anjaneya! Yes! Anjana had been Punjikasthala in her previous birth! As the realization dawned, Brhaspati looked at Anjaneya with new eyes and smiled fondly at him.

"Anjanakumar, I appreciate your thirst for knowledge of the scriptures but ... I cannot instruct you."

"*Gurudev!*" Anjaneya exclaimed in rude shock. "May I know the reason for this?"

"I cannot instruct you because I cannot accept you as my disciple," Brhaspati stated.

"Why, *gurudev*?" Anjaneya asked, "I beg you to tell me."

"I cannot impart knowledge to monkeys," Brhaspati admitted ruefully.

"*Gurudev* ..." Anjaneya faltered.

"Let me explain, Anjaneya," Brhaspati said. "Regardless of a person's greatness, he is bound by certain limitations and conditions. This applies to me also. I did not accept my own son, Taara, as my disciple. I did not give him an education!"

Disappointment oozed from Anjaneya's eyes. Brhaspati looked back compassionately at the young monkey with impeccable manners and innate courtesy.

"However," the *deva-guru* continued, "just as there are individuals whose actions are constrained by certain limitations, there are other individuals who are free from all such restrictions."

"*Gurudev*," Anjaneya asked eagerly, "Who are they?" The beginnings of hope stirred in his eyes.

"Look up into the sky above!"

Anjaneya obeyed Brhaspati.

"Who do you see spreading his light on the three worlds, Anjaneya?" the *deva-guru* asked with a smile.

"The sun, the god of light."

"Go to him," Brhaspati advised, "Seek refuge at his feet."

"*Gurudev*, are you suggesting that I approach the sun in the sky?" Anjaneya asked in bewilderment.

"Yes, my boy," Brhaspati reiterated. "The god of light will bless you with the light of knowledge."

Anjaneya folded his hands and bowed in reverence.

"May you achieve your objective," Brhaspati blessed him.

"After all, he is the mentor of the gods," Kesari sympathized with his son. "Perhaps that is why he looks down on the monkey race."

"No, father," Anjaneya remained fair. "We must not misjudge that great *guru* – his own son, Taara, is a monkey like us. Brhaspati declined to educate him too: the *guru* himself revealed this to me."

"Hanuman, follow Brhaspati's advice," Anjana was resolute. "Go and propitiate Suryadeva."

Doubt clouded Anjaneya's eyes. "Mother, as a little boy, I tried to swallow him – I humiliated him!" He heaved a rueful sigh. "He may be angry with me, mother!"

Anjana smiled at her son. "*Bhagavan* Surya is the king of the *grahas*. He is worshipped as the kinsman of all the world. His anger will be fleeting!"

"What if we change his anger into compassion?" Kesari suggested.

"That is an excellent idea," Anjana agreed. She turned to her son. "First, pray to Surya, asking his forgiveness. Then, pray for his munificence. The *deva-guru* would not guide you to *Bhagavan* Surya without a valid reason."

"Do you think Suryadeva will forgive me, mother?" Anjaneya asked wistfully.

"Of course, my son!" Anjana was emphatic. "He will certainly forgive you – for all we know, he may have quite enjoyed your childish prank!"

Anjaneya touched his parents' feet in respect. "Bless me ... I am on my way!"

Surya smiled at the young monkey standing before him.

"*Bhagavan*, the son of Anjana and Kesari salutes you," Anjaneya said with respectfully folded hands.

"Hanuman?"

Anjaneya flushed in embarrassment. "*Bhagavan*, in my childish ignorance, I mistook you for a ripe fruit and attempted to swallow you. Please forgive my foolish impetuosity."

Surya looked at the youth kneeling before him in abject repentance and smiled in amusement. "I forgave you then itself, Hanuman. It was but a childish prank, wasn't it?"

"*Bhagavan!*" Anjaneya exclaimed in relief. His face glowed with happiness. "Then, show me your mercy – please bestow on me the knowledge of the scriptures. Be my mentor!"

"Hanuman, get up, my boy!" Anjaneya came to his feet and stood with his head bowed in obedience. "Your birth has been predestined for great things. Your strength, which enabled you to approach me in spite of my intense heat, is incredible. Although you are born into the monkey race, you crave knowledge of the scriptures: this is extraordinary and highly commendable! I accept you as my student and disciple."

"*Bhagavan*, I am fortunate indeed!"

"Hanuman, I will teach you the eighteen disciplines, or *Astaadasa Vidyas* – this comprises of the four *Vedas* viz. *Rigveda, Yajurveda, Saamaveda* and *Atharvaveda*; the six *Angas*: *Siksha, Vyaakarana, Chandas, Nirukta, Jyotisha* and *Kalpa*; the scriptures called *Meemamsa, Nyaaya Sabda, Dharma, Artha ayurveda, Dhanurveda* and the *Puranas*.

"Mastery of even one of these eighteen disciplines qualifies one to be considered an eminent scholar. I will pay special attention to *Vyaakarana*, grammar being the life-blood of a language. I will make you a past master in all the nine grammars – you will become a *Nava Vyaakarana Pandit*."

"*Bhagavan*, I am truly blessed!"

"I will also make you adept in the discipline of pronunciation, or *Siksha*. I will teach you the flawless pronunciation of words and sentences," Surya continued.

Anjaneya folded his hands in speechless delight.

"However, there is one obstacle."

Anjaneya looked at Surya questioningly.

"I must be constantly on the move to dispense light and heat to the three worlds. This means that I cannot sit in one place and impart knowledge to you."

Anjaneya staunchly declared, "I will fly in your wake, as you travel across the sky, and receive your instruction."

Surya's eyes widened in surprise. Slowly, an admiring smile spread across his face. "If you do accomplish this feat, Hanuman, you will indeed prove yourself worthy to be my disciple!"

"Everything depends on your mercy, *Bhagavan!*"

"You have pleased me with your exemplary obedience and devotion. I will bestow on you all the disciplines of learning. From this moment, you are my student. Follow me and we will embark on our voyage of learning. I shall commence your education with the recitation of the primeval letter – the *Pranava*, which is the reflection of the Supreme God and the *Naada Brahma*," Surya said. In a solemn voice, which echoed through the vast reaches of space, the Sun god recited, *"Om!"*

Anjaneya, inspired by his new mentor, repeated the awesome *Omkar* after him.

<hr />

From dawn to dusk, Surya uninterruptedly imparted education to this most talented of students – one with unparalleled powers of comprehension. Surya was impressed by Anjaneya's unswerving perseverance, as he kept pace with his master's rapid transit across the skies, not stopping for even a brief moment of respite, and grasping every lesson at one telling. At the same time, Anjaneya's sterling obedience and devotion touched Surya's heart.

Moving closely in Surya's wake, like his shadow, Anjaneya completed his period of instruction in an incredibly short span of time. *Vedas, Vedaangas*, scriptures and *Puranas* – all the eighteen disciplines of education were soon stored in Anjaneya's prodigious brain.As a result of the special emphasis Surya placed on grammar, Anjaneya mastered all the nine significant grammars: a phenomenal feat of scholarship!

Bidding farewell to his dearest disciple, who had mastered all the disciplines, exceeding his wildest expectations, *Bhagavan* Surya said, "Your education is complete, Hanuman. While imparting knowledge to you, I have simultaneously tested your grasp on my earlier lessons. You have passed that test too with flying colours! The study of the *Saamaveda* having aroused your latent musical talent, you will become an expert in singing, composing tunes and creating new *ragas*. The mode of pronunciation you have mastered will become renowned throughout the three worlds."

Surya held out his hand in fond benediction. "You may leave, Hanuman – my blessings will always be with you, my boy!"

Hanuman gazed at his divine preceptor with brimming eyes and said, "*Bhagavan*, I am indebted to you. I would like to offer you a fee as a token of my gratitude to my master. Grant me this honour and name your *guru dakshina*."

Surya smiled enigmatically at him. "In time to come, you will perform a great service which will comprise my *guru dakshina*. That offering will be precious to me, your *guru*. You will realize this when you undertake that task. Fare thee well, my boy!"

Anjaneya folded his hands in deep reverence to the preceptor who had lavished on him a wealth of knowledge and affection.

⸻

"And thus, Anjaneya successfully concluded his course of education," Nirvikalpananda reached the end of this segment of his narrative.

"Master," Shivananda asked curiously, "what was the service Anjaneya rendered later, in order to fulfill his *guru dakshina* to his mentor?"

"During the period of Sri Rama's incarnation, Anjaneya rendered invaluable service to Sri Rama."

"But Master," Shivananda frowned in puzzlement, "how does Anjaneya's service to Sri Rama translate into Surya *Bhagavan's guru dakshina*?"

Nirvikalpananda laughed. "Sadananda, tell me: to which lineage did Sri Rama belong?"

"The solar lineage, master," Sadananda replied promptly.

"Surya was aware that the object of Anjaneya's incarnation was to serve the Rama *avatar* of Lord Vishnu as a true 'Arrow of Rama.' The Sun god hinted that Anjaneya would be offering him his *guru dakshina* by serving Sri Rama, who would be born in his lineage."

"That was so interesting, master," Vimalananda sighed. "Are there more incidents which demonstrate Surya's glory?"

"There are, my boy, there are! Both Sri Rama, during the *Tretayuga*, and Dharmaraja, the eldest of the Pandavas, during the *Dvaaparayuga*, were recipients of Surya's magnanimity.

"In the Lankan war, Sri Rama was unable to slay Ravana with his powerful arrows. Undeterred, Ravana persevered in his aggressive offensive against Sri Rama, showering him with missiles in his turn. Disturbed by this avalanche of weapons, the *grahas* moved from their ordained orbits. Sri Rama was in a grave dilemma. At that juncture, Sage Agastya visited the battlefield and explained that Surya's unfavourable influence was the cause of Rama's predicament.

"Ramachandra, it is the planets' malignant impact which impedes your victory. I will initiate you into the powerful *Aditya Hrdaya*. Chant the *stotra* with single-minded concentration. Aditya Surya *Bhagavan*, the fore-genitor of your solar dynasty – he who grants longevity and victory, will turn his magnanimous face towards you. Once that happens, slaying the demon, Ravana, will be easily accomplished!" Agastya advised.

"Sri Rama consented and received the sacred *Aditya Hrdaya* hymn from Sage Agastya. Having performed the ordained preliminary rites, he fervently recited the *stotra*, as directed by the sage. His single-minded devotion touched Surya's heart and the king of the *grahas* lavished his benignant rays on Sri Rama. With renewed valour, Sri Rama took up his bow and, in a short time, killed the demon, Ravana."

Nirvikalpananda paused and looked at his disciples.

"Master," enthused Chidananda, "your story linking Sri Rama's destiny in the *Tretayuga* with Surya's glory, is fascinating. Please tell us how Dharmaraja benefited from Surya's favourable influence."

"I am coming to it, Chidananda," Nirvikalpananda smiled indulgently. "This episode demonstrates how Dharmaraja gained Surya's mercy. Having lost everything in the notorious game of dice, Dharmaraja, accompanied by his four brothers and his wife, Draupadi, commenced his exile in the forest. They were followed by a group of Brahmin scholars who were devoted to the Pandavas.

"One day, Bhima, Arjuna, Nakula and Sahadeva went deep into the forest to forage for fruits and edible roots to satisfy their hunger ..."

With that, Nirvikalpananda resumed his narrative.

∞∞

Dharmaraja approached his *guru*, Dhoumya, who was relaxing in the shade of a tree.

The sage looked up and said, "Dharmaraja, why this sorrowful countenance? Is something wrong?"

Dharmaraja heaved a deep sigh and sat beside the sage. "*Gurudev*, it pains me to observe the sorry plight of the learned Brahmins, including you, who have followed us to the forest. You are entitled to reverence as gods on earth ... yet here you are, enduring the pangs of hunger and thirst. I am unable to provide you with proper food – I am reduced to offering you roots and leaves instead! What shall I do? I beg your advice."

Dhoumya stared thoughtfully at the eldest Pandava for a while. The sage closed his eyes … his right thumb tapped his fingers in brisk calculation.

His computation done, the sage looked up and locked eyes with the prince: "Dharamraja, it was Sani's malign influence which pushed you into playing dice and wagering all your worldly possessions, including your brothers and your wife. Consequently, you are now living in the forest. Here, the scarcity of food stares you in the face. The reason for your present hardship is Surya, the king of the planets – Surya does not look on you favourably."

"Gurudev!" Dharmaraja exclaimed in anguish at this news. Then, a smile dawned slowly on his face. "In that case, if I were to bring about the favourable influence of the planets, I would not have to live here like a destitute."

"Yes, Dharmaraja," Dhoumya nodded approvingly. "A man is duty-bound to attempt to rectify the adverse impact of the Navagrahas. You must earn Bhagavan Surya's mercy. He has not been anointed the Graharaju – king of the grahas, merely for the sake of form. He is considered to be kin to all living beings. Bhagavan Surya, who bestowed knowledge on Sage Yaajnavalkya and Anjaneya, is not only the dispenser of learning – he is also Annadaata: the Dispenser of Sustenance.

"Not just gods, demons and men – but also birds and animals … in short, all living beings, including trees and plants, depend on Surya Bhagavan for their food. He is also instrumental in providing the water essential for life. It is he who makes the water evaporate and fall on the worlds as life-giving rain. He who is fortunate enough to enjoy Bhagavan Surya's magnanimity will never want for food." Dhoumya urged Dharmaraja: "You must worship Surya immediately. Surya's merciful intervention is the only way out of your predicament."

"As you command, gurudev," Dharmaraja bowed in agreement. "But, what is the method involved?"

"I will teach you the prescribed rite of homage to Bhagavan Surya," the sage replied. "Bhagavan Surya is to be worshipped by reciting his one hundred and eight sacred names. Each of these names equals one mantra. Indra taught these 108 names to Sage Narada, who in turn passed them on to Emperor Vasu. I received the sacred names from the emperor."

"So, *Bhagavan* Surya's sacred names comprise the wealth of generations," Dharmaraja said admiringly.

"Yes, Dharmaraja," Dhoumya smiled. "And now, you are to inherit that priceless spiritual heritage. The recitation of the names requires mastery over two skills: one is comprehending the meaning of each name and the other is the correct pronunciation of the 108 names. I will now teach you the meanings and the accurate pronunciation of every letter of each name. Once I have completed my instruction, take a dip in the holy waters of the Ganga. Standing in the waters, face the east and pay homage to *Bhagavan* Surya by reciting his sacred names. The early hours of the coming day are particularly auspicious for this worship. At dawn, secure the *darshan* of the rising orb of the sun and commence your prayer."

Dharmaraja nodded in eager agreement and folded his hands in respect to Sage Dhoumya.

The flush of dawn was faintly visible in the eastern sky. Dharmaraja, having been inducted into the mysteries of Surya's 108 names, asked his *guru*'s permission to commence his worship.

"May Surya *Bhagavan* shower his mercy on you," Dhoumya blessed Dharmaraja. "May victory be yours!"

As the sun rose above the eastern horizon, Dharmaraja, standing waist-deep in the holy waters of the Ganga, commenced his recital of Surya *Bhagavan*'s names.

Armed with his knowledge of the true meanings of Surya's names, and with flawless pronunciation, Dharmaraja performed his *Surya aradhana*: worshipping Surya with his offering of the *Graharaju*'s sacred names. He kept his eyes fixed on the sun's red orb which appeared as a vermillion *tilak* on the beautiful forehead of the east. In single-minded concentration, Dharmaraja stared unblinkingly at the sun, opening his inner self to the all-pervading essence of *Bhagavan* Surya. In a while, his eyelids dropped over his eyes on their own accord.

With his inner eyes, Dharmaraja now perceived Surya's form ensconced in his heart. He continued to direct his rays of mediation towards the god of a thousand rays. He was oblivious to the passage of time. Minutes and hours, day and night – every distinction was blurred.

"Dharmaraja!"

The pleasant sound of his name reached Dharmaraja's ears and gently nudged him out of his deep meditation. His eyelids fluttered open ... his eyes widened in surprise at the enthralling panorama which emerged before him.

Against the azure background of the cloudless sky, hovered a single-wheeled equipage drawn by seven green horses. With Aruna on the vehicle's yoke, *Bhagavan* Surya sat majestically in the golden chariot.

Dharmaraja folded his hands and raised them in exultant homage above his head. "Oh *Bhagavan!* Dispenser of all sustenance ... a thousand salutations to you!"

"Dharmaraja," the Sun god replied, "your homage has pleased me with its single-minded devotion. Henceforth, my munificent face will be turned on you. I bestow on you the divine *akshaya-paatra*, an inexhaustible vessel – any food prepared by your wife with roots and fruits will be transformed into the four varieties of food: *bhaksya, bhojya, lehya* and *choshya*, to satisfactorily appease your hunger."

"I am blessed indeed, *Bhagavan!*

"Come, receive the inexhaustible vessel," Surya's voice resonated across the sky.

Dharmaraja bent forward in reverence and obediently held out his hands. In an instant, a gleaming copper vessel materialized in his open palms.

"*Bhagavan*, how blessed I am!" Dharmaraja's eyes brimmed with tears of joy.

"Dharmaraja, my beneficence towards you has made you fortunate. This divine, inexhaustible *akshaya-paatra* will sate your company's hunger till the end of your exile. May good fortune continue to be yours!"

Surya disappeared and Dharmaraja gradually emerged from his trance. Sending up a prayer of silent gratitude to Surya, he set out for his camp in the forest, where Dhoumya and his entourage of Brahmins felicitated Dharmaraja for securing the divine *akshaya-paatra*.

From that day, the food cooked by Draupadi metamorphosed into four varieties of dishes, satisfying the taste buds and stomachs of the Pandavas and their Brahmin followers.

"Dharmaraja, who successfully secured *Bhagavan* Surya's grace, is a role model for all of us who wish to worship Surya," Nirvikalpananda said.

"Master, it is good to know that Surya is the dispenser of both knowledge and sustenance!" exclaimed Shivananda in satisfaction.

"Yes," agreed the master, "without *Bhagavan* Surya, there would be no food or water for living beings. With that, we come to the end of our discourse regarding Surya's glory. We will now proceed to hear of the glory of the next *graha* – Chandra."

THE GLORY OF CHANDRA

"Dadhi Sankha Tushaaraabham Kshirodaarnava sambhavam!
Namaami Sasinam Somam Sambhormakuta bhushanam!!"

I offer my salutations to Sasi who is known as Soma (Chandra) who shines
like curds, the conch and snow, who rose from the Ocean of Milk, who is the
ornament on Sambhu's (Lord Shiva) crown.

"Now we come to the glory of Chandra, who is the overlord of medicinal plants, and exerts a powerful influence on the mind, particularly on water. We see how the ocean responds to the touch of Chandra's rays on a full moon night – its tides rising as if to reach out to him in the sky. This eternal phenomenon categorically establishes Chandra's influence on water."

Shivananda's eyes twinkled. "Master, I think several people in the *Puranic* age were influenced by Chandra's good looks!"

Nirvikalpananda joined in the general laughter and then continued,

"We have discussed this matter several times. Let me reiterate: the 'present' denotes the happenings of the current day, while 'history' refers to the events of the recent past – however, the *Puranas* are historical records which go back to the furthest reaches of time past. In order to enhance our understanding of some concept, or analyze an exemplary deed, we draw inferences from the historical or *Puranic* lives of people – this is an established scholarly practice. The individual we consider need not necessarily feature in epics such as the *Ramayana*, the *Mahabharata* or the *Bhagavata*. He may be a character mentioned in some other literary work."

The disciples nodded in comprehension.

"We will now consider an individual who does not find mention in the *Puranas*, but finds his place in more recent literature," Nirvikalpananda said.

"In which work does he feature, master?" Sadananda asked.

"Have any of you heard of the *Brhatkatha?*"

The four disciples exchanged puzzled glances and then shook their heads in unison.

"The *Brhatkatha* is a veritable ocean of literature. It was written by an ancient poet, Gunaadhya, in the *Paisaachi* language ..."

"*Paisaachi?!*" Chidananda exclaimed. "Who can understand that language?"

"Those who are familiar with the language can understand it!" Nirvikalpananda smiled in wry amusement. "However, such people are few! To redress this shortcoming, and make the *Brhatkatha's* literary wealth accessible to a larger body of readers, some poets have translated it into Sanskrit. Kshemendra's translation is the *Brhat Katha Manjari* which is not as exhaustive as the original. However, the poet Somadeva's version, the *Katha Sarit Saagaram*, has treated it in its full length."

"We are familiar with that title, master!" Chidananda said excitedly.

"The *Katha Sarit Saagaram* contains an episode which demonstrates Chandra's influence on events. Although the text does not explicitly state that Chandra's influence was the reason for the hardships faced by a particular individual, it is the logical conclusion which can be drawn from the narration. It is an irrefutable fact that every living being falls under the *Navagrahas'* influence."

"Your explication is eminently logical, master," Vimalananda declared staunchly.

"Any assertion, or explanation, which is not based on sound logic lacks credibility," Nirvikalpananda cautioned. "Now, let us hear the story of King Yogananda, who ruled his kingdom from his capital, Pataliputra. His son, prince Hiranyagupta, was a passionate hunter. One day, the prince decided to set out on a hunting expedition ..."

⸺⸻∞⸻⸺

As King Yogananda sat in consultation with his minister, Sakataala, and the court astrologer, Hiranyagupta entered the chamber.

The king smiled fondly at his beloved son. The extremely handsome and virile Hiranyagupta, his only son, took after his father in his regal demeanour.

"What brings you here, Hiranya, my boy?" asked the king indulgently.

"I seek your permission, father."

"Permission for, what, son?"

"I plan to go hunting in the forest, father."

"You have my permission and blessing," the king replied readily. "Take a large contingent of hunters with you and ..."

"Excuse me, my king, just a minute !" the court astrologer intervened.

"Yes, *Acharya*?" the king asked, "What is the matter?"

"According to his horoscope, the alignment of the *grahas* is not favourable to the prince."

"What does it matter if it is not favourable?" Hiranyagupta frowned and shot back at the astrologer.

"It is not safe to go hunting ."

"Not safe for whom?" Hiranyagupta's lips curled in contempt. "For me or the wild animals?"

King Yogananda laughed in appreciation of his son's wit, with Sakataala immediately joining in his monarch's mirth. The king addressed the astrologer. "*Acharya,* the prince is not leading a war party – surely we don't need be so particular about planetary alignments!"

The astrologer held his ground. "I beg you to understand, my king – the *grahas'* influence ..."

"*Acharya!*" shouted Hiranyagupta, "The planets, and their meaningless impact, apply only to the weak and those who lack self-esteem!"

"But , my prince ..." the astrologer remonstrated.

"I shall return safely from my hunting expedition and prove that your irrational fear lacks all logic – it is a mere farce!" Hirayagupta turned abruptly away from the astrologer and addressed his father: "Father ..."

"Happy hunting, my boy!" the king smiled in blessing.

On Hiranyagupta's exit, the king smiled at the astrologer and said conciliatorily: "*Acharya,* whenever you cast my son's horoscope, remember to factor in his self-esteem!"

However, the astrologer did not share the king's levity. His face was grave as he said, "Excuse me, my lord – it is the planets' malignant influence which is responsible for the prince's obstinacy and overweening self-esteem. I reiterate that this is not an auspicious time for the prince to go hunting."

———

Prince Hiranyagupta led his hunting party deep into the dense forest. Exhilarated by the cries of the wild animals, he spurred his horse on, eyes darting hither and thither in eager search of lions and tigers. Lured on by the distant roar of the animals, he plunged deeper and deeper into the forest, gradually leaving behind his band of soldiers, who were unable to keep pace with the prince's blistering speed. Hiranyagupta's reckless dash soon found him lost in the wilderness, without any visible track to follow. Strangely, in spite of the persistent calls which he heard, not a single animal was in sight. Hiranyagupta's horse continued its breakneck gallop, defying his efforts to rein it back.

The midday sun reached its zenith, scorching them with its fierce rays. Gradually, the horse slowed to a canter and Hiranyagupta sensed that his mount, like himself, was worn down by thirst and fatigue. He reined in the horse and listened for sounds of his hunting party: they were not to be heard.

The horse, unmindful of its rider's grip on the reins, walked purposefully on. Hiranyagupta realized that the animal was instinctively moving towards a source of water. Soon, the welcome call of aquatic birds greeted his ears and a large lake loomed into view. Hiranyagupta dismounted and let his horse make its weary way to the shore, where the thirsty animal eagerly lapped at the cool water. The prince looked up at the sun's position, which confirmed that he was lost and alone in the forest.

Suddenly, the sound of horse's hooves attracted his attention. He turned quickly to see his mount galloping away from him. Hiranyagupta whistled to summon his horse. However, the usually obedient animal ignored his call and plunged headlong into the wilderness.

Hiranyagupta's eyes widened in horror and a spasm of fear convulsed

his body as he saw the reason for his horse's impetuous dash into
the forest: a lion crouched low between two thorny shrubs, staring
unblinkingly at the prince with its hungry, yellow eyes. Roaring once, as
if in warning, the lion walked implacably towards him, never averting its
burning gaze.

Suddenly, it dawned on Hiranyagupta that he was unarmed – his bow
and arrows were on his runaway horse! All thoughts of thirst-quenching
water fled his mind and the prince turned tail and ran for his life. A quick
backward glance showed the lion in hot pursuit, and definitely gaining
on him!

Hiranyagupta burst out of the thicket: there before him, as though
offering him sanctuary, stood a tree. The prince darted to it and frantically
scrambled up the trunk.

Sitting on a branch, concealed by the thick foliage, he gave a sigh of
relief and cautiously peered down. To his astonishment, the lion squatted
determinedly on the ground beneath, staring up at him with its ravenous
eyes, its red tongue lolling menacingly.

An ominous rustle along the branch now drew his attention – a
colossal black shadow moved towards him, crushing the foliage. It was a
huge black bear! Hiranyagupta shivered uncontrollably, as panic gripped
him, and broke out in a cold sweat. The bear came to a stop near him
and stared unblinkingly into his terrified eyes.

Hiryanagupta, petrified by abject fear, looked alternatively at the lion,
which waited for him at the foot of the tree, and the bear, which was
crouched on the branch. His eyes protruded from his pale face …

"Don't be afraid. Like you, I have climbed the tree in order to escape
from the lion. Both of us are in the same dangerous predicament," the
bear assured him in flawless human speech.

Hiranyagupta could not believe his ears. "You … you … you can
speak?!" he stammered.

"When humans can behave like animals, tell me – why can't animals
speak like humans?" the bear retorted. "Our mutual fear of being torn
apart by the lion's claws has made us the dearest of friends. Don't worry,
I will not harm you!"

Prince Hiranyagupta heaved a great sigh of relief and introduced
himself to his new ursine friend. The bear moved closer to him, as if to
emphasize their solidarity. The lion, disappointed at missing its prey by a
whisker, crouched patiently at the foot of the tree, staring unblinkingly at
the man and beast perched companionably together on the branch above.

The sun set and darkness shrouded the forest. Hiranyagupta, tormented by the pangs of thirst and hunger, slowly surrendered to his fatigue and nodded off.

The bear, aware that the prince was in danger of falling to the ground in his sleep, said sympathetically, "Hiranya, you are exhausted. Place your head in my lap and go to sleep – I will keep watch. I will wake you in the middle of the night and then get some rest myself."

The exhausted prince took the bear up on its offer and placed his head in its lap. The bear clutched him protectively with its forelegs, securing him from falls. Within minutes, Hiranyagupta was fast asleep and snoring.

At the sound of the snores, the waiting lion came to its feet and addressed the bear. "Oh king of the bears! You are indeed naïve! The man belongs to the human race. He would not hesitate to hunt and kill us. There is no denying the fact that men and animals are sworn enemies. Push him down to me: I will sate the pangs of hunger by devouring him and go on my way, leaving you alone. Come – throw the man down and save yourself!"

"I have given him my word to protect him as he sleeps. I will not go back on my promise. Are you not aware that breaking a promise is a great sin?" the bear declared staunchly.

The disappointed lion gave up its vigil and stalked away into the forest, leaving the man and the bear on the tree.

At midnight, the bear roused the prince and said, "My friend, it is your turn to keep watch – be very careful. The lion has gone into the thicket: but, on no account must you climb down."

With this warning, the bear in turn placed its head in the prince's lap and sank into a deep slumber. The hours passed slowly. Hearing the soft pad of paws below, Hiranyagupta peered down. The lion had returned – it gazed back at him unblinkingly.

"Oh, prince, I will spare your life if you accept my only condition: you must satisfy my hunger. Heed my advice: push the bear down to me. I will feast on it and go my way, leaving you alone. You can depart safely in the morning and make your own way home."

Hiranyagupta stared at the lion in astonishment. Like the bear, the lion was also capable of speech!

"If you do not accede to my terms, I warn you that I will remain under this tree for any number of days. I will not go until I have sated my appetite by eating either you or the bear – the choice is yours!"

Hiranyagupta pondered awhile. Then, "Do you promise to leave me alone? Will you keep your side of the bargain?"

"I am the king of the jungle!" the lion declared haughtily. "Kings never go back on their words." The animal urged the prince: "Come on! The bear is fast asleep – shove it off the branch at once!"

Hiranyagupta thought quickly. He rationalized: the bear was a creature of the jungle; it would inevitably fall prey to the lion – if not today, then on another day. It was fated to be eaten by the lion. Whereas, if he sacrificed the bear to the lion, his own life would be saved. After all, survival was man's most basic instinct!

Having made up his mind, Hiranyagupta squared his shoulders and gave the peacefully sleeping bear a mighty push. However, the bear awoke into instant alertness and saved itself by instinctively clinging to a branch.

Seated securely on the tree, the bear glared at Hiranyagupta in overwhelming contempt. "You wretch! You have proved your inherent viciousness of character. You have stooped so low as to betray a comrade to save your own life. However, I will not throw you to the lion. I will inflict punishment for your betrayal with a curse: may you become insane!"

The lion kept up its nocturnal vigil through the long hours. When dawn broke, the disappointed animal gave up and went on its way. The bear descended from the tree and disappeared into the jungle.

Hiranyagupta remained on the tree. As the bear's curse took effect, he tore his clothes into tatters and jumped down from his perch. He wandered aimlessly in the jungle, gesticulating wildly to himself.

After combing the forest in futile search of Hiranyagupta, the prince's hunting party finally gave up and returned to Pataliputra in despair.

Days passed into weeks and weeks into months. King Yogananda persisted in dispatching search parties into the forest and to neighboring countries. Each one returned empty handed, unable to gather even a whisper of the missing prince's whereabouts.

The grief-stricken king and queen finally gave up hope and confronted the fact that their only son and heir was no longer alive. A pall of gloom descended on the palace.

Then, one day, a madman, incapable of speech, sought entry into Pataliputra. Fortuitously, one of the sentries at the gates recognized him to be their long-lost crown prince. The soldiers quickly ushered him to the royal palace. The king and queen were delighted to have their son back, but heart-broken at his pitiable state.

King Yogananda ordered the court physicians to treat the prince urgently. However, after long weeks of medical treatment, there was no perceptible improvement in Hiranyagupta: he remained speechless and insane.

The disconsolate King Yogananda called a meeting with his minister, Sakataala, the physician and the court astrologer.

"My king," the physician reported. "I have treated the prince for the past six months. In addition to following my own diagnosis, I have also consulted the learned royal physicians of neighboring countries and experimented with the medicines prescribed by them – all to no effect! The powerful medications I am using on the prince just disperse harmlessly like asafoetida in the waters of the ocean ."

"You could have at least attempted to restore his faculty of speech ," King Yogananda complained.

"My Lord," the doctor asserted, "I have tried every means at my disposal to cure his speech impairment. At all waking hours, I have subjected the prince to various techniques geared to make his speak." The physician was apologetic. "In fact, begging your pardon, I have even stooped to the crude method of burning him with a red hot poker – even then, he did not utter a sound!"

"Incredible!" Sakataala exclaimed.

"Based on his reaction to my treatment, and my own experience, I am forced to conclude that the prince suffers from irreversible, chronic speech impairment. He is dumb, my Lord – not observing an oath of silence!"

King Yogananda sighed and bowed his head in despair. He turned to the court astrologer.

"*Acharya,* have you consulted the prince's horoscope?"

"Yes, my king," the astrologer affirmed. "I have made an extended, in-depth study of his horoscope and persisted in my calculations for weeks. At the end of it, I must admit that I am unable to fathom the cause of the prince's malady – nor am I able to predict its duration or course." The *Acharya* could not resist adding, "If I may remind the king, on the fateful day, I voiced my objection to the prince's hunting expedition ..."

King Yogananda cut him off with a curt, "Anyone with access to an almanac would be capable of making that prediction, *Acharya* – we do not need a court astrologer to tell us that!"

"I will be frank, my king," the astrologer confessed, "My command over astrology is not strong enough to deduce the reason for the prince's condition."

"*Acharya* Vararuchi was adept at advising me on such matters," the king reprimanded his astrologer. "The horoscope you examined is based on his infallible calculations!"

The court astrologer folded his hands piously and turned his eyes to the sky. "*Acharya* Vararuchi was an astrologer and astronomer past compare! He was the ultimate authority in both those sciences! He was a matchless scholar – in fact, I would say that he was the male personification of the Goddess Saraswati herself! There can be no comparison between that *vidwaan* and my humble self. It is our misfortune that he is dead!"

The king, controlling his temper with difficulty, snapped: "Very well, *Acharya*, you may go!"

The astrologer rose and made his departure.

"What the astrologer said was absolutely true, *Maharaj*," Sakataala said. "*Acharya* Vararuchi could gauge the past, present and future: if he were now here with us, he could easily deduce the reason behind the prince's unfortunate plight."

King Yogananda nodded in silence.

"He could have suggested the appropriate measures to cure the prince's speech impairment and insanity."

"Vararuchi, with his knowledge of the past, present and future, has himself vanished into the past, minister!" Yogananda sighed.

"With due respect, my lord," the minister said, "that was our own transgression."

"Yes, yes," the king muttered, "I fully accept that it was my misguided judgement!"

"Have you heard of *Acharya* Vararuchi?" Nirvikalpananda paused to ask his disciples.

"We are familiar with his name but know little about him, master. Do tell us more!"

"Very well," said Nirvikalpananda and continued. "Vararuchi, King Vikramarka, Bhatti and Bhartrhari were cousins. They were born to one father who married four women of different castes. Vararuchi was born to the Brahmin wife and Vikramarka to the *Kshatriya* wife. Bhatti's mother was a *Vysya* and Bhartrhari's a *Sudra*.

"Vararuchi became an expert in the scriptures: the knowledge of the *Vedas*, *Puranas*, Grammar and Mathematics was at his fingertips. He was a past master in astrology. Based on his calculations of the *Navagrahas'* positions, he could accurately predict the past, present, and future. At that period, he was the only eminent scholar who was proficient in both astrology and astronomy.

"His proficiency in casting and reading horoscopes matched that of Brhaspati, the preceptor of the gods. In addition to forecasting events based on his study of an individual's horoscope, Vararuchi also possessed an uncanny ability: based on the alignment of the *Navagrahas* at that particular point of time, he could perceive and describe all the physical features of a person. This extraordinary skill posed a threat to his very life. Vararuchi was King Yogananda's court astrologer. The king held him in high esteem."

"Then why did the king order him to be killed, master?" Sadananda was bursting with curiosity.

"One day, a renowned artist visited King Yogananda's court. The king commissioned him to paint the queen's portrait. The king and queen were delighted with the artist's work, which was a faithful replica of the queen. One morning, in the the king and queen's absence, Vararuchi happened to be in the chamber in which the painting was displayed. While examining it, the astrologer realized that a small mole present on the queen's lower abdomen was missing in the portrait. Thinking to correct the defect, Vararuchi painted the mole on that particular spot and left.

"Later, to his shock, the king observed the mole, which had not been there earlier. Discreet interrogation of the maids in the queen's apartments revealed that the alteration was *Acharya* Vararuchi's handiwork.

"King Yogananda was outraged: how could Vararuchi be aware of this small mole on an intimate part of the queen's anatomy, which could have been observed only by himself and his wife? Had he been foolish in trusting Vararuchi and granting him unrestricted access to the queen's apartments? Was the astrologer a secret voyeur – had he spied on the queen's privacy on one of his frequent visits?

"In King Yogananda's eyes, Vararuchi's transgression was an unpardonable crime. The king summoned his minister, explained the details of the astrologer's depravity and ordered Sakataala to behead Vararuchi. In reality, Vararuchi had not seen the mole on the queen's abdomen: based on his study of the planets' alignment at the time of her birth, he visualized, in his mind's eye, that such a mole would be present at that spot." Nirvikalpananda paused.

"What irony, master!" Chidananda exclaimed. "Vararuchi was killed by the revelation of his own astrological insight!"

"But, master," Shivananda asked thoughtfully, "why did *Acharya* Vararuchi not have the good sense and discretion to avoid exposing the intimate details of the queen's anatomy to public view?"

"Minister Sakataala himself posed this question to Vararuchi before his execution. The astrologer's simple reply was, 'the *grahas'* influence.' Vararuchi explained that it was the malignant influence of the planets which had instigated him to unnecessarily meddle with the queen's portrait. He categorically declared that the *Navagrahas* were the basic catalysts of all thought and action. Let's leave it at that and go on with our story."

Nirvikalpananda picked up the thread of Vararuchi's tale.

"How I regret impetuously imposing the death penalty on Vararuchi," King Yogananda lamented to his minister.

"Your majesty: are you reproaching yourself?" Sakataala asked with an enigmatic smile.

"Yes," asserted the king. "If *Acharya* Vararuchi were alive, he would have discovered the reason for the prince's wretched condition." He disconsolately placed his chin on his hand and sank into despair. "What is to be done , everything is a matter of destiny, ordained by the will of God."

"If it pleases your majesty ... shall I bring *Acharya* Vararuchi here?" Sakataala asked.

"What?!" gasped the king. "Can you restore the beheaded Vararuchi to life?!"

"Majesty," the minister explained carefully. "On that day, you let yourself be carried away by your anger and humiliation. Ignoring a basic tenet of wisdom – always think twice before acting, you pronounced your harsh judgement on Vararuchi. Knowing *Acharya* Vararuchi well, I interrogated him and accepted his explanation. On your behalf, I ventured to commute his sentence: instead of beheading him, I have secretly imprisoned him in an underground cell ."

"Do you mean ... do you mean to tell me that Vararuchi lives?"

"Yes, my lord! If you pardon him, I will immediately bring the *Acharya* here."

"Pardon? Sakataala, I am impatient to beg the *Acharya's* pardon for my hasty, foolish deed!" King Yogananda said excitedly. "Please bring him here with all due respect."

⊶∞⊷

"*Acharya,*" the repentant king said, "please forgive me for my impetuous judgment and bless me."

"May all you desire be yours!" blessed Vararuchi. He continued: "The queen is akin to my own sister. Both physical and mental traits can be perceived with the aid of astrological calculations, based on horoscopes and the alignment of the *grahas*. This is what happened in the case of the queen's portrait. Due to the inimical impact of the planets on me at that particular time, I indiscreetly altered the painting: such an action was unworthy of me. I was awarded due punishment. You were just an instrument in the hands of fate!"

"Your words demonstrate your large-heartedness, *Acharya!*" the king said. "We are fortunate to have you with us again." He turned to his minister. "The credit goes to the wise Sakataala."

"Although I express my deep gratitude to our learned minister, I must emphasize one point," Vararuchi smiled serenely. "When the king sentenced me to death, the alignment of the planets did not support such an eventuality. That is why our able minister was inspired to save my head!"

King Yogananda smiled wryly. "For you, everything is ordained by the *grahas'* alignment!"

"Certainly," the astrologer emphasized. "Mercy or otherwise, everything depends on the planets' influence."

"Let me bring you up to date: Prince Hiranyagupta, our only heir, went missing while on a hunting expedition. He returned after a long absence, having mysteriously been struck dumb – to compound his sorry plight, he is also insane." The king's voice was grief-stricken. "*Acharya*, I beg you: please study our son's horoscope and suggest a remedy."

The queen quickly came to her feet. "I will fetch Hiranya's horoscope at once, *Acharya*."

"That will not be necessary, my queen," Vararuchi smiled reassuringly.

"All the three royal horoscopes are indelibly etched in my mind. Just give me a moment ..."

A tense silence, pregnant with expectation, fell on the chamber. Vararuchi narrowed his eyes in concentration – his nimble fingers twitched in rapid count.

The astrologer opened his eyes and looked at his three attentive listeners. "Chandra, standing in an adversarial position, has his malignant face turned towards our prince. Chandra *graha's* adverse influence is wreaking havoc on Hiranyagupta's mind: this is the reason for his madness."

King Yogananda and his queen exchanged anxious looks.

Vararuchi continued: "A forest creature's curse has further reinforced Chandra's unfavourable impact."

"Forest creature? What could that be, *Acharya?*" Yogananda frowned.

"In line with the prince's horoscope, it is an animal covered with thick, black hair."

"Your description suggests a bear, *Acharya*," Sakataala said thoughtfully.

"Yes," Vararuchi agreed. "My astrological insight also perceives a bear."

"But, this is ridiculous!" the king spluttered. "Incredible! How can a dumb animal pronounce a curse!?"

"Countless incredible phenomenon are part of this vast creation, my king," Vararuchi said sanguinely. "There can be no room for error in my calculations. Once he has recovered, the prince himself will validate my theory."

"*Acharya*, tell us the cure for my son's madness," Yogananda asked.

"There is but one cure: we must change Chandra's influence from the adversarial to the favourable. This can be accomplished by paying homage to Chandra *graha*."

"*Acharya*, I have a doubt ..." King Yoganada said hesitantly.

"Yes, *Maharaj?*"

"Earlier, you could perceive the mole on the queen's body based on the *grahas'* orbits. Now, you have deduced the cause of the prince's malady on the same basis. Please tell me, how is this possible?"

"In addition to the accurate position of the *Navagrahas* and their orbits, impeccable mathematical computation, instinctive perception and unbiased logic are essential. The wondrous human brain is capable of storing and processing vast amounts of information. The three factors I mentioned form the foundation of the knowledge of the past, present and future – the scriptures term such learning *Thirkaalajantha.*"

"Very interesting," said the king in admiration. "Now, please advise us as to how we can modify Chandra *graha*'s malignant influence."

"Certainly, *Maharaj*," said Vararuchi. "I will give my instructions to our royal *purohit* regarding the appropriate *homams*. He will oversee the rituals to be performed by you and the queen. Once the prescribed rites have been completed, the prince will be his normal self."

Nirvikalpananda smiled at his disciples, who gazed at him in rapt attention.

"Following *Acharya* Vararuchi's counsel, King Yogananda worshipped Chandra *graha*. The power of the rites, combined with the parents' unblemished affection, worked wonders. Prince Hiranyagupta was cured of both the ailments which had plagued him for months. Recovering his sanity and his power of speech, the prince narrated the details of his harrowing experience in the forest.

"King Yogananda and Minister Sakataala lavished praise on *Acharya* Vararuchi for the keenness of his inner vision, based on his vast astrological knowledge."

"Master," asked Sadananda, "are there other epic characters who were affected by Chandra *graha*'s malignant influence?"

"There would have certainly been innumerable such persons, Sadananda," Nirvikalpananda said. "Expert astrologers interpret the daily occurrences in the lives of people in the light of the *Navagrahas*' influence. In order to enhance our understanding of this, we studied Chandra's powerful influence. Let us now consider the glory of Kuja, the third *graha*."

THE GLORY OF KUJA

"Dharanee garbha sambhutham Vidyut kaanthi Sama prabham!
Kumaaram Saktihastam tam Raahum Pranamaamyaham!!"

I offer my salutations to Mangala (Kuja) who is born from the womb of the
Earth, who is resplendent like lightning, who is (called) Kumara, and who
holds the weapon, Sakti, in his hand.

"According to the scriptures, Kuja, the third of the *grahas* – he who was born from a drop of Lord Shiva's sweat, exerts his power over warfare and the acquisition of land. In acknowledgement of this, he is also known as *Yuddha kaaraka* and *Bhukaaraka* in Sanskrit. Kuja has a particularly significant influence on the unity and understanding between spouses in a marital relationship."

"Master," said Shivananda, "do tell us the story of an individual who acquired land under Kuja's benign influence."

"At the outset," said Nirvikalpananda, "let me make it clear that there is no specific mention of any individual who gained property through Kuja's intercession. However, by analyzing particular events in a person's life, it is possible to reach the logical conclusion that it was Kuja *graha's* malign or benign impact which dictated that particular course of events. This is what we shall now do.

"Who was that person, master?" Chidananda asked eagerly.

"Not one person, but two!" Nirvikalpananda smiled. "Both these individuals feature in our renowned epic, the *Ramayana*. One is the protagonist, while the other is , what shall I say , a character who did not receive her fair due. I refer to Lord Sri Rama and to Lakshmana's wife, Urmila. Some astrologers hold that Sita was also influenced by Kuja ."

"It is rather surprising to hear that Kuja held sway over the lives of such renowned personalities," Vimalananda wondered.

"There is nothing surprising about this, Vimalananda," Nirvikalpananda said. "It is evident that these characters from the *Ramayana* faced untold hardships due to Kuja's adverse influence. Let me make it clear to you once again ...

"The Telugu epic, *Ranganatha Ramayana*, claims that the unique position of the seven *grahas* at that particular time influenced Rama's birth. After all, this was no ordinary birth – it was the beginning of Sri Mahavishnu's incarnation as Sri Rama! So, it can rightly be accepted that Sri Rama's birth was determined and shaped by the position of the *grahas*.

"Again, we are acquainted with the fact that Sri Rama could kill Ravana only after reciting the *Aditya Hrdaya* in praise of Surya, under Sage Agastya's instructions. This ..."

"Yes, master," Chidananda intervened. "You touched on this in your discourse on Surya's glory."

"So, we are certain that Rama was under the influence of the *grahas*, both at the time of his birth and at the end of the Lankan war. It is but a logical extension to assume that the *grahas'* benign and malignant effect persisted through the intervening years of his life also. Every corporeal body is the combination of the *panchabhutas* and is rightly called the *panchabhutikam*: the five *bhutas*, or elements, being earth, water, fire, air and ether. This combination holds good even for God's incarnation in human form. Consequently, divine incarnations are also susceptible to the pangs of hunger and thirst, and experience hardship and sorrow like any other human being. Therefore, the Supreme God's incarnations are also subject to the *Navagrahas'* influence."

"Master, your explanation has given us new insight into the power of the *Navagrahas!*" Chidananda marveled.

"Yes, we now understand that every living being, without exception, is affected by the *Navagrahas*. Let us now analyze the lives of Rama, Sita and Urmila in the light of this undisputed fact.

"Lakshmana opted to serve his brother and sister-in-law during their forest exile. Urmila also offered to accompany them to the forest, but was turned down by Lakshmana, who left her behind in Ayodhya. Like her husband, the *Ramayana* too ignored Urmila! Urmila had to endure fourteen long years of separation from her husband, until Lakshmana returned from his voluntary exile and the Lankan war."

"Isn't it said that Urmila remained in a deep slumber during that fourteen year period, master?" Sadananda asked.

"Yes," Nirvikalpananda said, "*Urmiladevi Nidra* – the Sleep of Urmila Devi, is a popular Telegu song. However, we do not know for certain that Urmila slept throughout her enforced solitude. All we know is that she suffered the agony of separation from her beloved husband.

"Urmila's painful separation from her husband was undoubtedly the result of Kujagraha's unfavourable influence. Similarly, Rama and Sita also experienced Kuja's malign effect. Sita was separated from her lord; in Rama's case, this hardship was further compounded by the hazards of his battle with the demonic Ravana."

"So, we can conclude that Kuja's unfavourable influence was the cause of Urmila's long parting from her husband, Rama's separation from Sita and his war with Ravana," Chidananda commented.

Nirvikalpananda chuckled. "Obviously, if Kuja's benign countenance was turned towards Sri Rama and Sita, they would not have been separated from each other and Rama would not have suffered the trial of the Lankan war. The same goes for Urmila." He paused. "As we are all familiar with the story of the *Ramayana*, I will not delve any further into it. I have confined myself to pointing out the relevant incidents which highlight Kuja's power and glory."

"Yes, master," Vimalananda agreed, "there is no need to go into details of the *Ramayana*. Let us move on to the glory of Budha."

"Very well," said Nirvikalpananda, "let us hear of Budha's greatness."

THE GLORY OF BUDHA

"Priyangu gulikaasyaamam roopena apratimam Budham!
Soumyam Soumyagunopetam tam Budham Pranamaamyaham!!"

I offer my salutations to Budha who is of dark blue complexion like the
Priyangu bud, who is wise, who is of incomparable beauty, who is (called)
Soumya and who is of benevolent quality.

"Budha is the *graha* who bestows the gifts of wisdom, intelligence and skill. He is the master of *lipi* – the script. It is he who grants mathematical knowledge and poetic aptitude. He exerts his influence on other similar fields: but, let us confine our present narrative to his bequest of intelligence and knowledge.

"Panini occupies pride of place among all the renowned intellectuals who Budha blessed with uncommon intelligence and wisdom. It is Panini who gave the people of Bharat the *Paanineeyam*, the comprehensive theory of Sanskrit grammar. This monumental work of eight volumes is also known as the *Ashtaadhyaayi* ."

"Master," asked Vimalananda, "*Maharshi* Patanjali has authored an annotation of Panini's grammar, isn't it?"

"Yes, my boy," Nirvikalpananda said approvingly. "The *Mahabhaashyam*, Patanjali's explanatory comments on the *Paanineeyam*, is the greatest annotation of all time. Linguists hold the *Paanineeyam* to be one of a kind: comprehensive, logical and widely acknowledged as unique. In fact, it is not merely a treatise on grammar, but is accepted as a comprehensive and authoritative science of language.

"Panini, the author of this peerless text, was slow-witted in his childhood. In fact, he was so obtuse, that several teachers refused to accept him as a student! Panini was born in Saalaatura, a village near the city of Pataliputra. To his intense disappointment, on reaching the appropriate age, he was turned down by all the village teachers he approached for instruction. Panini reached Pataliputra in search of a master who would accept him as a disciple. He heard of a renowned *guru*, Varshaacharya, who ran a *gurukul paatasaala* in the city. This master was reputed to have the skill to turn even an ignoramus into an intellectual. Panini went to Varshaacharya's *ashram* and expressed his passion for knowledge, and his misfortune in being unable to find a preceptor. Panini requested the *guru* to accept him as his disciple and bestow an education on him. Varshaacharya, moved by Panini's sad tale, empathized with his enthusiasm. Believing that Panini's intense desire to acquire an education would ultimately make him a scholar, Varshaacharya accepted him as his pupil and commenced his tutelage.

"However, to Varshaacharya's deep chagrin, it soon became evident that his faith in Panini was misplaced. Panini clearly lacked both skills of comprehension and memory, failing to reach even the standard of the youngest novices. The seasons and years went by inexorably – but Panini showed no improvement. Varshaacharya permitted him to remain at his *ashram* for two reasons: Panini's unparalleled devotion to his *guru* and his stubborn effort to learn. However, finally, Varshaacharya was forced to concede that Panini's persistence would merely see him waste the remaining period of his life in hopeless endeavor. The *guru* summoned Panini to a private audience ."

Nirvikalpananda continued his narration.

Panini touched his master's feet in respect and stood before him with folded hands. Varshaacharya gazed intently at his pupil's face. "Panini, an education is indeed valuable. However, time is even more valuable! All human beings have a limited lifespan. I have come to a regretful conclusion: no matter how hard you try, an education is beyond your intellectual reach. You too should have grasped this truth by this time. You are patently unable to learn anything – you are merely wasting your valuable time here."

"Master, I am indifferent to the passage of time: I need the education!" Panini insisted respectfully.

Varshaacharya's voice was tinged with pity: "I am aware of that, Panini. But, a life should not be frittered away on hopeless endeavor. Every man must strive to achieve greatness with or without an education. Go into the world; take up a profession and live a fruitful life."

"Master ..." Panini's voice was choked with grief.

"Panini, you are an object of ridicule to disciples who are much younger than you. My own reputation is at stake, as I am unable to make you a scholar. You must undertake tasks which match your capabilities and lead a fruitful life. As of tomorrow, you are no longer a part of this *ashram!*" Varshaacharya pronounced his categorical decision and left the room.

Panini's tear-filled eyes followed his master's exit.

―――∞∞∞――――

That night, Varshaacharya's wife said, "*Swami*, I heard that you have asked Panini to leave the *ashram*. He loves and respects us more than a son could. Can you not change your decision?"

"It appears that Lord Brahma has decreed that Panini is to end his life without acquiring an education. He simply does not possess the intellectual capacity to comprehend and memorize lessons. I am constantly in a rage: either castigating Panini for his inability to learn anything, despite my continuous tutelage, or castigating his fellow-disciples for mocking him! This is certainly not a desirable state of affairs." Varshaacharya continued firmly: "Tomorrow morning, serve Panini a meal, give him some money for his travelling expenses and send him on his way."

―――∞∞∞――――

The next morning, as Varshaacharya instructed his disciples, Panini approached him with leaden feet and a heavy heart. He prostrated himself before his *guru* for the last time.

Varshaacharya blessed him: "My boy, don't worry. One's first priority is to nourish the body – the body is the only instrument through which a man can achieve anything. Discard your obsession for an education and live happily!"

Bidding his fellow disciples a tearful farewell, Panini made his way to the inner rooms of the hermitage to take leave of his master's wife.

Panini's tears gushed over her feet, as he prostrated himself before his *gurupatni*. She lifted him up tenderly and gazed into his eyes. She lovingly wiped away his tears, ignoring her own and consoled him: "My dear Panini, do not misinterpret your master's decision. It is just that you are incapable of studying – and my husband is incapable of teaching you."

"Mother," asked Panini, controlling his grief with difficulty, "if a great teacher like Varshaacharya himself cannot bestow the blessing of learning on me, who can?"

The master's wife smiled and said, "Panini, there is indeed a teacher who is greater than your *guru*, Varshaacharya! He is the *Guru* of all *gurus*!"

"Mother?!"

"Yes, Panini, there is a universal *guru* who authored the four *Vedas*, the six *Angaas*, the scriptures and the *Puranas*. He is none other than Lord Shiva! Go to the Himalayas and propitiate him with your penance. Beseech him to grant you the boon of learning."

"Mother," Panini said in a tremulous voice, "do you really advise this?"

"Go, Panini," his master's wife said persuasively. "I assure you that you will secure Lord Shiva's blessings. Chant the sacred *Panchaakshari mantra* devoutly, immersing yourself in dedicated penance."

Panini dried his eyes and touched his master's wife's feet in respect saying, "Mother, I will return after gaining the wealth of education!"

"May victory be yours!" his master's wife blessed him with the touch of her palm on his bowed head.

Panini commenced his single-minded penance in the Himalayas. Forgoing food and water, he immersed himself in the continuous, devout recitation of the *Panchaakshari mantra*. He was oblivious to the snow which piled and froze about him. The wheels of time rolled on. The frozen snow melted and rivulets of water formed canals above his motionless body – Panini remained indifferent to the changing seasons.

"Panini!" a sombre voice thundered across the skies.

Panini's eyelids trembled and opened slowly. The benign form of Lord Shiva stood before him!

"*Bhagavan*! Lord Shiva! The Universal *Guru*!" Panini's voice trembled in ecstasy. "Learning! Learning! I beseech you – bestow on me the boon of learning!"

Lord Shiva said sympathetically, "Panini, an obstacle stands in the way of your desire. Until it is removed, I cannot grant your boon."

"*Bhagavan* ..."

"Let me tell you the nature of this obstacle," Lord Shiva said with a smile. "It is Budha's malignant influence. Budha, the fourth of the *Navagrahas*, is unfavorably disposed towards you. His adverse effect must first be transformed into a positive attitude ..."

"*Bhagavan* ..." Panini attempted to interrupt.

Shiva silenced him with a raised hand. "I know what you are trying to say. However, each god has his individual, well-defined authority and duty. I will not change Budha's influence on you: it is you who must propitiate Budha and secure his blessing. Once that has been accomplished, I will grant you the boon of learning."

Panini prostrated himself at Lord Shiva's feet. "As you command, *Bhagavan*!"

"May Budha be magnanimous to you!" Lord Shiva raised his hand in blessing and vanished.

———

Without losing any further time in obeying Lord Shiva's command, Panini commenced his worship in propitiation of Budha. His single-minded, arduous penance reached the heights of intensity – then, Budha appeared before him. Panini, shedding tears of supplication, beseeched Budha to bless him with his magnanimous countenance.

Budha said gently, "Panini, my unfavourable influence was the consequence of your deeds in your previous life. Your penance has been fruitful. You will master all the arts. Lord Shiva himself will be your *guru!*"

"I am blessed, *Bhagavan!*"

"May good fortune be yours! Pray to Lord Shiva!" Budha advised and disappeared.

⚬⚬⚬

With renewed energy and confidence, Panini worshipped Lord Shiva. Almost immediately, Lord Shiva appeared before him, suffused in the glow of the setting sun.

"*Bhagavan*, I beg you to grant me learning," Panini asked respectfully.

Lord Shiva said, "Panini, concentrate on the sound of my *damaruka*. Consign those sounds to your memory."

Lord Shiva's hand was a blur of movement as the sound of his *damaruka* echoed across the calm dusk of the Himalayas. Interspersed with pregnant pauses, the drum resonated fourteen times, producing fourteen different types of sound. The anklets on Lord Shiva's feet chimed joyously in melodious accompaniment, as he danced to the beat of the *damaruka*.

Lord Shiva ceased his *Ananda Taandav* and smiled at the awed Panini. "Panini, you have heard the music of my *damaruka* and my anklets. The anklets' notes constitute the meanings of the *damaruka's* sounds."

Panini broke out in goosebumps. He prayed, "*Bhagavan*, the fourteen divine sounds of the *damaruka* will comprise the 'Fourteen Laws of Maheswara,' which I will constitute into the *Maaheswara Sutras*. Grant me your permission for this."

"So be it!" Lord Shiva serenely blessed Panini's endeavor.

"*Bhagavan*, I will formulate the science of grammar on the foundation of the Fourteen Laws of the *Maaheswara Sutras*." Panini's voice throbbed with eager excitement.

"Bravo! Just as health is essential to a body, grammar is essential to a language. I hereby bestow the title *Panineeyam* on the grammatical treatise to be written by you!"

"I am indeed blessed, *Bhagavan!* In honour of your eight divine forms, I will design my grammatical work in eight volumes."

"Your wishes will be fulfilled!" Lord Shiva raised his hand in blessing. "In future, you will be an integral part of my divine court."

⚬⚬⚬

Nirvikalpananda addressed his disciples: "Panini went on to write his treatise on grammar in eight volumes, based on the fourteen laws of the *Maaheswara Sutras*, also known as the *Pratyaahaara Sutras* – granted by Lord Shiva through the sounds of his *damaruka*. Based on its eight-volume format, the *Panineeyam* is renowned as the *Ashtaadhyaayi* – a work in eight chapters. Panini has established approximately four thousand grammatical rules in these eight chapters. *Maharshi* Patanjali, the incarnation of Aadisesha himself, has written his explication of the *Panineeyam* under the title, *Mahabhaashyam* – the Great Annotation.

"Varshaacharya and his wife rejoiced wholeheartedly at Panini's triumphant return with Lord Shiva's boons. Panini explained how Budha's blessings constituted the gateway to Lord Shiva's grace. In the course of time, the great Panini became a member of Lord Shiva's assembly in Kailash, along with Bhrngi, Bhrngiriti and Nandi. They were later joined by Patanjali, he of the human head and serpent body, who wrote the Great Annotation. Panini and Patanjali became intimate friends. We have now heard of Budha's glory through Panini's life," Nirvikalpananda concluded his narration.

THE GLORY OF GURU

"Devaanaam cha Rsheenaam cha Gurum Kaanchana sannibham!
Buddhimantam Trilokesam tam namaami Bhrhaspatim!!"

I offer my salutations to Brhaspati, who is the preceptor of the gods and sages,
who is resplendent like gold, who is the personification of wisdom and who is
the lord of the three worlds.

"Guru is the *graha* who bestows *Vedic* knowledge, devotion and concentration, fame and honour, education, children and wealth. Let us hear the story of an individual who obtained edifying knowledge, fame and wealth by propitiating Guru ..."

"Master," interrupted Sadananda in uncontrollable eagerness, "who was this fortunate person who received these numerous blessings from Guru *graha?*"

"Have you heard of the great Sanskrit poet, Bhaaravi?" Nirvikalpananda asked.

"Master, we have heard of him and his literary work, *Kiraataarjuneeyam*," Shivananda replied.

"*Kiraataarjuneeyam* is one among the five great *kaavyas* in Sanskrit. The other four are *Raghuvamsam* and *Kumaarasambhavam* written by Kaalidasa, *Naishadham* by Sriharsha and *Sisupaalavadham* by Maagha. Bhaaravi's *Kiraataarjuneeyam* is such a magnum opus that it also holds a prominent place in the celebrated trilogy, *Brhat Trayi* – the Great Three."

"Master," asked Vimalananda, "what are the other two works in the *Brhat Trayi*?"

"One is Sriharsha's *Naishadha* and the other is Maagha Mahaakavi's *Sisupaalavadham*. Another point of significance is that, while the renowned poet, Kaalidasa, is celebrated for his similes, Bhaaravi is reputed for his *artha gourava*. Bhaaravi's poetic skills bloomed in his childhood itself and emitted their fragrance when he was but a youth.

"The scholars of his period praised the young prodigy in his father's presence saying, "Narayanaswami is blessed to have a son like Bhaaravi!"

"However, Narayanaswami himself would airily declare, "Bhaaravi is just a child who does not know much about poetry .He lacks in-depth knowledge. He does not deserve your praise. There is much for him to learn." Narayanaswami persisted in treating Bhaaravi as an ignoramus.

"Bhaaravi, who relished the scholars' applause, was disgruntled by his father's criticism, which increased in proportion to his son's popular acclaim. Bhaaravi could no longer stomach his father demeaning him in public. His young blood boiled in indignation. Deciding that a father who insulted his own son was unfit to live, he plotted to murder his parent. One night, armed with a heavy boulder, Bhaaravi climbed into the loft above his father's bed and concealed himself there: his plan was to bash his father's head with the rock and kill him in his sleep. His father came to the room and prepared for bed. At that juncture, Bhaaravi's mother entered the chamber..."

"I was very unhappy with your behavior this morning," Bhaaravi's indignant mother complained to her husband.

"My behavior? What about it? Be more explicit!" Narayanaswami smiled indulgently.

"The whole world is praising our Bhaaravi as a 'great poet.' Instead of basking in the acclaim of the scholars, you are demeaning him in public by saying, 'He lacks in-depth knowledge ... He does not deserve your praise.' Do you realize how hard this is for Bhaaravi and how grief-stricken he is at this public humiliation by his own father?"

Narayanaswami broke into peals of laughter at his wife's criticism. "Oh, is this what bothers you? You are very naïve – remember, applause is intoxicating. If this intoxication goes to Bhaaravi's head, his intellectual development will come to a standstill and his ego will assume monstrous dimensions. Bhaaravi will deviate from the path of wisdom. Our son must continue to develop in order to achieve greatness. It is my fondest hope that Bhaaravi will become a great poet: my son must shine as the brightest star in the literary firmament! With this in mind, I consistently remove the barriers of applause which could stunt his intellectual growth."

"Really?!"

"What other reason could I have? My heart exults in joyous pride when people praise my Bhaaravi. But I keep a tight rein on my happiness in order to promote my son's development. Bhaaravi is now merely a poet – he must grow into a great poet! Bhaaravi is now just a scholar – he must mature into a great scholar! Very soon, this will come to pass!"

"*Swami*, how large-hearted you are!"

"My ambition for my son has given me a large heart! He will overcome the hazards of praise and applause and achieve excellence!"

"*Swami*, you do not know how happy your words make me!"

"It is evident, my dear," Narayanaswami smiled. "What could be more obvious than the tears of joy which course down your cheek?!"

At that juncture, to his parent's astonishment, Bhaaravi jumped down from the overhead loft. He fell at his father's feet and burst into sobs of recrimination.

"Father, my poet's heart failed to understand your father's heart! My proud, shameless heart could not comprehend your love. Misinterpreting your criticism, I planned to murder you in your sleep with this boulder ..."

"Bhaaravi!"

"Yes, father! Public acclaim has turned my head and pride has blinded my eyes. Please forgive me!"

"Son, you have realized your mistake: your father will forgive you," said his mother, wiping her own tears.

"No, mother," Bhaaravi cried emphatically. "Forgiveness alone is not sufficient. Father must first punish me and only then pardon me." He turned to his father. "Father, pronounce a fitting sentence on this cruel son who plotted to murder his own father!"

"*Swami!*" Bhaaravi's mother exclaimed in consternation.

"Sins call for expiation, and misdeeds for punishment. That is the rule of law! That is the call of justice! It is punishment which liberates an individual from the guilt of sin." Narayanaswami said sombrely. "I must impose some appropriate form of punishment on Bhaaravi."

"As you wish!" Bhaaravi's mother murmured weakly.

"Bhaaravi, here is the punishment which befits your crime: you must live in your father-in-law's house for six months. You will leave for his house tomorrow, along with your wife," Narayanaswami concluded seriously.

Bhaaravi's mother heaved a sigh of relief: that did not seem too bad!

Bhaaravi prostrated himself at his father's feet in obedience and prepared for his departure.

Bhaaravi's mother and father-in-law welcomed him warmly to their house. They were overjoyed to see their daughter and son-in-law. However, that joy and affection was short-lived – and vanished into thin air when they heard that the couple was there on an extended, six month visit.

There was a gradual erosion in the hospitality and respect offered to Bhaaravi in their house. Subtle slights and negligence became the order of the day. Soon, his father-in-law's house became a living hell for Bhaaravi, who was now subject to overt hostility and humiliation.

It dawned on Bhaaravi that his father's punishment was worse than a prison sentence. He was awed by his father's discernment in condemning him to this miserable experience. He confronted the naked truth: a father-in-law's house is heaven for a short sojourn, but hell when extended! Indeed, his father had punished him in a truly befitting manner!

One day, Bhaaravi's father-in-law summoned him and said, "Look here, my boy: it is accepted wisdom that work is an integral characteristic of a man. This implies that anyone who is born a man must take up some profession and work in order to earn his keep. Eating one's fill, and sitting idly digesting the meal, is not the hallmark of a man – nor should it be!"

"Father!" exclaimed the distressed Bhaaravi.

"Do my words anger you? Surely, you have come here forsaking your anger and self-respect, right? It is high time you worked to earn the food you eat and the comfort you happily take for granted!"

"Father ..." Bhaaravi's wife attempted to silence her father.

"What?" he asked sarcastically, "Do you think your husband is too high and mighty to work? Perhaps you think he should take his ease lolling on the swing all day?"

"Nothing of that kind, father ... it is just that he is unaccustomed to hard labour ..."

Bhaaravi's mother-in-law jumped into the fray. "He is unaccustomed to hard work?! Very well, let him learn – even buffaloes can be taught to work: why can't a man?" She glared at her daughter and son-in-law.

"Mother!"

The mother ignored her protesting daughter and turned to her husband. "Do one thing – terminate our cowherd's services and let our son-in-law take his place!"

"Excellent idea!" Bhaaravi's father-in-law exulted. "The job does not require hard labour. All he has to do is keep the cattle from straying." He turned to command Bhaaravi: "Go! Take the cattle from the barn to the grazing fields!"

"Father!" Bhaaravi's wife pleaded in a tremulous voice, shedding copious tears.

Unmoved by her grief, her mother roared, "Your husband will be occupied tending the cattle from dawn to dusk. He cannot return home for his meals. You shall cook his food and take it to him in the fields."

Bhaaravi walked slowly to the barn with bowed head.

⸻

Bhaaravi, now a cow-herd, tended to the animals under the blistering sun, taking care to see that the cows did not wander into the paddy fields.

Bringing him his food, his wife regarded her perspiring husband with tear-filled eyes. Bhaaravi washed his hands and feet and came to sit under the shade of a tree.

"Your father has given you a very harsh and cruel punishment indeed," she said, as she placed a mouthful of food in Bhaaravi's hand.

"This is but a befitting expiation for my heinous sin. Father is very wise! Condemning me to live in my father-in-law's house is like cauterizing a wound with a medicine-smeared knife!" Bhaaravi smiled ruefully.

"You have even stopped writing poetry after coming here!"

"Yes, I seem to have sunk into depression. It is commonly held that poetry emerges from pain. However, although I yearn to write about the agony of my ordeal in my father-in-law's house, I am unable to summon the words! I fear I have lost my poetic skills!" Bhaarvi heaved a deep sigh.

"*Swami*, once we leave my father's house at the end of your term of punishment, we must find a way to live comfortably. You must earn the money required for our needs."

Bhaaravi shook his head dejectedly. "Here, we are fated to lead a life devoid of both self-respect and wealth."

"*Swami*, I heard that the reason for our sorry plight is the *grahas'* malignant influence. Can this be true?"

"Who said this?"

"An astrologer, who is older than my father, said that your horoscope shows Guru *graha* in an adversarial position – it is he who exerts an unfavourable influence on your life."

Bhaaravi sighed. "Perhaps that is true. Maybe that is the reason for our hardships and the deterioration in my literary proficiency."

"Guru's malignant influence is the reason?"

"Yes ."

"*Swami*, the astrologer also said that Guru *graha* can be appeased by worshipping him through the prescribed rituals. Why don't you attempt to propitiate Guru?"

"No , I will not ."

"*Swami*! But, why not?"

"I will endure the just punishment meted out by my father!" Bhaaravi declared stoically.

"Then, on your behalf, I will worship Guru *graha*. Will you grant me your permission to do this?" Bhaaravi's wife asked hopefully.

"How can I object to you worshipping a god?" Bhaaravi asked.

―――∞∞∞―――

This conversation took place on a Thursday, when the star, Anuradha, was in the ascendant.

Bhaaravi's wife commenced her worship of Guru *graha* at an auspicious time on that day. She recited the original Guru *mantra* one thousand and eight times a day, repeating this procedure for nineteen consecutive days.

The days passed. Bhaaravis' wife faithfully continued her ritual worship for the restoration of her husband's literary skills – through which he could earn fame and wealth. On the nineteenth day, she went to the fields as usual, with food for her husband who was tending the cattle. She found Bhaaravi engrossed in deep thought – he was oblivious to her arrival.

"*Swami*," she caught his attention. "You are here in body, but far away in mind! What is the matter?"

Bhaaravi gave a start and came back to earth. Wordlessly, he took her to the shade of a tree and gestured to her to sit on the ground beside him. He smiled beatifically at his wife and recited a *sloka* sparkling with mesmerizing cadence and significance.

"*Sahasaa vidadheeta nakriyaam avivekaha*
Parama aapadaam padam
Vrnate hi vimrsyakaarinam gunalubdhaaha
Swayameva sampadaha!!"

"*Swami* ... this *sloka* ..." Bhaaravi's wife hesitated.

"Is my own creation!" Bhaaravi exclaimed joyously. "I do not know why – but, since this morning, *slokas* have been rolling off my tongue in one continuous flood of words!"

"*Swami*! My worship of Guru has been fruitful. The preceptor of the gods has turned his munificent face towards you!" Bhaaravi's wife brimmed with excitement. "Today is the nineteenth day of my prayers!"

"*Om Gurave namaha!*" Bhaaravi raised his folded hands in salutation towards the sky. "*Devi*, this *sloka* is the inherent expression of my own life experiences. Do you know its meaning? 'One should not act impetuously! Ignorance is the root of all misfortune! Wealth will come voluntarily to one who acts after due, intelligent deliberation!'"

"*Swami*, your *sloka* encapsulates the truth of life!"

"This morning, I was inspired to write an epic titled *Kiraataarjuneeyam*. I have completed two chapters in my mind and the *sloka* which you just heard is from the second chapter."

"Guru has blessed us both," Bhaaravi's wife wiped away her tears of joy.

"You rightly said that we need money for our future. I will write this *sloka* on a palm leaf for you to sell to some rich man." Bhaaravi declared.

"Yes, *Swami*!"

Nirvikalpananda looked at his entranced disciples.

"As Bhaaravi suggested, his wife sold that *sloka* to a wealthy businessman, who appreciated its deep meaning and gave her a huge sum of money. Six months passed and Bhaaravi returned home with his wife. Narayanaswami joyously blessed Bhaaravi who had successfully endured the strange punishment he had inflicted on him for his self-development. Bhaaravi's mother hugged her son warmly.

"In due course, Bhaaravi completed his work on the *Kiraataarjuneeyam*. Narayanaswami was exultant on reading his son's creation. He embraced his son and poured his heart out in fulsome appreciation. He declared that he was indeed proud to have a son like Bhaaravi. Scholars showered encomiums on Bhaaravi and acclaimed his rise to greatness in an incredibly short span of time. Bhaaravi insisited that he owed his knowledge, fame and wealth to Guru *graha's* favourable influence.

"So, we see how the worship of Guru *graha* resulted in the three-fold benefit of knowledge, fame and wealth. Bhaaravi was enshrined as the Pole Star in the literary firmament! His fame continues to shine even today!"

Nirvikalpananda concluded his account of Guru's glory.

THE GLORY OF SUKRA

"Himakunda mrnaalaabham Daityaanaam paramam Gurum!
Sarvasaastra pravaktaaram Bhaargavam pranamaamyaham!!"

I offer my salutations to Bhargava (Sukra) who shines like snow, like the
Kunda flower and lotus fiber, who is the great preceptor of the demons and
who is the expert orator of all the scriptures.

"Sukra is mainly the bestower of wealth, happiness, prosperity and fame. Sukra also exerts some other influences but we need not go into those for now. Let us hear the example of a renowned *Puranic* character who regained all the wealth and prosperity he had earlier lost.

"I hope you remember the story of the Churning of the Ocean of Milk. We heard of King Bali who collaborated with Indra and the other gods in obtaining the *amrita* and was later disappointed at not receiving a share of the nectar. After the distribution of the *amrita*, King Bali lost his life in the ensuing war between the gods and the demons. Sukra brought him back to life, using the Mrtasanjeevani and the grateful Bali organized a grand felicitation in honour of Sukra's feat.

"Sukra, pleased with Bali's gesture, advised his disciple to perform the *Viswajit Yaaga* – a sacrifice that would enable him to conquer the entire universe. On the successful completion of the *yajna*, a cornucopia of gifts emerged from the sacrificial fire: a chariot bearing golden vestments, horses resembling Surya's handsome steeds, a lion pennant, a wondrous bow, two quivers and a suit of armor. Agnideva, the god of fire, presented these marvels to Bali. Prahalada, Bali's grandfather, gifted him with a garland of lotuses which would never wither. Sukra, on his part, bestowed a pristine white conch on his disciple. Emperor Bali, radiating happiness, offered his salutations to his *guru* ..."

Sukra exhorted Bali: "Bali, although it is true that we do not possess the *amrita*, what does that matter? We have the priceless Mrtasanjeevani *mantra*. You also have the wonderful chariot, bow, arrows and armor required to wage war. Blow the white conch I have presented you and declare war against the immortals!"

Bali demurred. *"Gurudev*, I am unsure of victory after the debacle on the shore of the Ocean of Milk. Do you think this chariot, and the bow and arrows, are sufficient to defeat the gods?"

"No, they are not enough!"

"Then, bestow your favourable influence on me and bless me with victory!"

"That too is not enough. I will also turn my malignant influence ..."

"Gurudev?!"

"Not on you and your *asura* army, my boy! Indra shall be the target of my negative impact. My malignant influence on Mahendra will strengthen your fighting arm a thousand times! Go to war, Bali! Victory will certainly be yours this time!" Sukra locked eyes with Bali.

At Indra's court, the king of the *devas* sat in a trance of delight, savoring Rambha and Urvasi's sensuous dance. The nymph's anklets beat a delightful musical tattoo on the floor. Suddenly, two of Indra's spies rushed into the court. Brhaspati noticed their pell-mell entrance and

held up his hand, signaling Rambha and Urvasi to end their dance. The
melodious beat of the anklets ceased abruptly.

"Victory to the king of the gods! Lord, Bali has surrounded Amaravati
with a huge army!"

"What?!" Indra exclaimed in utter disbelief.

"Yes, Lord!" the second spy declared in tremulous tones. "The *rakshasa*
army has encircled the fort. All the entrances are under enemy control!"

The blood-curdling sound of countless *asura* conches confirmed the
spies' ominous tidings. Indra dismissed his court and conferred anxiously
with Brhaspati.

"*Gurudev*, Bali, who has only recently tasted unequivocal defeat at our
hands, has again declared war. This timeframe strongly suggests that he
is in possession of some new power," Indra said.

Brhaspati gazed into the void for a moment and then turned to Indra.
"Mahendra, on Sukra's advice, Bali has performed the *Viswajit Yaaga*.
As a consequence, the *rakshasa's* strength has increased thousandfold.
Bhrgu's descendants, who are *brahmavaadins*, have invested Bali with
extraordinary power. With the exception of Lord Vishnu and Lord Shiva,
none can defeat him."

"*Gurudev!*"

"Yes, Indra. According to my calculations, the present time is not
favourable for you!"

"Then guide me as to my best course of action!"

"Indra, you are well aware that there can be only two end results in war:
one is victory and the other is a heroic death. Our present strength and
weapons overrule any chance of our victory. At the same time, the *amrita*
will ensure that there are no heroic deaths!" Brhaspati was in despair.

Indra heard him out helplessly. "*Gurudev*, your analysis of our
predicament only exacerbates my anxiety. Please tell me what to do now!"

"You are left with only one option: surrender the kingdom of *Swarga*
to Bali and leave!"

"*Gurudev!?*"

"Don't worry, Mahendra," Brhaspati consoled him. "This renunciation
is not irreversible – it is merely a temporary solution."

Indra heaved a sigh of resignation and bowed his head in defeat.

At Indra's command, the gods and *apsaras* left *Swarga* and sought asylum in various other places. Indra, accompanied by his family, also reached a safe haven. Sage Narada visited Kasyapa *prajapati's ashram* with the sad tidings that the gods under Indra had become refugees.

Aditi, the mother of the *devas*, was grief-stricken at the sorry plight of her children. She lamented to her husband. "*Swami*, my children are very gentle by nature. The evil *rakshasas* have robbed them of their wealth and happiness and reduced them to a pitiful condition. Please restore Amravati to Indra and the other *devas*. Punish the *rakshasas* and save my children!"

Kasyapa heaved a sigh of regret on hearing Aditi's grief-filled plea. He gently wiped her tears and said, "Aditi, I do not have the strength to fulfill your wish. No one in the three worlds possesses such power except the Supreme Lord."

"The Supreme God, *Swami*?"

"Yes, Sri Mahavishnu alone has such power!" Kasyapa smiled. "He is the Supreme Power who can punish the *asuras* and rescue the *suras*: pray to him, the Father of the Three Worlds!"

"*Swami*, will he bless me?"

"There is a special procedure prescribed for his worship. If you devoutly conform to that format, the Supreme God will surely bless you."

Aditi attended keenly to her husband's instructions.

"The *payobhakshan vrat* is a vow of extraordinary significance. I will tell you the procedure involved, the rules and regulations which govern it, and the appropriate time and duration for its observation. I will impart to you the special *mantra* of the *payobhakshan vrat*. Tomorrow is the day of Padyami in the light half of the month of Phaalguna – this is an auspicious day to commence the vow."

"It shall be as you command, *Swami*! I will begin my observation of the vow tomorrow morning itself!" Aditi said excitedly.

"My good fortune be yours!" Kasyapa said. "Remember, you must commence the vow with *maha sankalp*."

Heeding her husband's advice, Aditi commenced her observation of the *payobhakshan vrat* the following day and adhered to it for twelve consecutive days with the greatest devotion. On the last day, to her delighted surprise, Lord Vishnu appeared before Aditi.

"Mother ... Aditi!"

"*Bhagavan*, you have heard my call!" Aditi's voice trembled in ecstasy and she shed tears of joy.

"How can I ignore the mother's call?!" Lord Vishnu replied smilingly.

"*Bhagavan!*" Aditi was speechless in awe.

"Mother, I know your heart's desire. I will restore the gods' glory by taking birth as your son!"

"Oh, *Bhagavan*! I am fortunate indeed!" Aditi's astonished eyes brimmed with happy tears.

"Mother," the Lord smiled tenderly. "I share your good fortune. I will bask in the secure comfort of your womb, frolic in your lap and imbibe nourishment from your milk."

Aditi trembled and broke out in goosebumps. "*Bhagavan* ... Oh, *Bhagavan!*"

"Serve your husband with your body, keeping my image firmly in your mind. I will enter your womb like ghee into the sacred sacrificial fire!"

"I am blessed, *Bhagavan!*"

"You will bear a great son!" With this blessing, Vishnu vanished.

⁓⁕⁓

Aditi's vow was fulfilled. The Supreme God's boon took flesh and Aditi joyfully carried her divine pregnancy. An extraordinary effulgence engulfed her body and her natural beauty was amplified a thousand times.

Brahma recited a paean of praise to Lord Vishnu, the resident of the Ocean of Milk, who now resided tranquilly in Aditi's womb, ready to assume his incarnation. Sage Narada lost no time in carrying the tidings of Aditi's pregnancy, and the reason behind it, to Indra and the other gods.

⁓⁕⁓

Brhaspati addressed Indra: "Mahendra, the *deva*'s hardships will soon end. You must do your own part to regain your past glory."

"What must I do, *gurudev*?"

"The main reason for the transformation of the kingdom of the gods into the kingdom of the *rakshasas* is ..."

Indra interrupted indignantly: "Emperor Bali!"

"Bali may be a contributing factor, but there is a deeper root cause for this state of affairs."

"What is that, *gurudev*?"

"Sukra's malignant influence on you!" Brhaspati directed a keen glance at Indra. "Sukra's unfavourable impact holds firm sway over you. It is essential that you gain his favour."

"Hmmm ... show me the way."

"Meditate on Sukra, the sixth of the *Navagrahas*: worship him with staunch devotion."

"*Gurudev!*" exclaimed the shocked Indra. "Sukra is the preceptor of the *rakshasas*, our sworn enemies! He himself is our adversary! How can he bless me? Impossible!"

"Indra, cast aside your doubts and pray to Sukra," Brhaspati reiterated seriously. "Sukra will bless you!"

"*Gurudev*, tell me one thing: would you bless the *rakshasa* king, Bali, if he attempted to propitiate you?"

"I certainly would! I have no choice: it is my ordained duty!" Brhaspati smiled. "The Holy Trinity has invested us, the *Navagrahas*, with the authority to bestow on each and every individual in the universe good and bad influences, mercy and wrath. You can obtain the blessing of any god only when you enjoy the *Navagrahas'* favourable influence. Have faith in me Indra – worship Sukra *graha*, the giver of wealth."

"As you command, *gurudev*," Indra agreed obediently.

⸙

It was the month of Sraavan, in Abhijit Lagna, with the Sravanaa star in the ascendant. In the second half of that *Dwaadasi* day, when Surya blazed in the middle sky, and Chandra and the other *grahas* and stars stood in auspicious positions, Aditi gave birth to a son.

The infant came forth with four hands – holding the conch, the discus, the mace and the lotus. He was resplendent in tawny attire and wore crocodile-shaped earrings. The crown on his head, the divine *Kaustubha* gem on his neck, and the ornaments which adorned his body, wrapped him in an extraordinary glow.

Aditi gazed in awe at her little baby and wondered how this miraculous infant with four hands, divine weapons and ornaments could have remained cocooned in her small womb. The joyous Kasyapa and Aditi sang a paean of praise to Lord Vishnu who had deigned to be incarnated as their son. In that instant, the divine form of Lord Vishnu gave place to the features of a normal child. In another instant, the child metamorphosed

into a dwarf at the age appropriate to undergo the *upanayana* ceremony.
Recovering from her shock, Aditi gathered her newborn dwarf child to
her breast and suckled him tenderly.

Nirvikalpananda looked around smilingly at his disciples. "You must have
realized that this is the story of the Vamana *avatar*. Lord Vishnu assumed
the Vamana *avatar* in order to retrieve Indra's domain from King Bali.

"We are all familiar with the story of Vamana attending King Bali's
yajna and asking for three paces of land, Sukra attempting in vain to stop
Bali from consenting to this, Sukra assuming a miniature form in order to
block the spout of Bali's *kamandalam,* and Vamana piercing the spout with
a twig – resulting in Sukra losing an eye. Finally, Lord Vishnu obtained the
kingdom of *Swarga* as a donation from Bali and bestowed it on Indra."
Nirvikalpananda concluded his gist of the Vamana *avatar*.

"Master," asked Chidananda, "what about Sukra ?"

"I am coming to that, Chidananda," Nirvikalpananda said with a
smile. "In due course, Indra completed his worship of Sukra. The pleased
asura-guru turned his benign face towards Indra."

"Master, I have a doubt ," Vimalananda intervened respectfully.
"Sukra's malignant influence on Indra , Indra's propitiation of Sukra ,
Sukra blessing Indra – this chain of events is unfamiliar. Did these events
really take place?"

Nirvikalpananda smiled indulgently and said: "Pay attention to my
explanation. One method of analysis is to gauge an event on the basis of
its cause. Another method is to gauge the cause, in retrospect, based on
an event. Both methods are equally logical and applicable. Let me give
you an example: suppose you sleep through an entire day and wake up
after sunset. You would not question whether the sun rose that morning
while you slept. Although you did not witness the sunrise, you are certain
that the sun did rise. That is the immutable truth!

"Similarly, when an individual's horoscope is subjected to astrological
analysis, it is possible to predict in advance that a particular *graha* is going
to have an adverse impact on that individual. Using the retrospective
method, if the horoscope is examined after the individual has endured
hardship, it is possible to pinpoint the particular *graha* responsible for his
suffering. We have used the second method to conclude that it was the

malignant influence of Sukra, the giver of wealth and glory, which was responsible for Indra's misfortune.

"Another noteworthy point is that Sukra is the preceptor of the *asuras*: this makes him a natural enemy of the *devas*. It is perfectly reasonable to conclude that he exerted an unfavourable influence on Indra, the king of the *devas*. Do not forget that the *Navagrahas* are divine forms. As such, all gods, demons and humans are equally susceptible to their mercy and wrath. That is the greatness of the *Navagrahas*. Therefore, it is not surprising that Sukra adversely impacted Indra, in order to facilitate his disciple, Bali's, victory. Likewise, he later withdrew his malignant influence by accepting Indra's worship and deigned to show his magnanimous face to the king of the gods."

"Master, one more doubt ..." said Shivananda.

Nirvikalpananda inclined his head in patient attention.

"As a consequence of Sukra's magnanimity towards Indra, Bali lost the kingdom of *Swarga*. Does this not reflect badly on Sukra's position as the preceptor of the *asuras*?"

"No! In practical terms, Sukra attempted to be fair towards both Bali and Indra. As the *asura- guru,* he attempted to dissuade Bali from making his donation to Vamana. He blocked Bali's *kamandalam* and lost an eye for his trouble. This makes it evident that he remained true to his obligations as the preceptor of the *rakshasas*. At the same time, he blessed Indra in his role as a *Grahadeva*."

"Master, your analysis is founded on sound logic, as always!" Sadananda exclaimed in admiration.

"When things are not clear, they should be subjected to logical analysis. I will give you another example to enhance your understanding. A couple gets married and in due course, they have a son. It is not decorous to openly enquire whether their marriage has been consummated. Instead, we accept that their son is the visible proof of that consummation. Similarly, we conclude that Sukra's malignant influence was responsible for Indra's loss of wealth and fame. This is a perfectly logical conclusion. Now, let us move on to the glory of Sani *graha*!"

THE GLORY OF SANAISCHARA

"Neelaanjana Samaabhaasam Raviputram Yamaagrajam!
Chaaya Maartaanda Sambhutam tam Namaami Sanaischaram!!"

I offer my salutations to Sanaischara who shines like dark blue collyrium, who is the son of Ravi (Surya), who has Yama as his elder brother and who is born of Chaaya and Maartaanda (Surya).

"The mere mention of the name, 'Sani,' is enough to evoke instant devotion laced with dread! Sanaischara is unique among the planets, in that his malignant influence causes one-fold harm, while his benign influence is doubly beneficial. His anger rouses our fear while his mercy gives us courage and confidence. In fact, it is Sani who bestows upon living beings the one thing they crave above all others: the gift of longevity. As the only *graha* to grant longevity, Sanaischara is known as the *Ayurdaaya Kaaraka* – the bestower of long life.

"An individual who rouses Sani's wrath must navigate his life through a jungle of thorns. On the other hand, if Sani is pleased with him, his life becomes a pleasant journey through fragrant meadows. There is an episode in King Dasaratha's life which categorically proves this. I will now narrate this particular story to you. This was the period when King Dasaratha ruled Bharat, with Ayodhya as his capital. One morning, the court astrologers who routinely perused the almanac, and interpreted the movement of the *Navagrahas*, announced the imminent approach of a great threat.

"The astrologers foretold that Sani was poised to enter the orbit of the star, Rohini. This heralded the coming of a terrible drought which would persist for twelve long years. They warned that there would be a dire scarcity of food and water during this period – a dreadful famine would wipe out all life on earth.

"The anxious Dasaratha consulted his mentor, Sage Vasishta, and begged him to suggest a way to save the country from the ravages of the predicted drought ...

Sage Vasishta said, "Oh King! It would be meaningless to offer relief to your subjects after the onset of the drought! Your bounden duty as a king is to prevent the very occurrence of the impending calamity."

"Prevent the occurrence of famine?" King Dasaratha asked. "*Acharya*, do you suggest that we conduct the *Maha Varuna yajna*?"

"The *graha* who is poised to enter Rohini's orbit is no ordinary planet – it is Sanaischara himself! Mere sacrifices and rituals cannot divert him from his course!"

"Then, kindly advise me as to the appropriate course of action."

"There is only one thing to be done," Vasishta said. "You must stop Sani *graha* from entering Rohini's orbit!"

Dasaratha, astonished at Vasishta's bold suggestion, said: "This is a very complicated issue. Let us discuss it with our ministers, *gurudev*."

Dasaratha summoned his eight ministers – Drshti, Jayantha, Vijaya, Siddhartha, Arthasaadhaka, Asoka, Mantrapaala and Sumantra and acquainted them with the state of affairs and Vasishta's counsel.

"Stop Sani from entering Rohini's orbit ... how is that possible? We need Sage Vasishta's explicit advice," Minister Sumantra said.

"Let us attempt to propitiate Sani with *homams* and rituals," suggested Minister Mantrapaala.

The other ministers nodded in agreement.

"According to the calculations of our court astrologers, Sani may have already commenced his journey towards Rohini's orbit. If he is to be stopped, immediate action is called for. There is no time to be lost with rituals: and let me repeat my warning – such rituals would serve no purpose. We must not forget that Sanaischara is a fierce *graha*!" Sage Vasishta cautioned.

The ministers exchanged looks of consternation. Dasaratha turned to Sage Vasishta with a worried frown.

"King Dasaratha, there is no time for further consultation and discussion. Sani must be stopped in mid-course. That is the only solution!" Sage Vasishta said urgently.

"*Gurudev*, you are the only person capable of achieving this great feat," Dasaratha appealed to his mentor.

Sage Vasishta smiled. "Have you forgotten the past, Dasaratha? At Indra's request, you rode to heaven on your chariot and valiantly engaged the demon, Sambarasura. Sambara assumed ten forms and showered arrows on you from ten different directions. Unfazed, you drove your chariot at lightning speed to simultaneously cover all the ten points of attack, and killed the marauding demon. Awed by your valour and your inimitable charioteering skills, Lord Brahma appeared before you. In acknowledgement of your proficiency, he bestowed on you the name 'Dasaratha,' instead of your original name 'Nemi.' Now, board your trusty chariot and rush to the vast reaches of the stars and planets!"

At this exhortation, Dasaratha looked intently at his mentor and said, "Reaching the plane of stars and planets is easy enough, *gurudev* … stopping Sani is another matter altogether!"

Sage Vasishta held the king's gaze. "Meet Sanaischara face to face and appeal to him for mercy. If he refuses to oblige, attack him!"

"Hear, hear!" the eight ministers chorused in approval.

Dasaratha, attired in cloth of gold, and adorned with golden ornaments, wore his jewel-studded crown and mounted his aureate chariot, drawn by magnificent white horses. He signaled to his steeds and his trusty chariot dashed forward into the vastness of space.

Rivalling the speed of the wind, Dasaratha covered one and a quarter lakh *yojanas*. On reaching Rohini's orbit, Dasaratha halted his chariot in Sani *graha's* anticipated path and waited expectantly.

Seated in his iron chariot, drawn by ten multi-hued horses, Sani sped towards Rohini. Suddenly confronted by Dasaratha's golden equipage, Sani braked to an abrupt halt. Frowning darkly at the king, he bellowed: "Dasaratha, do you realize that you are obstructing my passage? Reverse your chariot and move aside!"

"Salutations to the holy feet of Sanaischara!" Dasaratha said, respectfully raising his folded hands to his forehead.

"First move your chariot out of my way – we will then see about your salutations!" Sani thundered.

"*Bhagavan*, I have deliberately halted my chariot in your path: not to make way for you but to stop you in your tracks!" Dasaratha said, a calm smile on his face.

The furious Sani roared, "Dasaratha, if my passage is impeded, chaos will result!"

"And, if I do not block your present course, you will enter Rohini's orbit. This will cause a dreadful, twelve-year long famine on earth. I beseech you to reverse your course and retreat!" Dasaratha pleaded.

Sani's sardonic laughter resonated through the vast reaches of space like a thunder-clap.

"Retreat!? Sanaischara never retreats! Be gone!"

Sani urged his horses onwards. Without a moment's hesitation, Dasaratha too drove his chariot forward. Stopping a short distance away, Dasaratha folded his hands in supplication.

"*Bhagavan*, your intended path will unleash a wave of destruction on life on earth. On behalf of all humankind, I beseech you: do not enter Rohini's orbit."

"Impossible!" Sani roared furiously. "I, the son of Surya *Bhagavan*, will not yield to entreaties or prayers!"

"Then, I have only one option: I have to stop you with my valour!"

"A mere mortal attempting to stop Sanaischara!" Sani's mocking laughter echoed across the skies. "Go ahead and try!"

Dasaratha smiled and bowed his head. "How can I turn down the wish of one of the *Navagrahas*?"

The king took up his bow in his left hand, tautened the bowstring and released it. The mighty echo of the '*tamkaar*' reverberated through all the eight directions. Sani's horses, spooked by the thunderous twang of the bowstring, neighed in terror and backed nervously. The sound echoed in Sani's ears.

Dasaratha took an arrow from his quiver and notched it to his bow. He locked eyes with Sani and declared in a loud, clear voice: "Sanaischara, in order to discharge my obligation as a king, and protect my subjects on earth, I must attack you with my arrow of destruction. Save yourself – if you can!"

In one fluid movement, Dasaratha raised and drew his bow, taking aim prior to releasing the arrow.

Sani, astounded by the king's temerity and courage, shouted: "Dasaratha! Stop!"

Dasaratha froze in his aggressive stance.

"Lower your bow, Dasaratha," Sani said gently.

Dasaratha looked at him in surprised interrogation.

A smile lit up Sanaischara's face. "Put down your bow and quiver and come here!" he commanded.

Reassured by Sani's serene demeanor, Dasaratha placed his bow on his seat, dismounted from the chariot and approached Sani on foot.

Sani looked intently at the king. "Dasaratha, I am the son of *Bhagavan* Surya and you are a descendent of Surya's lineage! It was to test your personal courage and your commitment to your role as the protector of your subjects that I refused to heed your prayer."

"*Bhagavan* ..."

"I am pleased with your valour. Ask for any boon you desire."

Dasaratha humbly extended his cupped palms towards Sani. "*Bhagavan*, I beg you to grant me a boon which will ensure the wellbeing of the three worlds. From today, do not enter Rohini's orbit. As long as this universe exists, you must not cross Rohini's circuit. This is the boon I ask from you."

"Your concern for the welfare of the three worlds is commendable! I willingly grant your boon. I give you my word that I will never cross Rohini's trajectory!"

"I am blessed, *Bhagavan*! Indeed, I am blessed!" Dasaratha exclaimed with respectfully folded hands. His grateful eyes transfixed on Sani's benign face, Dasaratha broke into an extemporaneous hymn in praise of the *graha*.

Sanaischara listened benignly to the hymn and raised his hand in benediction. "Dasaratha, I bestow the title *Dasa vidha stotra* to the hymn you have composed. All those who recite this hymn with true devotion will receive my blessings and will be immune to the adverse effects of the *grahas!*"

Dasaratha gazed at Sani through tears of joy. Sani smiled at the king and reversed his chariot. Dasaratha stood as still as a statue, his eyes following the retreating Sani until the iron chariot was lost in the mist of the distance ...

Nirvikalpananda paused and looked questioningly at his disciples.

"Master, we expected you to narrate the experience of an individual who bore the brunt of Sani's wrath and secured his blessings by worshipping him ," Sadananda said.

Nirvikalpananda chuckled. "We have already heard the stories of individuals who suffered the adverse impact of the *grahas* and gained their favour by duly performing the ordained rituals. Now, through Dasaratha's tale, we have learnt that it is possible to pre-empt the *Navagrahas'* unfavourable influence by paying heed to astrological predictions and worshipping the planets. I chose this episode in King Dasaratha's life to impress this on you."

"Yes, master," said Vimalananda. "It is now clear to us that man can save himself from the hardships which result from the *grahas'* malignant effect."

"Very well, let us proceed to the story of the eight *graha*, Rahu," Nirvikalpananda said.

THE GLORY OF RAHU

"Ardhakaayam Mahaaveeram Chandra Aditya Vimardanam!
Simhikaagarbha sambhootam tam Raahum Pranamaamyaham!!"

I offer my salutations to Rahu who is half-bodied, who is distinguished and valiant, who is the oppressor of Chandra and Aditya and who is born from Simhika's womb

"The scriptures say that the malignant influence of Rahu, the eight *graha*, results in eight kinds of hardship. Under Rahu's adverse impact, an individual is exiled from his native land and compelled to live in the burial ground."

"Master, the term, 'eight hardships,' is commonly used. What exactly are these eight hardships?" Vimalananda asked curiously.

"The scriptures categorically list the eight hardships, which are more accurately eight curses on mankind. The eight hardships a man should never have to face are – living in exile, separation from his wife, visits from relatives when in poverty, the eating of left-overs, the merger of his rivals, dependence on others for food, humiliation and destitution."

"Master, it is widely known that King Harischandra suffered the eight hardships, went into exile and lived in a burial ground. Is it right to conclude that Rahu's malignant influence was the reason for his sorry plight?" asked Sadananda.

"Undoubtedly! Astrologers are of the same view," Nirvikalpananda replied. "In fact, I intend to narrate Harischandra's story as an example of the consequence of Rahu's influence.

"When under the unfavourable influence of the *grahas*, a man's thoughts and deeds will gravitate towards the wrong path. During this adverse period, the concerned individual will blindly ignore the cautionary signs of bad omens and planetary alignments. According to the *Markandeya Purana*, Harischandra set out on a hunting expedition, although his kingdom was well provided and secure, and did not face any threat from wild animals.

"It is essential that a king select an auspicious day and time to wage war, or to go on a hunting expedition. This is the traditionally accepted practice. However, King Harischandra's overweening self-confidence and egoism made him deliberately ignore this tradition and surrender to his weakness for hunting. In fact, it was not merely a weakness ... it was an addiction!"

"Master," asked Sadananda doubtfully, "can hunting become an addiction?"

"Certainly! Hunting is an addiction. Our wise forefathers included hunting in the list of *Sapta Vyasanas* – the Seven Addictions.

"Harischandra's addiction to hunting made him a victim of Sage Viswamitra's wrath and enmity. As a consequence of his financial indebtedness to Viswamitra, the pitiable Harischandra was forced to surrender his entire empire to the sage – except for the substantial lands previously donated to the Brahmins and temples. He was compelled to leave his native land and go into exile. He had to sell his wife and son. As if all this hardship was not enough, he had to sell himself to the keeper of a crematorium and undertake the task of burning corpses.

"We are all acquainted with King Harischandra's various hardships and his miserable life burning corpses as a crematorium keeper. I will not elaborate on these familiar episodes. Suffice it to understand that it was Rahu's malignant influence which was responsible for Harischandra's suffering."

"Master, Harischandra's hardships also resulted in his earning the meritorious title, 'Satya Harischandra'," remarked Chidananda.

"In addition to that unique recognition, he was blessed by Brahma, Indra and the other gods," added Shivananda.

"Yes, King Harischandra was fortunate to secure the blessings of the gods, who acclaimed his integrity. He earned the title, Satya Harischandra and his name became a synonym for truth. It is fair to assume that Rahu's favourable influence effected these fortunate developments in his life," Nirvikalpananda said.

"In short, we can conclude that Satya Harischandra's life exemplifies both Rahu's positive and negative impact," remarked Vimalananda.

Nirvikalpananda considered at his disciples. "You may wonder why King Harischandra did not attempt to ward off his sufferings by propitiating Rahu and securing his grace. Right?"

"Yes, master," agreed Vimalananda. "And one more doubt: we may concede that King Harischandra himself may not have been aware of Rahu's malignant influence. However, the wise Sage Vasishta was his preceptor. Surely the sage could have advised Harischandra to worship Rahu and gain his mercy. Why did this not happen?"

"Excellent question!" Nirvikalpananda said approvingly. "Harischandra was born into the great lineage of Ikshvaaku – the solar dynasty, descended from *Bhagavan* Surya himself. It so happened that King Harischandra unilaterally took the decision to donate his kingdom to Sage Viswamitra. A king must keep his given word: in order to uphold this principle, Harischandra had to surrender his empire to Sage Viswamitra. Again, after forfeiting everything and becoming a destitute, he could not shirk his moral responsibility to clear his debt: this entailed his miserable stint in the crematorium. Sage Vasishta was aware of the moral principles involved. Therefore, he could not in good conscience advise the king to evade his hardships by propitiating Rahu.

"Again, Sage Vasishta was a renowned seer who could envision the past, present and future. He was confident that Harischandra would keep his word, uphold his integrity and remain a synonym for truth through all eternity as Satya Harischandra."

"Master, your explanation is enlightening!" Chidananda exclaimed.

"Yes, master," agreed Vimalananda. "We are now able to grasp the moral complexities involved."

"Good," the master said. "You have heard of Rahu's glory. Let us now take up Ketu's fame."

"Yes, master," said Shivananda enthusiastically, "we are sure to enjoy it!"

THE GLORY OF KETU

"Palaasapushpa sankaasam taarakaagraha mastakam!
Roudram roudraatmakam ghoram tam Ketum pranamaamyaham!!"

I offer my salutations to Ketu who shines like the palaasa flower, who is foremost among the stars and planets, who is Roudra, whose form is fierce and horrible.

Sadananda asked: "Master, what does 'Palaasapushpa' mean?"
"It is *Butea frondosa* in botanical terms, and is commonly known as the Flame of the Forest.. Ketu's complexion is as red as the *moduga* blossom. As in the case of the other *grahas*, Ketu, the ninth of the *Navagrahas*, has his own unique characteristics and impact. The most extraordinary of his influences is the one which grants *moksha* – liberation from the cycle of birth and death. Ketu's favourable influence is essential in order to attain *moksha*. Let us now hear the story of a Puranic character who was unable to attain liberation, no matter how hard he tried, as

he lacked Ketu's grace." Nirvikalpananda smiled benignly at his four disciples.

Vimalananda, Chidananda, Sadananda and Shivananda looked up at him in eager anticipation.

"We just heard the story of Harischandra. Do any of you know who his father was? ... He was Satyavrata Maharaj, popularly known as Trisanku."

"Master, how did Satyavrata Maharaj obtain the name, Trisanku?" asked Vimalananda curiously.

"Satyavrata became Trisanku as the result of Sage Vasishta's curse ... Trisanku means one who has committed three sins."

"What were those three sins, master?" Sadananda asked.

"When Satyavrata was young, he abducted a bride from the marriage platform when she was about to be wed. That was one sin.

"Furious at his son's misdeed, his father, King Trayyaaruna, punished Satyavrata by expelling him from the kingdom. Earning his father's wrath was Satyavrata's second sin.

"Satyavrata then sank into a mean, lowly life, indiscriminately killing and eating the forest animals. One day, he killed Nandini, Sage Vasishta's holy cow, and ate its meat. Consuming beef was his third sin. Sage Vasishta cursed him to be called Trisanku henceforth, as he had committed three *sankas*, or sins. From that day, Satyavrata was known as Trisanku," Nirvikalpananda elaborated. "King Trayyaaruna was soon filled with remorse for sending his only son to the forest in exile. He recalled Trisanku to the palace and anointed him as the king. After ruling the kingdom for many long years, Trisanku reached a state of detachment towards life. He yearned to obtain *moksha* and enter *Swarga* – but without dying or giving up his gross body. He expressed his unusual wish to Sage Vasishta ..."

Nirvikalpananda was once again in the thick of his narrative.

———

"Master, I am tired of this existence. I can no longer summon up the energy, or the interest, to govern the kingdom. I am repelled by life and its routine compulsions."

Sage Vasishta smiled serenely. "Trisanku, these feelings are but natural at your advanced age. "Harischandra has reached adulthood. Anoint him as the king and lead a life of renunciation."

"I am not inclined to an ascetic's life, although I yearn to attain liberation. Master, I wish to enter *Swarga* with this corporeal body."

A smile flitted across the sage's countenance. "Trisanku, gaining access to *Swarga* is not under your control. Unless a person dies, it cannot be determined whether he deserves to go to *Swarga* – heaven, or *Naraka* – hell. Death is not in your hands. If an individual commits suicide in his desire to reach *Swarga*, he will undoubtedly suffer the torments of *Naraka*."

"Master, let me be more explicit: I wish to enter *Swarga* in my gross body – this obviously precludes my death."

Sage Vasishta's face reflected his shock. Had Trisanku lost his mind?! He said, "Trisanku, let me reveal an immutable truth: leaving aside your desire to enter *Swarga* with your corporeal body, even if you die a natural death, it is not possible for you to obtain *moksha* and enter *Swarga*."

"Master!"

"I'm afraid this is true. The reason for this is that you do not enjoy the favour of Ketu *graha*, who is the giver of *moksha*. It is impossible to obtain liberation without Ketu's benignant influence."

King Trisanku locked eyes with Sage Vasishta. "Master, let us ignore the vagaries of fortune and the influence of the *grahas*. I request you to perform a prodigious *yajna* with the objective of sending me to *Swarga* in this gross body. I know this to be within your capabilities. After all, you performed a *yajna* to enable my ancestor, King Vaivasvata, to obtain progeny."

"Trisanku, that was completely different! You desire the impossible – it cannot be achieved. In fact, your wish is merely an absurd desire!" Sage Vasishta declared frankly.

Trisanku persisted: "In that case, I ask you to convert my absurd desire into a deserving wish and ensure its fulfillment. Perform the required *yajna* which will liberate me and gain me entry to *Swarga* in this body."

"Oh king, is this a command?"

"I have requested and pleaded to no avail. Now, I command you!"

"I refuse to obey your command!"

"Master!"

"Trisanku, I repeat that you do not enjoy Ketu *graha's* favour. In these circumstances, the *yajna* will fail – it will not be fruitful. I refuse to perform a *yajna* which has no chance of success."

Turning his back on the dumbstruck Trisanku, Sage Vasishta stalked out of the room.

King Trisanku made his way to Viswamitra's hermitage and respectfully touched the sage's feet.

"May your wishes be fulfilled," blessed Viswamitra.

"*Maharshi*, your benediction is indeed apt! I come to you burning under the humiliation of Sage Vasishta's rebuff."

"Indeed? What transpired, Satyavrata?" Viswamitra's tone was conciliatory. "I will not demean you by addressing you by the name conferred on you through Vasishta's curse."

"I am blessed, *Maharshi*! I am repulsed by my kingly life and duties. I begged Sage Vasishta to conduct an appropriate *yajna* in order for me to obtain *moksha* and enter *Swarga* in this corporeal body. However, he rudely declined my request." Trisanku's voice throbbed with anger.

"What was the reason for his refusal?"

"He holds that Ketu, the bestower of *moksha*, exerts a negative impact on my fortune," Trisanku said with a mocking smile.

Viswamitra roared with laughter. "Satyavrata, you must not task an individual beyond his capabilities! Vasishta is a nobody! His powers are negligible! All he has is the empty title of *Brahmarshi*. Just as a person who is incapable of kindling the sacrificial fire resorts to blaming the twigs, Vasishta blames Ketu for his own inadequacy."

"Master, I beg you to fulfill my desire," Trisanku pleaded.

"Satyavrata, only a *Maharshi* who can hold his own with the Creator with respect to his task of creation can send you to *Swarga* in your gross body. I will prove to Vasishta that I can fulfil your wish," Viswamitra declared proudly.

"Master, you have given me your word. I no longer doubt that I will enter *Swarga*!" Trisanku was overjoyed.

"Make all arrangements for the *yajna*. First extend your invitation to the sages who are to be the *brahmavaadins*. I myself will officiate as the chief priest and perform the *yajna*," Viswamitra announced.

Trisanku prostrated himself gratefully before Viswamitra.

"May you enter *Swarga* in your corporeal body," said the sage in benediction.

As he proceeded to invite the various sages required for the conduct of the *yajna*, Trisanku met Vasishta's sons.

"Your father has declined my request to perform the *yajna*. I have now secured Sage Viswamitra's consent to conduct the sacrifice. Kindly participate in the *yajna* and give me your blessings."

Vasishta's son, Sakti, replied: "We are prohibited from attending a ceremony proscribed by our father. Furthermore, we cannot participate in a *yajna* conducted by a *Kshatriya*."

Trisanku returned to his palace burning with humiliation. The ministers he had dispatched with invitations to other Brahmins also reported to him in despair: "Lord, all the Brahmins have declined your invitation. They insist that it is a sin to participate in a *Kshatriya yajna* conducted by Viswamitra."

Trisanku hurried to acquaint Viswamitra with these developments.

The outraged sage declared: "It is the misfortune of those mean Brahmins that they fail to recognize my power as a *Brahmarshi*. Satyavrata, I give you my word – I will single-handedly perform the *yajna* and send you to *Swarga*. As long as you are fortified by Viswamitra's blessings, you will be immune to adverse influence: even that of the *grahas*! Go and proceed with your arrangements."

<hr>

Cursing all those who had spurned Trisanku's invitation to the *yajna,* Viswamitra exhorted the king to commence the sacrifice on a grandiose scale. Viswamitra recited the appropriate *mantras* and urged the various gods to accept the offerings of the *homas*. However, the gods failed to grace the sacrifice – they chose to reject a *yajna* which was conducted on the basis of a patently absurd wish.

"Master, what do we do now?" King Trisanku lamented. "The *yajna* will not be complete if the gods turn down our offerings."

Viswamitra rose in a towering rage against the recalcitrant gods. He evoked an instrument of sacrifice called the *sruvam* and declared, "Satyavrata, do not worry. I will conduct this *yajna* single-handedly, in spite of the absence of the sixteen prescribed priests – Brahma, Udgaata, Brahmanaacchamsi, Hota, Adhvarya, Prastota, Pratiprasthata, Pota, Maitraavaruna, Pratihaarta, Acchaavaaka, Veshta, Agnidhra, Subrahmanya, Gaavastuta and Unneta. I will ensure the success of the *yajna* even in the face of the gods' rejection of its offerings. I will make it fruitful!"

"Your blessings, *Maharshi*," Trisanku saluted Viswamitra with folded hands.

"I will send you to *Swarga* in your corporeal body by sacrificing the formidable powers which I have accumulated through my long years of intense, rigorous penance. Salute Yajneswara and me and stand up," Viswamitra commanded.

Trisanku dutifully obeyed the sage.

Viswamitra closed his eyes in deep meditation. After a while, he opened his eyes slowly and gazed intently at Trisanku. "Your entrance to *Swarga* is beyond the reach of normal human beings. My phenomenal power will be the invisible *vimana* which transports you to heaven. *Om*! Go, Satyavrata, go to *Swarga*! Reach heaven with your corporeal body!"

At Viswamitra's command, Trisanku's body rose into the air and sped towards heaven. Trisanku looked down at the receding sage and folded his hands in obeisance. Viswamitra followed the king's trajectory with a complacent smile and raised his own hand in benediction.

Trisanku hurtled towards *Swarga* with the speed of light, crossing the orbs of all the *grahas*, including the great Surya. Indra's spies rushed to him with news of Trisanku's imminent arrival. Indra hurried to *Swarga's* entrance, accompanied by the startled gods, nymphs, *siddhas*, *gandharvas* and *saadhyas*.

Trisanku reached the gateway to heaven. Assuming the gathered assembly to be a warm reception committee, he folded his hands in salutation to Indra and said: "Mahendra, I am King Trisanku. Sage Viswamitra has sent me to *Swarga* in my gross body by conducting a *yajna* and using his formidable powers. Please accept me as a denizen of *Swarga*."

"Yes, I am familiar with your unnatural desire, and the *yajna* conducted by Viswamitra in his hedonistic pride. You are an accursed person. Furthermore, your body is constituted of the five elements of earth, water, fire, wind and ether. Individuals inhabiting such corporeal bodies are forbidden from entering *Swarga*. Go! Turn back and return to earth!" Indra proclaimed and gestured angrily with his hand.

Immediately, Trisanku turned upside down and dropped like a stone towards the earth. As he reached the midpoint between heaven and earth, overwhelmed with panic, Trisanku called out to Viswamitra: "*Maharshi* Viswamitra! Save me! Please save me!"

Furious with Indra for foiling his objective, Viswamitra was determined to prevent Trisanku's return to earth.

"Satyavrata!" Viswamitra commanded. "Stop! Stop right there!"

Viswamitra's powerful command immobilized Trisanku and the king froze in his upside-down position in the sky.

"Oh king," declared Viswamitra, "my promise to send you to *Swarga* with your gross body will not be in vain. I shall create another *Swarga* in the space where you remain suspended. This will be your own heavenly domain and will be called Trisanku's *Swarga*. You will be the sovereign of this *Swarga*."

———

Nirvikalpananda paused and considered his disciples. "As he promised, Viswamitra created a second heaven, particularly for Trisanku, midway between the earth and the sky. The sage demonstrated that he was powerful enough to compete with the Creator in the task of creation. However, Trisanku's *Swarga* is merely a limbo which hangs in the sky and belongs nowhere. This is why a useless person is derogatively said to inhabit Trisanku's *Swarga*. Do you understand that Ketu's malignant influence was the reason behind the creation of Trisanku's *Swarga*?"

"That is clear enough, master," remarked Vimalananda with a rueful smile. "Harischandra endured untold suffering due to Rahu's adverse impact and his father, Trisanku, was subjected to hardship on account of Ketu's malignant influence."

"I repeat: in these stories, we have analyzed the hardships experienced by an individual and retrospectively deduced the particular *graha* responsible for his suffering," Nirvikalpananda explained.

"Master, hearing your detailed, captivating exposition of the *Navagraha Purana* has been a sheer delight!" Sadananda exclaimed.

"You have given us a clear understanding of the *Navagrahas* and their glory," added Shivananda.

"Hearing the *Navagraha Purana* has stimulated my interest in visiting the *Navagraha* temples in our country," said Chidananda excitedly.

"Master," Vimalanada was enthusiastic. "Shall we go on a pilgrimage to all the *Navagraha* shrines?"

"Certainly, Vimalananda," the master said with an indulgent smile. "Now, let us listen to the assured benefits to be gained by reading the *Navagraha Purana*."

Nirvikalpananda paused and his voice assumed a solemn, prayerful timbre: "The *Navagrahas* will shower their blessings in abundance on all who read or listen to the *Navagraha Purana*!"

The *guru* bowed his head in reverence and intoned:

"Om! Aadityaadi Navagraha arpanamastu!"
"Om! Offered to the Nine Planets, of whom Surya is the fountainhead!"

GLOSSARY

Aarya	A person of noble birth
Acharya	Spiritual teacher
Adharma	That which is not in accordance with the teachings of Dharma
Agnikaarya	A Vedic ritual dedicated to Agni, the god of fire
Akshata	Rice grains smeared with turmeric
Akshaya-paatra	An inexhaustible vessel
Amla	Gooseberry
Amrita	Nectar *Amsa* Portion
Ananda Taandav	Lord Shiva's Dance of Bliss
Anga	Category
Anthariksha	Space
Apsara	Celestial nymph
Aradhana	An act of adoration
Arghya	Ritual ablution
Artha gourava	Literary Content
Ashram	Hermitage
Ashtami	Eighth day in a lunar fortnight
Ashtadikpalakas	Guardians of the eight cardinal directions
Avabrdha snanam	Ritual bath which concludes a yajna
Avatar	Incarnation
Avyaya	Imperishable
Balabrahmacharis	Young ascetics under lifelong vows of celibacy
Bimba	The fruit of the *Momordica Monadelpha*
Bhagavan	Divine person
Bhaksya	Fried food
Bhojya	Delicacies

Bhoochara	Terrestrial life
Bhutas	Elements
Brahmanda Roopa	Universal Form
Brahmavaadins	Exponents of the Vedas
Chaaranaas	Demigods
Chakra	Wheel
Chaturmukha	Four-faced god: Brahma
Chintamani	Wish fulfilling jewel
Choshya	Beverages
Daanavas	Demons: the offspring of Danu, one of the Kasyapa's wives.
Damaruka	Small, two-headed drum
Daitya	Demons: the offspring of Diti, one of Kasyapa's wives.
Darbha	Sacrificial Grass: *Desmotachya bipinnata*, used in Hindu rites.
Darshan	Auspicious sight
Deva-guru	Preceptor of the gods
Devas	Demigods
Devi	A married woman or a female deity
Dharma	The eternal law of the cosmos according to Hinduism
Dikpaalaka	Guardian of a cardinal direction
Diya	A small clay lamp
Dwaadasa Aadityas	Twelve names of the sun
Dwapara Yuga	The third of the four ages described in Hindu scriptures
Gandharvas	Celestial musicians
Garudas	Celestial beings belonging to the clan of eagles
Gothra	Family name
Guru	Teacher
Guru dakshina	Teacher's fee
Gurukul Paathasaala	Residential school with pupils living with the *guru*
Gurupatni	The *guru's* wife
Havis	An oblation made to a god through the sacrificial fire
Homam	Vedic sacrificial ritual with Agni (the god of fire) as intermediary

Jaatakarma	Religious rite celebrating the birth of a child
Jalacharas	Aquatic life
Japa	Prayer
Jnana	Enlightenment
Kaalakeya	Demons: the offspring of Kaala, one of Kasyapa's wives
Krttika	One of the twenty-seven stars in Hindu astrology
Kalasa	Water-pot used for religious purposes
Kalpa	A time period (a day according to Brahma's divine count)
Kalpavrksha	A wish-fulfilling divine tree
Kamandalam	A water-pot used by ascetics
Kaamadhenu	Divine cow of plenty
Karma	Action
Khechara	Avian life
Kimpurushas	Divine beings with equine faces and human bodies
Kinnaras	Divine beings with equine faces and human bodies
Kshatriya	Member of the warrior caste
Ksheeraannam	Rice and milk pudding
Kumara	Son
Lehya	Medicinal food
Lipi	Writing
Loka	Plane of existence
Maanasaputra	Mind-born son
Maanavas	The human race: descendants of Manu
Maharshi	Great sage
Maha sankalp	Great will: preparatory mind-set for penance or puja
Mahayogi	Great ascetic
Mahathi	Sage Narada's lute
Makara kundala	Crocodile-shaped ear ornament
Mangala	Auspicious
Manmatha	The god of love
Mantra	Sanskrit religious incantation
Matsyakaantha	Mermaid
Moolarupa	Original Godhead
Namo Namah!	Salutation meaning 'I bow.'

Navagrahas	The nine planets
Navarathnas	The nine precious gems
Nirhetuka Krpa	Unconditional grace – a divine quality
Omkar	The primordial sound of 'Om'
Paanigraham	Marriage
Parabrahma	The Supreme Lord
Paramathma	The Supreme Soul
Pithamaha	Paternal grandfather / Chaturmukha Brahma
Prajapati	Lord of the people
Pralaya	Annihilation
Pramodoota	Fourth of the sixty years of the Hindu calendar
Pranam	Obeisance
Pranava mantra	The primordial sound, 'Om.'
Prasnopanishat	Question-and-answer method of oral instruction in the Upanishads
Purohit	Family priest
Pushya	One of the twenty-seven stars in Hindu astrology
Raasi	Sign of the zodiac
Rakshasas	Demons
Rakshas vivah	Marriage performed forcibly with an abducted virgin
Rajoguna	The quality of passion and activity
Rudra Veerya	Lord Shiva's semen
Saadhana	Consistent effort
Saadhyas	A clan of demi gods
Saamkhya Yoga	School of Indian philosophy
Saatwic	The quality of balance, harmony, virtue and peace
Saiva	Branch of Hinduism devoted to the worship of Shiva as Supreme God
Samidhas	Twigs offered into the sacred fire during religious rites
Sankha	Sacred conch shell
Sathapatha Brahamana	A Hindu religious text
Satyaloka	The world of Brahma
Seshatalpa	Vishnu's serpent-bed
Siddhas	A clan of demigods
Sishyas	Disciples
Sloka	Verse

Soumya	Soma's (Chandra) son
Srshti	Creation
Sruvam	Wooden instrument used to pour ghee into the sacrificial fire
Sudra	A man of the lowest caste
Sukram	Semen
Sukta	Vedic aphorism
Suras	Gods
Swaathi	One of the twenty-seven stars in Hindu astrology
Swami	Hindu honorific for Master
Swarga	Heaven
Taamasic	The quality of imbalance, lethargy, ignorance and destruction
Tapas	Penance
Teertham	Holy water
Tejas	Splendour
Tejomandala	Corona
Thirkaalajnata	Knowledge of the past, the present and the future
Tilak	An ornament or mark worn by a Hindu on the forehead to indicate caste
Tretayug	The second of the four ages described in Hindu scriptures
Trimurti	The holy trinity of Brahma, Vishnu and Shiva
Trinethra	Three Eyed: a name for Lord Shiva
Trishul	Trident
Upanayanam	Investiture with the sacred thread before commencing religious study
Vanavasam	Exile in the forest
Varaaroha	A woman with fine hips
Vasantham	Spring season
Vasus	Elemental gods in Hinduism
Vaikuntha	Abode of Lord Vishnu
Vedas	Earliest Hindu scriptures
Vidwan	Scholar
Vidya	Education
Vimana	A self-moving aerial vehicle
Virat Purusha	Immense cosmic form: Lord Vishnu's universal form

Vishnupriya	Beloved of Vishnu
Viswa kartha	Creator of the Universe
Viswa bhartha	Lord of the Universe
Viswaroopa	Universal Form of Lord Vishnu
Vysya	A caste
Yajna	Ritual sacrifice
Yajus or Yajurveda	The Veda of prose mantras
Yojana	Measure of distance
Yuga	Cycle of time

SLOKAS

Ardhakaayam mahaaveeram Chandraaditya vimardanam!
Simhikaa garbha sambhootam tam Raahum pranamaamyaham!

I offer my salutations to Rahu who is half-bodied, who is distinguished and valiant, who is the oppressor of Chandra and Aditya and who is born from Simhika's womb.

Dadhi sankha tushaaraabham ksheerodaarnava sambhavam!
Namaami sasinam Somam Sambhormakuta bhooshanam!

I offer my salutations to Sasi who is known as Soma (Chandra) who shines like curds, the conch and snow, who rose from the Ocean of Milk, who is the ornament on Sambhu's (Lord Shiva) crown.

Devaanaam cha rsheenaam cha Gurum kaanchana sannibham!
Buddhimantam trilokesam tam namaami Brhaspatim!

I offer my salutations to Brhaspati, who is the preceptor of the gods and sages, who is resplendent like gold, who is the personification of wisdom and who is the lord of the three worlds.

Dharanee garbha sambhootam vidyut kaanti samaprabham!
Kumaaram sakti hastam tam Mangalam pranamaamyaham!

I offer my salutations to Mangala (Kuja) who is born from the womb of the Earth, who is resplendent like lightning, who is (called) Kumara, and who holds the weapon, Sakti, in his hand.

Harih Om!
Adityaadi navagraha devataabhyo namah
Adityaaya cha Somaaya Mangalaaya Budhaaya cha
Guru Sukra Sanibhyascha Raahave Ketave namaha.

Salutations to Aditya and other Navagrahas.
I offer my salutations to   Aditya, Soma, Mangala, Budha, Guru, Sukra,
Sani, Rahu and Ketu.

Himakunda mrnaalaabham daityaanaam paramam gurum!
Sarvasaastra pravaktaaram Bhaargavam pranamaamyaham!

I offer my salutations to Bhargava (Sukra) who shines like snow, like the
Kunda flower and lotus-fiber, who is the great preceptor of the demons
and who is the expert orator of all the scriptures.

Japaakusuma samkaasam kaasyapeyam mahaadyutim
Tamorim sarva paapaghnam pranatosmi divaakaram.

I offer my salutations to Divaakara (Surya), who shines like the japa
flower, who is the son of Kasyapa, who is resplendent, who is the enemy
of darkness, and who is the destroyer of all sins.

Kara aravindena pada aravindam
Mukha aravindena vinivesayantam
Vatasya patrasya pute sayaanam
Baalam mukundam manasaa smaraami.

I meditate on that Holy Child who sleeps on the banyan leaf with His
lotus-like foot in His lotus- like hand, placed in His lotus-like mouth.

Neelaanjana samaabhaasam Ravi putram Yamaagrajam!
Chaayaa Maartaanda sambhootam tam namaami Sanaischaram!

I offer my salutations to Sanaischara who shines like dark blue collyrium,
who is the son of Ravi (Surya),who has Yama as his elder brother and
who is born of Chaaya and Maartaanda (Surya).

Palaasa pushpa sankaasam taarakaa graham mastakam!
Roudram roudraatmakam ghoram tam Ketum pranamaamyaham!

I offer my salutations to Ketu who shines like the palaasa flower, who is foremost among the stars and planets, who is Roudra, whose form is fierce and horrible.

Priyangu kalikaa syaamam roopenaa apratimam Budham!
Sowmyam Sowmyagunopetam tam Budhaam pranamaamyaham!

I offer my salutations to Budha who is of dark blue complexion like the Priyangu bud, who is wise, who is of incomparable beauty, who is (called) Soumya and who is of benevolent quality.

Saptaasva rathamaaroodham prachandam Kasyapaatmajam!
Swethapadmadharam Devam! Tam Suryam! Pranamaamyaham!!

I offer my salutations to Surya who rides the seven horse-chariot, who is very passionate, who is the son of Kasyapa, who holds the white lotus and who is God.

SELECT BIBLIOGRAPHY

Andhra Mahabharatam
Bhagavatam
Devi Bhagavatham
The Eighteen Puranas
Mahabharata (Sanskrit)
Ranganatha Ramayanam
Srishti Prakarana
Uttara Ramayanam
Valmiki Ramayana (Sanskrit)

ACKNOWLEDGEMENTS

Navagraha Purana is more than a book – it is the culmination of years of ongoing research. This research has truly been an epic journey through the divine forests of Hindu mythology, and I feel privileged to be able to lead the reader down the jungle paths I so meticulously forged. When I discovered the task had not yet been undertaken to represent the life and glory of the Navagrahas (the nine planets), I felt that God had granted me the opportunity to tell this story, just as He had granted me the gifts with which to tell it.

A *purana* is a religious text identified by five particular elements: the Creation of worlds, the Destruction and Renovation of worlds, the Genealogy of gods and heroes, the Rein of the Manus, and the Transactions of their descendants. As each of these elements has a role in the story of the Navagrahas, I have decided to call my work *Navagraha Purana*.

It would be far too simple to say that *purana* is pure fiction. As teams of researchers continue to discover the many ways that Mars resembles Earth, those who have read the *puranas* just smile, for they have known for generations that the planet Kuja (Mars) is the son of Mother Earth.

Even those who question the scientific foundations of such writing must admit that it is representative of a spiritual truth. Nevertheless, while writing the story of the Navagrahas, I took care to maintain harmony between the scriptures themselves and the way they have come to be interpreted and practiced by human beings.

I would like to express my deep gratitude to Jaico Publishing House for making possible the translation of my *Navagraha Purana*, so that a valuable Indian story may be shared among an English audience as well.

I owe my sincere thanks to Ms. Sandhya Iyer , Managing Editor, Jaico Publishing House, for selecting my work for publication, and overseeing the publication of Navagraha Purana, Ms. Mugdha Guru for her efforts in every aspect of getting the book printed, Ms. Dipti Patel of Wordfamous for taking the initiative as my literary agent and Ms. Preetha Kannan for her expert and significant efforts in editing the book.

And many thanks with my blessings to my beloved daughter Umarji Anuradha for her continuous endeavors in bringing this book to light.

V S Rao
Hyderabad

ABOUT THE AUTHOR

V S Rao (Vakkantham Suryanarayana Rao) is a celebrated Telugu author, playwright and script writer. He was born in 1942 at Arikela, a remote village near Punganuru in Andhra Pradesh and has a high school education.

He wrote his first story, which was for children while still a child himself. His father Mr. Varadaiah, who was a lover of literature recognized his son's incipient talent and encouraged him to read extensively. Mr. Rao thus went on to become a voracious reader and writer par excellence. Later Mr. Temporau, the pioneer of Telugu pocket detective fiction, became his mentor.

Mr. Rao's works include short stories, novels, plays and philosophical articles. Mr. Rao has a number of titles to his credit under the nom de plume V S Rao, Baatasaari, Koundinya, Suryaatreya and Chitrabhanu. While working as translator in one of the wings of Tirumala Tirupati Devasthanams, he has translated a number of Kannada religious books into Telugu.

His extensive epic-based works include *Navagraha Puranam* which has sold more than one lakh copies. His plays explore societal issues and mythology, while his books run the gamut from philosophy and social concerns to thrillers and drama. His writing is largely women-centric, and passionately highlights women's issues.

Mr. Rao is the recipient of numerous literary awards for his plays and prizes for novels. His short story MODEL was anthologized in the Bharateeya Jnanapith's Visishta Bhaarateeya Kahaniyan and his literary work has been the thesis of a doctorate awarded by Sri Venkateswara University.

Mr. Rao is the father of three sons including Vakkantham Vamsi , a reputed Telugu screen writer. He lives in Hyderabad with his family.

JAICO PUBLISHING HOUSE
Elevate Your Life. Transform Your World.

ESTABLISHED IN 1946, Jaico Publishing House is home to world-transforming authors such as Sri Sri Paramahansa Yogananda, Osho, the Dalai Lama, Sri Sri Ravi Shankar, Sadhguru, Robin Sharma, Deepak Chopra, Jack Canfield, Eknath Easwaran, Devdutt Pattanaik, Khushwant Singh, John Maxwell, Brian Tracy, and Stephen Hawking.

Our late founder Mr. Jaman Shah first established Jaico as a book distribution company. Sensing that independence was around the corner, he aptly named his company Jaico ('Jai' means victory in Hindi). In order to service the significant demand for affordable books in a developing nation, Mr. Shah initiated Jaico's own publications. Jaico was India's first publisher of paperback books in the English language.

While self-help, religion and philosophy, mind/body/spirit, and business titles form the cornerstone of our non-fiction list, we publish an exciting range of travel, current affairs, biography, and popular science books as well. Our renewed focus on popular fiction is evident in our new titles by a host of fresh young talent from India and abroad. Jaico's recently established translations division translates selected English content into nine regional languages.

Jaico distributes its own titles. With its headquarters in Mumbai, Jaico has branches in Ahmedabad, Bangalore, Chennai, Delhi, Hyderabad, and Kolkata.

SINCE 1946